THE RETURN OF THE WILDLIFE – *PHINDA IZILWANE*

1990 – 2000

THE RETURN

BARBARA
HAPPY MEMORIES
JEAN & MIKE

PHINDA PRIVATE GAME RESERVE

THE RETURN

THE STORY OF PHINDA GAME RESERVE

PUBLISHED BY SHAN VARTY

WRITTEN BY MOLLY BUCHANAN

PHOTOGRAPHY BY RICHARD DU TOIT

DESIGN AND ILLUSTRATIONS BY JOHAN HOEKSTRA

Reproduction:
Beith Digital, South Africa
Typesetting:
Molly Buchanan Productions
Johannesburg
Printing:
Tien Wah Press, Singapore

ISBN 0-620-24584-0

First edition,
first impression 1999
Published by:
Londolozi Publishers CC
P.O. Box 4752
Rivonia 2128 South Africa
E-mail: shan@ccafrica.com

Conservation Corporation Africa
E-mail: reservations@ccafrica.com
Tel: +27 11 775 0000
Fax: +27 11 784 7667
Web site: www.ccafrica.com

To the Getty Family
without whom Phinda would have been short-lived,
the animals would never have been returned,
and Phinda's rural neighbours
would have little cause for hope.

A FOREWORD FROM THE PEOPLE OF PHINDA

The rural communities bordering Phinda Game Reserve were ordinary people. They never thought that one day they could have better jobs and the opportunity for tertiary education. When Phinda started ten years ago, for the most part, they did not think that changing a pineapple farm and cattle ranch into a game reserve was a good idea. They believed that there was every chance that the dangerous game would destroy their farm stock, and perhaps even worse. We couldn't believe that this belief would change so quickly and so easily. But this is what happened when our people started to work there.

There were many discouragements for the men who had a dream of creating Phinda. It needed intelligence and commitment to overcome these hurdles. Phinda started with bringing in the wildlife. They also promised communities job opportunities and training. In 1992, the establishment of the Rural Investment Fund opened many doors that had been closed to the communities. More and more students are given golden opportunities to further their studies in tertiary institutions. Today Phinda is considered a role model, enhancing cross-cultural understanding, changing poachers to businessmen, linking the rich with the poor, and helping to unite everyone in the environmental equation.

We, as the Phinda Committee, believe that in a successful family, as we have become, there is always a need for collective action, shared responsibility and the pooling of ideas. This alone holds the key to our long-term survival.

Gladys Zikhali
Convenor of the Phinda Committee

Left: **The Phinda Committee, from top left to bottom right: Gladys Zikhali, Musa Mtsbali, Dumi Mpanza, Caroline Bukhosini, Caroline Mngadi, Octavia Masinga, Comfort Khumalo, and Lucy Khumalo.**

GLOSSARY

Phinda Izilwane	**The return of the wildlife. As in most Zulu words which have an 'h' following a consonant, Phinda is pronounced 'Pinda'**
AmaZulu	The Zulu people – 'the people of heaven'
AmaThonga	The Zulu name given to the people who live to the east, meaning 'dawn people', pronounced 'Tonga'
Assegai	A sharp light spear
Bakkie	A small truck or pick-up
Biodiversity	The diversity of species
Biosphere	A part of the earth inhabited by living species
Boma	An enclosure usually made with reeds or brushwood
CCAfrica	Conservation Corporation Africa
Fonya drive	A spectacular form of fishing undertaken by large numbers of people when the pans are low
Gubu	A stringed instrument used by the AmaThonga
Impi	A group of Zulu warriors
Inxala	Zulu name for nyala
KwaZulu	The land that is heaven
Lobola	The bride price
Mfecane	The scattering of the tribes of Africa when Shaka invaded his neighbours
Mpumalanga	Where the sun rises, previously Eastern Transvaal
Munyawana	The river of salt
Mvubu	Hippo
Mzinene	Probably from mzaneno, the Zulu word meaning 'coming towards'
Nagana	Cattle and antelope disease carried by tsetse fly
Nagana campaign	A 30-year war on wildlife in a futile attempt to rid the land of nagana, during which an estimated 100 000 head of game were killed
Nduna	Zulu chief or overseer
Nguni	The people who spoke a common language who settled along the south-east coast of Africa.
Nkosi	Zulu community leader
Pallah	Zulu name for impala
RIF	Rural Investment Fund
Rinderpest	Virulent cattle disease which spread through Africa at the end of the 19th century
Rondavel	Round thatched hut
Tilapia	Fresh water fish
Vlei	Wetland, pronounced 'flay'
Voortrekkers	The Afrikaner settlers who migrated from the Cape Colony in the 1830s
Wildtuin	Game reserve

CONTENTS

INTRODUCTION

THE RETURN is as much a story of the people of Maputaland as it is of Phinda – a reserve created out of a group of derelict farms in the midst of Maputaland's rural poverty. The reserve is a narrow strip of land about thirty kilometres from north to south, covering an area of 150 square kilometres. Phinda holds seven magical ecosystems ranging from dry sand forests to montane grasslands and to riverine forests of fig and fever trees. Of much greater significance than its size is its strategic position between the state-owned Mkuze Game Reserve to the west and the Sodwana State Forest and St Lucia Game Reserve to the east, and its key role in showing what private enterprise can achieve.

Phinda was born out of a belief that the beauty of Maputaland was worth saving from the spiral of destruction into which it had been drawn. Its first target was to repair habitat damaged by almost a century of cattle farming, to return the wildlife which had once roamed the Maputaland plain, and to build luxury, world-class destinations for visitors without whom there would not be a viable plan. The second task was to reconnect the rural communities with the land by giving people the opportunity to participate at every level in sustainable conservation development by providing employment, training and the infrastructure for small business development. As soon as Phinda was up and running, CCAfrica then embarked on its second major goal: the establishment of the Rural Investment Fund. In the past seven years, the RIF has become a catalyst for social and economic change, not only in the communities to the east of Phinda, but wherever CCAfrica's infrastructure and management presence can be used to benefit its rural neighbours.

Two hundred years ago, the Mkuze River, just to the north of Phinda, formed the border between the Thonga and Zulu people. Over the past two centuries this border has become blurred and the lives of the rural people have changed dramatically. Their history, which is briefly set out in this book, puts into perspective the problems the people of Maputaland face today, their weaknesses and their untapped strengths. We believe that the future of wildlife is inextricably linked with these people. Both their economic development and the conservation of the land must be driven by partnerships; between the rural people with their wisdom and accumulated knowledge of the natural world, the government and the cash-strapped but technically skilled and experienced KwaZulu Natal Conservation Service, and private enterprise with its ability to raise funds and take calculated risks.

Our goal is that everyone will work together, participating in, and establishing, an internationally recognised Greater St Lucia Wetland Park which will link the state-controlled reserves, the wetlands and wilderness areas owned by the communities, and the private estates such as Phinda. Our objective should be to ensure that every sustainable economic activity should form part of a single comprehensive plan.

One of the most ambitious conservation programmes, and one that was endorsed by President Nelson Mandela and leaders of other states in southern Africa, is the creation of transfrontier parks which will unify fragmented ecological habitats and re-open the migratory routes of elephants and other animals. Under President Thabo Mbeki's enlightened leadership, and in the spirit of the African Renaissance, the governments of southern Africa may well take the quantum leap needed to create a transfrontier park, linking the Reserva d'Elefantas d'Maputa in Mozambique with the reserves of northern Maputaland and southern Swaziland. The formation of this park is being facilitated by the Spatial Development Initiative and the Peace Parks Foundation. It would result in a unique combination of pristine coastline, big game country and wetlands. If it was then linked with the Greater St Lucia Wetland Park in southern Maputaland, the combined wilderness areas would form one of the most exciting conservation developments of the 21st century.

Dr Ian Player, founder of the Wilderness Leadership movement and a passionate advocate of Maputaland's natural wealth, said: "We are the last generation which will have the choice: whether to rebuild this great park or watch it slip away towards an ever-degraded environment which eventually can no longer support life, including that of the people who live there. We cannot let this opportunity pass."

Phinda has shown in microcosm what is possible. Population pressures and changes in land ownership, as a result of claims which go back almost to the beginning of this century, decree that the wilderness of Maputaland must be used. But it must be used wisely. We need all the ideas and ingenuity that we can muster. Already the development of a Greater St Lucia Wetland Park has been under discussion for half a century. We cannot afford to wait any longer before we act. We need decisions now.

Dave Varty

ACKNOWLEDGEMENTS

PHINDA owes its existence to many people. At the start Kevin Leo-Smith and Trevor Coppen had a dream of making the magic of Maputaland accessible to people from all over the world. They were joined by Alan Bernstein, whose considerable financial ability was a great asset in turning their gossamer-light dream into a reality. Dave Varty became the fourth member of a team whose combined influence and energy made things happen. When it seemed that the way forward was impenetrable, they managed to bring together international and local funders and, through a variety of coincidences, Phinda was born. Although Kevin, Trevor and Alan have gone their separate ways, they can take much of the credit for the founding of Phinda which, I believe, will prove to be a milestone in conservation history.

Without the unshakeable faith of its shareholders, Phinda in all likelihood would never have appeared on the Maputaland map. We have many people to thank. Christopher Sporborg, deputy chairman of Hambros Bank, Jan Newman and his dynamic colleagues, Jonathan Klein and Mark Getty who was instrumental in persuading all four of the Getty family trusts to invest in the fledgling company. We owe a huge debt of appreciation to Mark and to his brother Tara who have taken an active interest in conservation developments in Africa, to Gordon Getty, the two Getty trustees, Judge William 'Bill' Newsom and Jan Moehl, and Neale Axelson, chairman of the African Explosives & Chemical Industries' Pension Fund. Despite the many difficult years, they have all continued to be tremendous supporters of CCAfrica's long-term goals.

The early days at Phinda were not easy. Money was always in short supply: to buy Land Rovers and equipment, to pay for wildlife and land rehabilitation, and for salaries. A kaleidoscope of people known as the Phinda Pioneers, too many to mention individually, gave of their time, talents and unstinting effort. There was no challenge that they did not meet head on: no problem that they could not solve. Les Carlisle, who will

one day be known as 'the father of Phinda', and his team have turned Phinda into a vibrant and exciting wilderness and have earned both our admiration and appreciation.

CCAfrica director and great friend, Tony Adams, and his wife Dee, have brought Phinda to a point where it runs on well-oiled wheels. Lodge managers and staff, under Tony's guiding hand, have created a wonderfully happy and caring atmosphere. There is nothing that is too much trouble, no guest who cannot feel the friendly hospitality that starts at the front gate and runs through the organisation of great holiday adventures and romantic evenings, day in and day out. Steve and Nicky Fitzgerald, CCAfrica directors, also played a major role in transforming Phinda into a world-class adventure destination.

Molly Buchanan and I would like to thank all those people who gave so willingly of their time to talk about their involvement with Maputaland and with Phinda. *The Return* would not have become a reality without the invaluable input of my husband, Dave, and Steve Fitzgerald and Tony Adams, who guided us through a maze of issues. Les Carlisle was both an entertainer and an inspiration in retelling his Phinda experiences. Dr Ian Player, Dr George Hughes, Charles Tinley and Paul Dutton talked about Maputaland and their involvement with the Natal Parks Board. Keith Cooper, director of conservation of the Wildlife and Environment Society of South Africa, was particularly helpful. Trevor Coppen, Jane Conyngham, Martin Rickleton and Mark Tennant shared their early Phinda experiences. Peter Goodman's thesis on the ecology of the Mkuze Game Reserve, and Luke Hunter's on the lions and cheetah of Phinda, were much appreciated. David Rattray kindly read the chapter on Zulu history and then expanded on the fascinating story, keeping everyone entranced. Andrew Venter introduced us to the community leaders who are participating in his ecopartners programme at Mkuze, and Andrew Zaloumis talked about the exciting vision of the Lubombo Spatial Development Initiative.

At Phinda everybody made time: Sam Nguni while preparing partridge for a bush dinner, Yvonne Short while facing a camera for a video production, Eric Buthelezi between welcoming guests at Phinda Mountain Lodge, Gavin Hulett at Forest Lodge, Jason King at Mountain Lodge, Ansel Biesenbach at Rock Lodge, Hugh Marshall who temporarily quelled Molly's fear of snakes, Isaac Tembe while driving to meet community leaders, Nicole Young and Anthea McGregor between a busy schedule for the Rural Investment Fund, and Karl Rosenberg, Carl Walker, Anton Louw, Michael Gumede and Andrew Lewis during their busy schedule at Phinda. Nkosi Simon Gumede made time between parliamentary sessions, as did Tinky van Rensburg when visiting Lulubush, while Tara and Jessica Getty, Judge Bill Newsom and Jan Moehl found a few moments during their visits to South Africa. Jenny Gillis, Dr Murray Short and Dr Liz Standing talked on health problems in Maputaland. We would also like to thank the Brenthurst Library, the Johannesburg Reference Library, the Don Africana Library, the KwaZulu Natal Conservation Service's Library, the National Army Museum, London and the London Illustrated News for the pictures of the Zulu War, and Caroline Tinley who lent us the engraving of Piet Retief.

Richard du Toit did a superb job in tackling an almost impossible 'shopping list' of pictures and was supported by Roger and Pat de la Harpe who photographed many of the Phinda and rural African people. Peter Pinnock, Martin von Fintel and Geoff Nichols gave us permission to use their photographs of fishes and flowers, while Andrew Lewis, Mark Tennant and Lex Hes provided early Phinda photographs. Johan Hoekstra, with his genius and inimitable style, has produced yet another book designed with flair and imagination. We are grateful to Libby Husemeyer for her patience and guidance in editing the manuscript, for the many useful comments provided by Liz Campbell and Harold Fridjhon, for assistance with research provided by Andi Durow, for the maps prepared by Judith Campbell and for Lynn Payne's proof reading and encouragement. We also thank Werner Bothner and his team at Beith Digital for the outstanding quality of the reproduction.

Last of all, I would like to thank Molly Buchanan, the author of this book. Molly, who is one of the most efficient, organised and energetic women I have ever met, has recorded a fascinating story of KwaZulu Natal and its people, the problems facing Maputaland today and Phinda's first ten years. If this book can influence a few people to help the rural communities and save Maputaland's wilderness from destruction, it will have done its job.

Shan Varty

Shan Varty

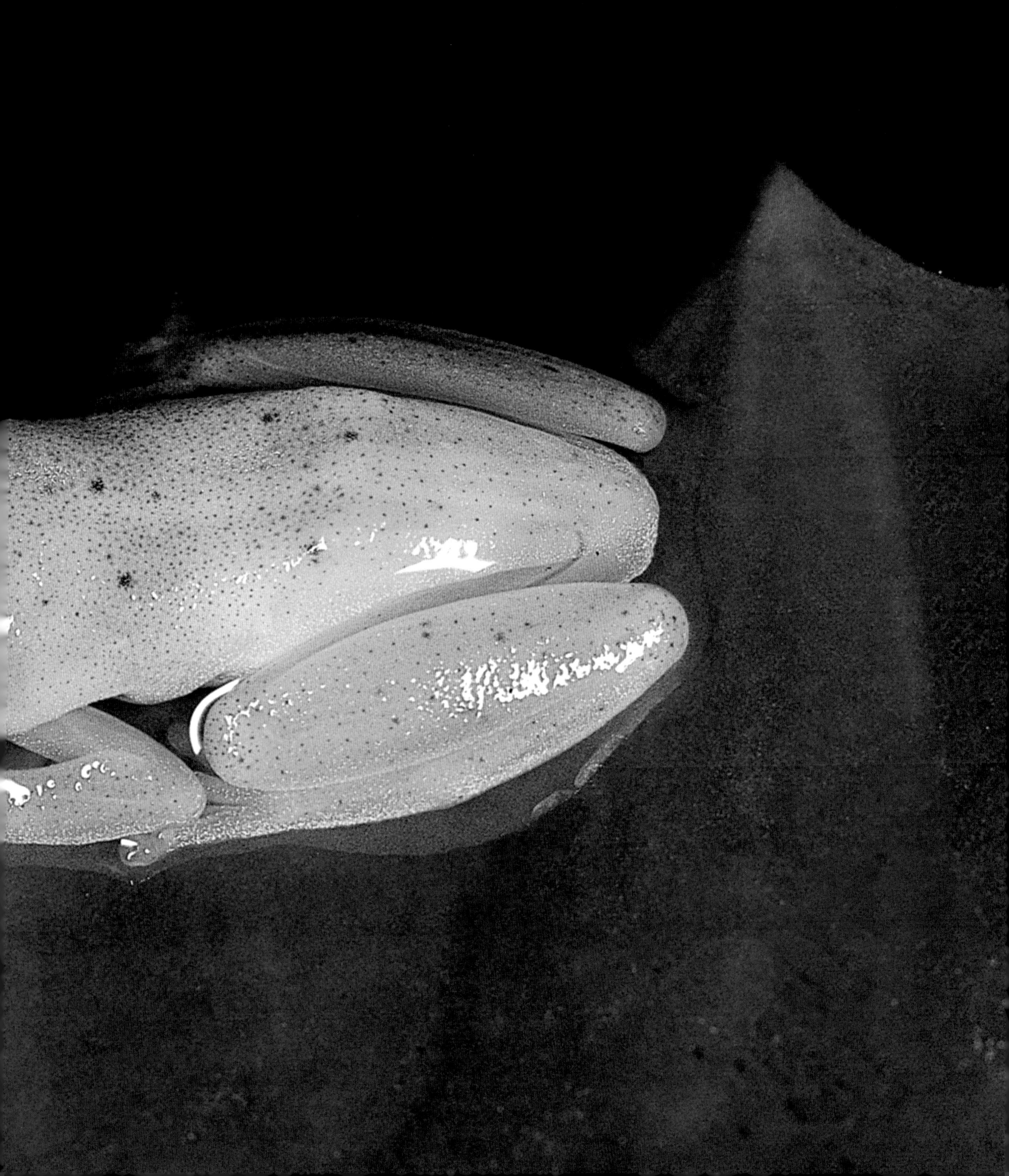

PHINDA – THE RETURN

For a brief moment time lost all meaning. The dawn could have been centuries before men from Europe arrived on the African subcontinent. It was easy to imagine that the wilderness had been little different two hundred or even a thousand years earlier.

During the night the dust and heat had been swept away. Rain had filled the pools. The rivers, long dry, flowed once again. Before dawn the thunder had receded over the hills and a gentle breeze had replaced the gale-force winds. As the early morning light flooded the plain all nature sparkled in the clear morning air. The hills, which had yesterday disappeared in a dull, dry haze, now appeared in sharp relief, each detail on their slopes clearly defined.

It was possible, on a morning such as this, to hope that the wilderness in all its beauty could be the same forever. Even after all that had happened. After all the abuse of the land. All the droughts and dust of past years. All that the people had suffered. And the animals too. Few mammals had survived the avarice and greed of men from beyond Africa's shores, their search for wealth and their determination to impose a European-style agricultural system on a fragile, nutrient-poor land. Yet there is a resilience in nature that man cannot easily destroy. Unwittingly, he had tried damned hard.

This was Phinda in 1999. In a single decade the reserve on the Maputaland coastal plain had become a model of what could happen all over Africa. Once again nature had the upper hand. It had taken imagination, faith, a little luck and a great deal of hard work. Phinda had put back, albeit in microcosm, the most important element of life in Africa – it had provided a reason for hope.

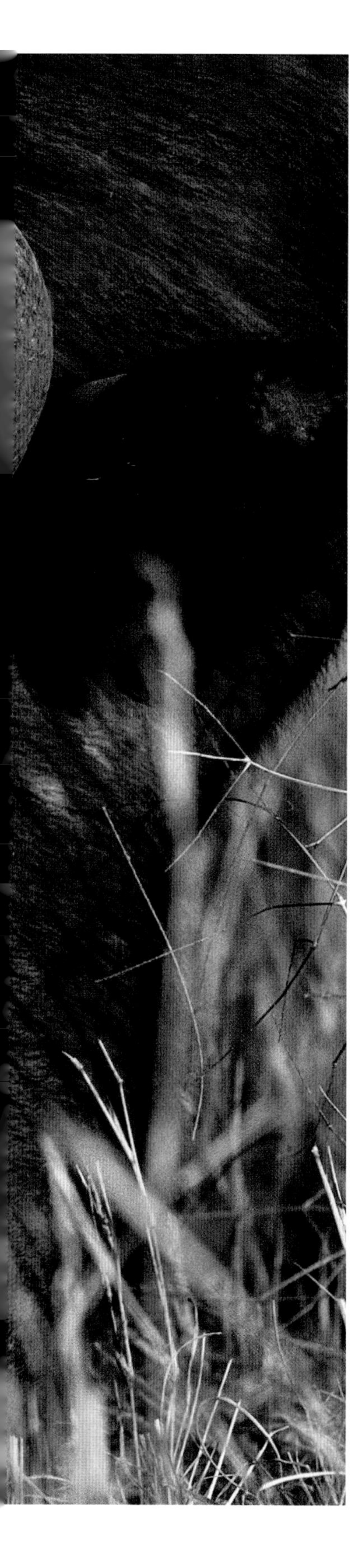

Twenty buffalo were not going to make an impact on Phinda's 15 000 hectare reserve but they were a start. More animals were in the pipeline and one day, in the not too distant future, Les Carlisle hoped to see a herd of a thousand buffalo roaming the Mkuze wetlands in a free-ranging Greater St Lucia Wetland Park.

WITH THEIR SILVERY LEAVES still wet from the storm of the night before, the *Terminalia* trees appeared to glisten in the soft light of dawn. Beneath the trees a group of twenty buffalo stood warily watching their captors. They had never become accustomed to the presence of man despite daily interaction during the year of their captivity. Now the gates of their boma were open. They were free to go. Les looked at the sun rapidly climbing away from the horizon. The shadows were still long but it was important to give the buffalo a whole day to settle in their new environment. The first night would be the most dangerous of all. Les had watched every stage of their progress. It had taken five years to get the buffalo to Phinda. Five years of hard work. Of continual grind. Two paces forward, one back. And now this day had dawned and the last of the Big Five mammals was being released on Phinda – on land where buffalo had once roamed in their thousands.

Les Carlisle had overseen the reintroduction of very nearly two thousand animals to Phinda. He wanted to make sure that the buffalo left the boma in a group. It was a pitifully small herd but big enough for their protection if they stayed together. There were no big prides of lions, their only serious predator. Les had deliberately kept the prides small to give buffalo and other large prey species a better chance of surviving their first months in a strange habitat. Bringing a new species into an area with an established predator population was no easy matter. This had been proved when eland had been reintroduced. He had wanted to buy forty eland at a time to give the animals a better chance, but only twenty had arrived. When they were released they scattered far and wide. Their protection is in numbers. Scattered, they were vulnerable. It could not have been easier for the lions. In a little over a month fourteen had been taken and some had jumped the fence. Les did not want that to happen again.

The buffalo were important. Not just because of the time and money spent on them, or because guests expected to see them. The Big Five had become a major tourist attraction – as important as the Empire State Building, Buckingham Palace or the Eiffel Tower. The fundamental importance of buffalo was that they were a vital link in the ecology of the African wilderness – a link that had been missing since the 1870s, by which time hunting had virtually wiped out the big game on the east coast of South Africa. Buffalo feed on tall grass while wildebeest, zebra and sometimes white rhino follow behind, grazing on the shorter grasses and on the sweet young shoots encouraged by the cropping. Buffalo are also heavy. They break the crust of the soil and recycle nutrients, improving the carrying capacity of the land.

Turning the wasteland back into dynamic wilderness had been a dream. The land had been farmed for a century and almost destroyed in the process. Few people had succeeded in scraping a living off the land and it was doubtful whether even the most successful farmers in the area

Les Carlisle had many helpers with the buffalo project. *Below:* Jimson Ndhlovu, skilled in animal care, saw to the health of the captive buffalo during their quarantine. *Opposite:* A juvenile oxpecker forms a symbiotic relationship with a buffalo, feeding on parasites and in payment giving early warning of approaching danger.

could continue forever: the odds were not in their favour. The weather was too fickle and the soil too poor. The cycle was always the same. Clear the bush and trees. Plant a crop once, perhaps twice. And then move on, leaving a desert behind. Phinda promised a sustainable alternative.

When the Phinda project was started in 1990 it was up against a political and legal system that favoured a failing agricultural system. Les Carlisle said: "You could have as many head of cattle as you wanted. But if you didn't already have wildebeest, a far more viable option, you weren't allowed to bring them onto your land. The same law applied to all other indigenous wildlife. The first thing we had to do was to get legislation in place for the establishment of a Big Five game reserve. We also had to get permission from all our neighbours, which included the Biyala Farmers' Association, the Mnqobogazi, Nibela and Mduku communities to Phinda's east, as well as the KwaZulu Natal Department of Veterinary Services and the state conservation bodies."

It was a case of declaring war. Phinda was caught up in the aftermath of a 100-year history of conflict between conservationists and the farmers who had erroneously blamed the wildlife for the spread of nagana, the deadly disease carried by tsetse fly. Although the tsetse fly had disappeared, the farmers still saw game as a threat to their cattle. From time to time lions escaped from the reserves and they were not recompensed when their cattle were killed. The farmers disparagingly called the Natal Parks Board 'die Natal se Varke Raad' – the Natal Pigs Board. At the first meeting of the Farmers' Association Les set about trying to change their attitude. He thought he was going to be lynched when he told them it would not be long before all the farms in the area would be under wildlife. What he meant was that they would switch to game farming. It was no use telling them. Phinda had to set the example. It took nearly ten years but Les now has some satisfaction in seeing that all Phinda's neighbours are farming game or mixed cattle and game.

"Eventually we had the legislation in place," Les continued. "Before the ink was dry on a legally binding document signed by our neighbours which gave us permission to introduce buffalo onto Phinda, we struck another problem. Tuberculosis was discovered in the buffalo populations in the Hluhluwe and Umfolozi Reserves where we had arranged to source the animals. That put us back to a new round of talks with the conservation and veterinary authorities. We met with fierce resistance initially but in the end we formed a team which made an enduring contribution to the restoration of Phinda.

"At capture the buffalo were tested for the tuberculosis virus. Because of an error reading in the testing of blood samples, each animal had to be put through five successive tests before it could be released. With each test the animal had to be immobilised twice, once to inject the tuberculin and the second time three days later to take skin readings to check reactions. It was neither easy nor cheap, and if one animal in the herd tested positive, then it was back to the beginning. Each animal cost

When Les and Lynette first arrived at Phinda they often saw hyena. You don't see them very often now. After the lions arrived, the hyena took the easy way out and crossed the fence into Mkuze Game Reserve where there are still no lions. This is one of the weaknesses of fences between reserves. Neither Mkuze, without lions, nor Phinda, without hyena, could function as nature intended. But while the lions frightened away the hyena on Phinda, it was not long before other species reappeared. Today a spiral of vultures or a bateleur, flying low over the bushveld looking for carrion, is a common sight.

Next page:
In relocating white rhinos, the huge animals are first darted from a helicopter. They are then blindfolded and partially revived so that they can be led, with a few hefty tugs, into transport vehicles. The twenty-six white rhinos relocated from Malachite to Phinda, have been more than enough to establish the white rhino population, which has grown to just under sixty, proof of nature's ability to recover under ideal conditions. It has even been possible to sell some of the rhinos to finance the relocation of other animals, improving Phinda's biodiversity.

us R10 000 and then a further R11 000 to feed and test over the twelve to eighteen months of its captivity. Any animal that tested positive was culled. There were no shortcuts to the procedure but in the end a healthy herd of buffalo was released on Phinda."

Les Carlisle grew up close to the Kruger National Park. He and his three brothers, all fearless and bounding with energy, must have been the scourge of schoolboy rugby. It was those same qualities that made him the key person at Phinda during its developing years when his wealth of experience in animal relocation was invaluable. There was nothing he was not prepared to tackle, whether it was facing a formidable audience, a man threatening murder with a gun in his hand, or lions and elephants. Les had the ability to quickly stamp his authority on any situation, yet his humour was never far below the surface and frequently bubbled over. Like Dave Varty, co-owner of Londolozi Game Reserve and one of the founders of Phinda and CCAfrica (Conservation Corporation Africa), Les met and fell in love with his wife while still at school. Together they wove the dreams for their future and then proceeded to live those dreams to the full, Les moving ahead like a tornado while Lynette anticipated his every move and quietly kept their lives in order, helping with his work wherever she could.

Les's reaction to Phinda was instantaneous: "We arrived at Phinda in January 1991 and fell in love with it. Lynette and I never left the area for nine months. There just wasn't time. So much was happening. Every single day was a roller-coaster adventure. There was just so much to learn. Everything we did from my early days in cheetah research and then catching game professionally was pioneering. And every day was full of challenge and excitement. There is simply nothing I would rather do.

"We lived in a prefab house under a huge *Albizia adianthifolia,* a flat-crown tree, in a beautiful setting. Wonderful views of the grassy flood plain in front of us." When Les and Lynette first moved in there were only a few nyala about but within a short period of time they had cheetah walking across their front lawn. Soon after that they had hyena treeing five young lions in front of their house. The hyena had been without any serious competition for decades and ruled the roost at Phinda when they first arrived. It was not long before the lions got bigger and the tables were turned.

Before the reintroduction programme could get off the ground, Les had to secure the Phinda property for wildlife. He persuaded the Kwa-Zulu Natal conservation authorities that a two-metre-high electric fence would contain the animals. A higher fence would not deter antelope like kudu and waterbuck from jumping, but the extra half-metre would lead to broken legs and necks. What keeps animals from getting out of the reserve are the three strands of high voltage wire. The lowest is for lions, the middle one is for rhino and buffalo and the top one is for elephants.

A few months after their arrival, Les and Lynette went to have a look at Malachite, a farm about 65 kilometres to the north. A multi-national

corporation was in the process of destroying an area of biodiversity and converting the farm into a monoculture sugar producer: a sad loss for conservation but, at the time, a great opportunity for Phinda to acquire a wide range of species. Les recalls that they caught everything they could lay their hands on. The most important item on the shopping list was white rhinoceros. Malachite had twenty-six of them. There were also wildebeest, zebra, giraffe, nyala, impala, warthogs, terrapins and tortoises, quail, francolins and snakes.

The first animal Lynette and Les saw on Malachite was an impala with its feet in the air. "A python had just killed it," said Les. "We grabbed the python. It was a Sunday morning and we didn't have any equipment with us, only a cooler box with our lunch in it. We emptied the box and stuffed the python in. A 4.2-metre python in a cooler box is not a happy snake. I sat on the box holding onto the handles while Lynette drove back to Phinda as fast as she could. The python was so strong it was lifting me against the top of the vehicle. I was also concerned that Lynette would hit a pothole and bounce me right off the box!"

The rhinos were relocated from Malachite to Phinda by the capture unit of the Natal Parks Board which moved twenty-one of them in one day. About thirty-five tons of rhino. They would have moved all twenty-six that day if it hadn't been for the rain and getting stuck in the mud. It was probably the biggest relocation of rhino that has taken place in one day anywhere. Dave Varty remembers the day vividly: "Alan Bernstein and I arrived on the scene in the pouring rain. With us were some prospective South African and US investors who were all very smartly dressed and who we were trying to impress. As is usual in the bush, things never work out the way they are planned. When we arrived a bearded guy, plastered with mud, came over to us and asked us who the hell we thought we were, 'driving unauthorised into the reserve and parking our kombi in the damned way'. And then, without waiting for our answer, he told us in unequivocal terms to get the hell out of the way so that he could manoeuvre the next crated rhino into position for release. That was our first meeting with Les Carlisle who has become a friend and has been of immense value to Phinda.

"We watched as Les directed a really dangerous operation. One Land Rover had already been seriously damaged by an irate rhino. Even in that hour we could see his talent and dedication. Nothing deterred him. He was afraid of nothing. But he was also thoroughly professional. Later we were introduced to Les Carlisle for the first time. I still have the same problem with Les – I still seem to get in the damned way!"

Les had several close encounters when moving animals onto Phinda. He escaped with only a few broken ribs when a wildebeest that he was trying to get out of a truck smashed into him. "The other two guys were supposed to jump in and grab the wildebeest's back legs at the same moment that I grabbed his horns. They thought I was joking and their delayed reaction was nearly very expensive for me. Then once we were

out of the truck the wildebeest nearly took me out a second time. It came flying for me as I ran down the ramp. I managed to dive over the bushes. One gets accustomed to living on adrenaline!"

As soon as the relocation programme was running smoothly, Les was off to the Pilanesberg to collect cheetah. "We had a very definite strategy of first bringing in the cheetah, getting them established and later bringing in the lions. We also needed to give reintroduced prey species time to get accustomed to their surroundings and we wondered how the nyala would react to the sudden influx of predators.

"Phinda's first lions were caught in the Sabi Sand Game Reserve. We travelled with them by road through the night and had a formidable welcoming committee when we arrived the next morning at Phinda. It was part of our strategy to explain to our neighbours what we were doing. We could not guarantee that a lion would not get under our electrified fence. Warthogs burrow holes and lions often follow. In the soft sand even lions can dig. What we could do was show our neighbours how concerned we were about their worries. That first morning when we drove in with the five lions we were met by the chiefs and tribal elders from the three local communities, representatives from the Biyala Farmers' Association, other interested neighbours and the press.

"We got off to a bad start but it all ended well. We had caught the lions just after they had eaten a kudu. The drug, Zoletil, which we use to anaesthetise the lions, does not stop natural functions, so both the lions and those of us who had travelled in the back of the truck monitoring the cats were covered in faeces. When we opened the truck we just about knocked our audience out with the stench. But after a quick clean-up we were able to fit the cats with radio-collars and demonstrate the transmitter and monitoring system. Subsequently we have shown that if lions leave the reserve we are able to track them quickly. We have also guaranteed that our neighbours will be compensated for any livestock killed by our predators. What was most significant was that the community were the first to agree with our plans to return the wildlife. Nkosi Simon Gumede, the leader of the Makasa Tribal Authority and the Mduku community, had far more sympathy with what we were trying to do than most of the other farmers. 'The animals were here long before us,' he said. 'We should let them come back.'

"For the most part we flew lions in. We collected two big females from Hoedspruit near the Kruger Park in a little Cessna 206. It had been an uneventful day – rather unusual for game capture operations. We thought we would liven things up. While the pilot was talking to ground control and preparing to land we put a paw on his knee. The next second we had an on-board emergency. If he could have, he would have jumped out of the aircraft. But he had no need to worry. The drug we use has a wide margin of error. While it is safe, it is slow acting and not ideal for a quick capture and release. The animal could be injured or killed by other lions during the seven or eight minutes before the drug has taken effect.

The sedated cheetah (left) was amongst the first of the predators to be reintroduced to Phinda where it has thrived on the restored grasslands. After half a century of having no lions or cheetahs and only a few leopards and hyenas on the farms, the nyala had flourished. It turned out that they had no idea how to handle the predators. The cheetahs and lions would kill one nyala and the others would come to see what all the noise was about. The predators would then feel threatened and kill three or four more. It was not long before the nyala's flight instinct returned and the natural predator-prey dynamic was back in place.

The Phinda relocation programme brought together many talented conservationists and wildlife technicians. John Raw, Colin Bennett, Karl Rosenberg, Andrew Lewis and Carl Walker formed the nucleus of the team, which often worked around the clock caring for lions, cheetah and elephants. Many others shared Phinda's dream: Martin Rickleton was contracted to run the buffalo pens, Dr Dave Cooper from the KwaZulu Natal Conservation Service, Dr Rob Bagnall, deputy director for Veterinary Services for KwaZulu Natal, Dr Marina Nel, the State Veterinarian, and her assistants Alicia McCall and Debbie Rizzato, gave their time unstintingly.

"On one occasion I had grabbed a darted lioness by her tail and was pulling her backwards as fast as I could when the whole pride of about eighteen cats came rushing at us. Tony Adams, who is now a director of CCAfrica, said it sounded like the start of a Grand Prix. I was more interested in keeping the lioness from turning around and biting me. She was about 13 or 14 months old and could have spoilt my day completely! Fortunately we were able to intimidate the pride long enough to get back to our Land Rover, by which time the lioness was immobilised.

"Our first young elephants – a group of eighteen – arrived from the Kruger National Park at the end of 1991. They would have been culled if we had not taken them. We kept the herd in a boma for three months to let them get used to the electric fencing. Once they had stopped hitting the fence and we knew that it would keep them in, we released them. For the first few days they would return to the boma at night where they felt safe. Then one morning they took off for the thickest, densest, darkest bush they could find – hardly ever to be seen for eighteen months. Occasionally someone would catch a glimpse of them eating in an old pineapple field planted by one of the previous landowners, but the minute they saw us they would duck back into the forest. We had planned to clear the pineapples but the elephants did the job for us.

"The following year we brought in a second group of twenty immature elephants. They joined up with the first group but there was still a problem: the orphaned elephants needed the anchor of a mature female. Our first adult elephants came in from Gonarezhou in southern Zimbabwe where Klem Coetzee had developed a special technique for their capture. Very soon after that we had the opportunity to move a full breeding herd of eleven Kruger Park elephants. The matriarch reacted to her new surroundings immediately. She did not like the electric fence. She did not like the boma and she did not like us. She put her 1.2-metre tusks under the boma fence, rearing up when she was shocked and ripping about fifty metres of fence out of the ground. She continued attacking the fence until we decided to let the herd go. She was going to break out anyway.

"They stayed on the property for two nights, coming into contact with the fence twice but never breaking out. On the third night the matriarch walked up to the fence and again tried to push it over with her tusks. This time when she was shocked she ripped up hundreds of metres of boundary fence which, unlike the boma fence, was not reinforced with cable. She got such a fright that she ran back into the property dragging the fence behind her. During the night she broke out again and again, destroying hundreds of metres of fencing, but she was unable to persuade the herd to follow her over the tangled wires. Eventually she succeeded in dragging the fence out of the way and the herd went with her. Our elephants were off to visit the neighbouring communities. When I phoned the Kruger Park to tell them what had happened, they immediately put all further capture operations on hold. I was told that if I did not get the

The declining free range for wildlife in Africa presents stark choices: relocate or cull. Fortunately modern capture methods make relocation a practical and commercially viable option. Les Carlisle says: "What is needed are much larger contiguous areas set aside for elephants through which they can migrate as they did long ago. Even with all the problems that are unavoidable when relocating big animals, I would rather move them into areas where they can thrive than see them culled."

elephants back within 24 hours they would consider all adult elephant relocation unsuccessful. The pressure on us was enormous." Les then called Dave and said: "We're in real trouble. I've got a herd of elephants heading for the Hluhluwe supermarket. The sun is setting and it's going to be a long night." If his words were flippant, his attitude was not. Dave was convinced that by the next morning the elephants would all be dead. He also expected that their critics would not wait long to pounce.

When Dave called Les the next day, he could not believe his ears: "They're back in the boma and I'm off to breakfast." Dave says: "Without Les those elephants did not have a chance. It was an incredible effort. That's the kind of man he is. There are simply no half measures."

Les recounts what happened that night. "The herd was in the middle of rural KwaZulu Natal on a grassy plain surrounded by small villages. The elephants would become more aggressive every minute. Once it was dark there was a strong possibility they would start killing people. That's how elephants behave. I got together with Kevin Leo-Smith, our CCAfrica director and co-founder of Phinda, and Martin Rickleton, who had shared many years' experience on game capture with me. By nightfall the animals had to be either asleep or dead.

"We sent out calls to everyone who could help us. Dr George Hughes put all the resources of the Natal Parks Board at our disposal. Their capture unit was at Weenen, a four to five hour drive away. Mark Cook, head of the unit, and Dr Peter Rogers, their vet, responded immediately. They arranged for their helicopter to fly down as soon as it was available. Two construction companies working in the area made arrangements to bring us low-bed carriers to move the elephants. We were simply not equipped to handle the emergency. I had enough of the morphine-based M99 capture drug for four darts and I hated the idea of killing the animals. We took the decision that we would do everything to save the elephants even though we had been given an explicit instruction to the contrary by the conservation officials. We chose to ignore those instructions. But we could not take any risks.

"Peter Bell, a director of Bell Equipment based at Richards Bay, was the first to arrive to help us. He took us up in his helicopter and we found the elephants in a thicket surrounded by a flat open grassy plain. In front of them were the Mkuze wetlands. Behind them was a village. We could take no chances with the safety of these people. The matriarch kept taking her herd into the reeds but she could not take them across the wetland. She did not know how deep it was and she had two babies with her. We tried to chase the elephants away from the village. When they wouldn't move I darted the matriarch. That immediately anchored the herd.

"I managed to get two more darts in so we had three sleeping elephants and eight very active ones. It was dusk when we saw the Parks Board green bakkie bouncing towards us in a big cloud of dust. Peter Rogers had the M99 and the darts. Then Mark Cook arrived with the Parks Board helicopter. In no time we had all the elephants asleep. It was only

Previous page: For Phinda and other fledgling reserves, the most important aspect of the escape of Phinda's elephants was that the future of mature elephant relocation hung in the balance. If the project failed, the rebuilding of Big Five game reserves would be in jeopardy. If they succeeded it was possible that the vast plains of Africa, where elephants have disappeared altogether, would one day be restocked.

Waterbuck and kudu have no problem with electrified fences. They will not hesitate to jump even a three-metre fence, especially if they have lions behind them. One other species that has not been brought in to Phinda is wild dogs. The fence would not hold them and the territory is far too small for this nomadic species. In the Serengeti the home range of wild dogs extends over as much as 4000 square kilometres.

when we landed that we realised there was going to be no moon. We were stuck 45 kilometres from Phinda in the middle of rural KwaZulu Natal. We had eleven sleeping elephants and no lights. Verre van Heerden, the Parks Board pilot, took off immediately and flew to Phinda Mountain Lodge. He loaded as many paraffin lamps as he could and brought them back to us, flying unaided through the inky darkness with only a few vehicle headlights to guide him in.

"We put a lamp on the belly of each elephant. When a lamp started to wobble it was time to top the elephant up with a bit more M99. You couldn't see your hand in front of you but we managed to load the two baby elephants into rhino recovery crates. We then tried to work out how we were going to load these tons and tons of sleeping elephants onto the flatbed trucks. We broke every rule in the book. You're not supposed to roll elephants. We had to roll them to get them onto the nets. If we were going to save them we had no option. All of this happened on a cold, dark night. And I had three broken ribs from a car accident. The only animal we could not bring back was the matriarch. Before dawn we were close to running out of M99. We had to choose between saving two of the younger animals or the matriarch which had caused all the trouble. We had received further instructions to put her down, so in the end the tough decision was taken out of our hands. The next day, with the elephants safely back, the Kruger Park resumed its elephant capture operation.

"As soon as the mature herd had settled down under a younger matriarch and was released on Phinda they made a beeline for the orphaned babies which had been without guidance for over a year. You could have drawn a line with a ruler between them. The only explanation I have is that they must have sub-audible communication. There was no other way they could have known where those baby elephants were. It has been proved in Namibia that they can communicate over vast distances. We can't hear them but they can hear each other. Once they linked up, the babies settled down. Elephants sense the atmosphere of a place. Here at Phinda, in ideal elephant country, they have become relaxed. The result is that we have had good elephant viewing ever since.

"In the early days we brought in waterbuck, kudu and hippo. They were all difficult. The problem with waterbuck and kudu is that they are not easy to contain. The hippo arrived in 1992 when we were in the middle of a major drought and our big dams were not built. They took one look at the massive waterways of St Lucia and were off. Before we brought in the next lot of hippo we established lots of good permanent water. We even named our big dam, Mvubu, the Zulu name for hippo, so we were pretty confident they would stay.

"Several methods of game capture have been developed. We found that the most effective for mass capture was to use an opaque plastic curtain, a technique discovered by Jan Oelofse in Hluhluwe Game Reserve. On one occasion in the sixties, he ran out of heavy nylon netting and used plastic bags to fill a gap in a temporary fence. He found that the antelope

"With few exceptions, all the animals we have relocated have settled down well," says Les Carlisle. "There was one little orphaned elephant that just pined away. Our entire staff was committed to helping him. He got pneumonia so we had gas heaters to warm him and we set up drips hanging from the tree above him because he was so dehydrated. But he was broken-hearted at being separated from his mother and did not pull through."

stopped in their tracks in front of the opaque curtain: they would not run where they could not see. The technique he developed was to drive the animals through a funnel created by brushwood and into a boma made with plastic curtain walls. Once there a team would quickly draw the curtain closed behind them and then step by step concentrate the animals into one corner of the makeshift boma. From there it would be a relatively simple manoeuvre to direct the animals into a waiting truck without injury and with very little stress. Rhino and elephants, because they are so big and dangerous, are more difficult. From the helicopter we have to fire a heavy-gauge dart, which leaves a big bruise. More often than not this turns into a massive abscess which we have to treat by packing the wound with antibiotics until it heals.

"We did not invent animal relocation. As far as I know, the man who did was Noah. There is much that can be criticised in our handling but we do the very best we can. Without the modern drugs and techniques that have been developed in recent years, a creative conservation and restocking project, such as at Phinda, would be impossible. We still have much, much more to do. We want to bring back some of the smaller, more rare species like serval, aardvark and pangolin. The Maputaland plain was a paradise once with an incredible diversity of wildlife. We want to make it that way again."

At the turn of the 19th century, Africa was still the 'dark' continent to the western world. The discoveries of Livingstone, Stanley, Burton and Speke all lay in the future. But far from its shores, events were being set in motion that would change Africa forever. Napoleon was the key to the emergence of Egypt from the poverty and intellectual bankruptcy into which it had declined during the Medieval Age. Of much greater significance was his brilliance on the battlefield, which acted as a catalyst accelerating scientific advances in every aspect of gunnery. By the time of the American Civil War in 1861, called the first of the modern wars, and the Anglo Zulu War in 1879, weapons were more accurate and, with breech-loading, far more efficient. These guns were to be the death knell for the wildlife of Africa and for men who tried to defend their land with spears.

The Napoleonic Wars, which overlapped the American War of Independence, affected Africa in many other ways. The New World had been a major supplier of goods to Britain, which now had to look elsewhere for cotton for uniforms, and for sugar, coffee and food for the army. Trade with Brazil flourished and, in turn, increased the demand for slaves. Although the slave trade was largely focused on West Africa, Delagoa Bay on the south-east coast of Africa became a thriving slave port. This land had been inhabited by the AmaThonga for many centuries. They were the true hunter gatherers of the coastal plain, living in harmony with their environment and with a knowledge of the plants around them that was unique. It was a culture based on the omnipotence of nature. The AmaThonga respected every living animal, even those they hunted. Nothing had prepared these peaceful people for slavery or for the subsequent disasters that were to hit them.

After the Napoleonic Wars, Britain's economy slumped. Bad harvests, high food prices and industrial unemployment led to social and political unrest and the first of the major waves of immigrants from Britain to Africa. Men arrived with guns and shovels. Both were dangerous. But for good or bad, Africa was on a path to be drawn into the world arena.

William Charles Baldwin and many other hunters came to South Africa in the 19th century to make fortunes in ivory and for adventure, hunting lions and buffalo. They shot kudu, inxala and pallah (Zulu words which have been adopted into the English language as nyala and impala). Africa also attracted many artists. The impala (left) was drawn and engraved by S. Daniell and published in 1804.

FOR HOW LONG the African subcontinent had been inhabited was a subject of debate for many years. In the past, schoolbooks taught that black men arrived from the north at about the same time as men from Europe landed at the Cape. Today those books are being rewritten. With the exception of Kenya and Tanzania, South Africa is the only country in which fossils representing virtually the full evolution of man have been discovered. Border Cave, situated on the western slopes of the Lebombo mountains (the Ubombo range is renamed the Lebombo north of the Pongolo River) and, as the crow flies, less than sixty kilometres from Phinda, was first excavated by Professor Raymond Dart in 1934. It has yielded an archaeological treasure trove of nearly 70 000 implements dating back about 130 000 years. The remains of at least five *Homo sapiens* belonging to the Middle Stone Age, about 100 000 years ago, have also been discovered there, together with an anatomically modern *Homo sapiens* dated about 1000 years ago.

A little further north in Swaziland, in the same mountain range, Lion Cavern reveals that men mined haematite there 40 000 years ago. They crushed the iron ore to make a pigment which they used to decorate their faces and bodies. Later they smelted the ore to make primitive weapons. A smelting furnace discovered by Paul Dutton, at the time working for the Natal Parks Board at the Ndumu Game Reserve on the Pongolo River, has been carbon-dated to about 600 AD. Traces of human habitation dating back to this period have also been found on the eastern shores of Lake St Lucia and in the Mkuze River area.

With all this evidence, it is reasonable to assume that when Arab traders landed on the south-east coast of Africa, about 700 years ago, the area around Delagoa Bay, with its abundance of rivers and freshwater lakes, mammals and birds, was inhabited. Perhaps a monsoon swept the Arab dhows further south than their usual route and they put in for water at Delagoa Bay. They did not stay long, but they did venture into the interior, probably searching for gold, ivory and slaves – the object of their voyages to the east coast of Africa. Venetian beads which they used for trading have been found on the Ndunakaze Hill in Mkuze Game Reserve, on Phinda's western boundary.

In 1497, some twenty years before Magellan's ships circumnavigated the world, finally disproving the fallacy that the world was flat, Vasco da Gama sailed from Lisbon under the patronage of Don Manuel, king of Portugal. He followed the route to the Cape discovered a decade earlier by Bartholomew Diaz, but once he had rounded the Cape, he sailed north into uncharted waters searching for the spice islands and for the Indian port of Goa – at that time the diamond trading centre of the world. In December 1497 he named the fertile green hills along the African coast Terra de Natal – 'the Christmas land'. Further north he sailed into a large bay which he named Delagoa, 'the way to Goa'. For the next 300 years the coast received little attention from Europe although ships passed by more

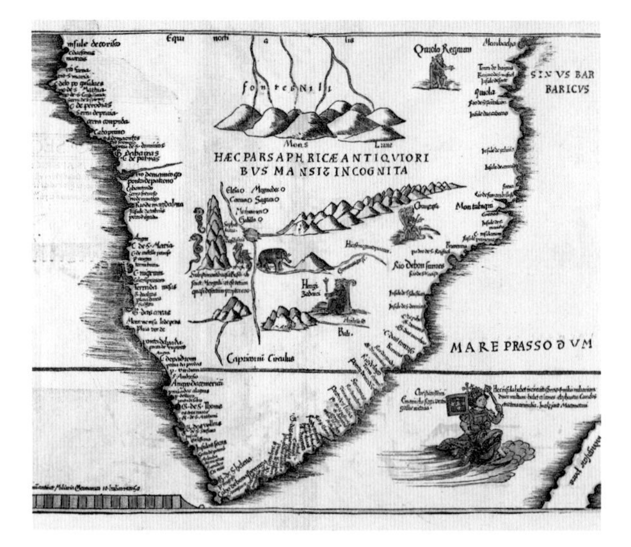

A map drawn in 1525 shows the southern African coast already well defined, although it would appear that Madagascar was as yet undiscovered. Delagoa Bay and Terra de Natal are shown clearly. After the return of Vasco da Gama to Portugal, the route to India and the Orient was open. However, it was Magellan's ship, which rounded the Cape and arrived back in Lisbon in 1522 with its almanac one day out, that made it possible to draw maps with some degree of accuracy. *Opposite:* A group of Zulu girls and a boy play an age-old pebble game called *'amagende'* which involves throwing stones and catching them.

and more frequently as trade between Europe and the East flourished. Many ships were wrecked on the inhospitable southern African coastline. Until the port at Delagoa Bay was established, survivors had a 500-mile journey north along the fever-ridden coast to reach Sofala, near the Zambezi River delta, where the Portuguese had established a base. Few completed the journey.

In 1554 the Portuguese chronicler Manuel de Mesquita Perestrello explored the east coast. He called the land south of Delagoa Bay, Terra del Fumo, 'land of smoke', because of the ubiquitous fires that played an essential role in the life of the AmaThonga. These gentle people lived in harmony with their surroundings and with their neighbours. To the south, beyond Lake St Lucia, the green hills were the home of about fifty independent Nguni clans, all speaking the same language and observing the same customs. Their songs and folklore recall a time when their ancestors travelled down the east coast of Africa through fever-ridden country and arid bushveld to the well-watered, grassy hills which provided ideal grazing for their cattle. When one of the clans first set foot in these hills, they called the territory KwaZulu, which means 'heaven', naming themselves the AmaZulu, or 'people of heaven'. At the time the most powerful Nguni chief, Dingiswayo, had reorganised his army, laying the foundations for his successor, Shaka, who had been conscripted into his army from the Zulu clan, and who was to become the most powerful of all Nguni chiefs.

In 1787, the year in which George Washington drew up the constitution of the United States, Shaka was born in the hills south-west of Lake St Lucia in KwaZulu. His exploits were to have a profound impact on the indigenous people of southern Africa, and particularly on the Thonga people, his closest neighbours to the north. But all his knowledge and military skills, which were to make the Zulu army so powerful, were insufficient to ward off the tidal wave that was to engulf his kingdom half a century later.

In his early years Shaka had been despised. He was illegitimate. It is also said that he was sexually undeveloped, but he grew into a huge and powerful man who, when the time came, heaped retribution on all those who had scorned him and his mother. When his father, Senzangakona, died in 1816, Shaka took over as chief of the Zulu clan with an escort provided by Dingiswayo. Applying all he had learnt from his years in Dingiswayo's army, he honed discipline to a fine art, forbidding his warriors to marry until they were in their forties and training them to run barefoot and at great speed over long distances. He also discarded the traditional throwing assegai for a much more effective short stabbing spear. Disloyalty, disobedience and cowardice were punishable by death.

Two years later, in 1818, Dingiswayo was killed and Shaka took over as the strongest chief north of the Tugela River. There is much speculation about what motivated Shaka to begin his reign of terror. It is unlikely, as some writers have suggested, that it was because of pressure

The rural people of KwaZulu still retain many of their old traditions although beads are now made of glass and not of seeds. The type of skin used in a warrior's headband indicates his rank and also shows that the wearer is a man of stature within the community. Leopard-skin cloaks and headbands are worn by the king.

The Zulu people learnt the skills of mining iron ore and forging weapons many centuries before Shaka welded together the Zulu kingdom. The short stabbing spear, which he introduced, revolutionised warfare in Africa. The Zulu impi discarded their long throwing spears and were trained in fierce hand-to-hand combat.

from the slave trade in the north and the influx of white people from the south. It would have taken an immensely strong Arab contingent to venture so far south of Delagoa Bay, through the wild country inhabited by the AmaThonga, and then to face the might of a well-trained Zulu army numbering 30 000. In any event, Arab traffic through Delagoa Bay fell significantly after Britain abolished the slave trade in 1807. Nor could the arrival of white men in Natal have been considered a threat at that time. Their numbers were too few.

A more likely motivation for Shaka's subjugation of his neighbours was a combination of the age-old motives of power and greed, a bloodthirsty disposition and a territorial imperative. Over many decades Shaka's kingdom had prospered. The Zulu clan's cattle had multiplied and they had become one of the wealthiest tribes in all Africa. At the same time their lands had become overgrazed. Then the east coast of southern Africa was struck by successive years of drought. The desperate need to find more grazing for their cattle would have provided sufficient reason for war. On the hills north of the Buffalo River, the scars of erosion, caused by heavy rain on land bared of its protective mantle of grass, probably started about this time.

For ten years tribes fled from Shaka's formidable fighting force, trespassing on the domains of other tribes to the north, south and west in what became known as the *mfecane*, or the scattering. Few tribes south of the Zambezi River were unaffected as the more powerful in turn annihilated or enslaved their weaker neighbours. Among those who fled northwards, parallel with the coast, were three Nguni chieftains: Sobhuza, who retreated to the mountains north of the Pongolo River and laid the foundations for the Swazi kingdom, Shoshangane, who fled north of Delagoa Bay where he established the Gaza kingdom, and Manukosi, who settled in the territory inhabited by the AmaThonga. Fearful of their lives, the AmaThonga had no choice but to submit to slavery or escape. It was small wonder that when the first Europeans met the AmaThonga they found them terrified and starving. One outstanding Nguni chief, Mzilikazi, fled into the interior to escape Shaka's army in the early 1820s. After coming into conflict with the Afrikaner Voortrekkers in the Transvaal Republic, he crossed the Limpopo River with his regiments and founded the Matabele kingdom in Zimbabwe.

In a decade Shaka had consolidated the Nguni people under his leadership and formed the Zulu kingdom. There were no malingerers in his army. Defeat was the prelude to a massacre. On one occasion an entire regiment was put to death together with their wives and children because they had retreated in the face of overwhelming numbers. The hill where the tragedy took place is called 'the place of slaughter'. Shaka never married. Any of his concubines who fell pregnant were put to death. He wanted no competition from his progeny.

Before the *mfecane* the Zulu people had lived south-west of Lake St Lucia, keeping to the hills and well away from the fever-ridden coastal

The AmaThonga have two distinctive methods of catching fish: fishtraps, a common feature of the Kosi lakes, and fonya drives, which involve hundreds of people. Ian Player records that he once witnessed a crocodile swimming towards a line of about 500 women in a fonya drive. There was no panic. The women simply parted, allowed the crocodile to pass, then reformed their line. When they had encircled the fish, they closed in, catching tilapia in their large reed baskets. Even the baskets show their understanding of nature: they are loosely woven to allow the smaller fish to escape.

The AmaThonga make use of a wide variety of plants. Twigs from the tinderwood tree (*Clerodendrum glabrum*) are used to make a fire. Aromatic *Combretum* or *Acacia* logs are burnt when cooking their evening meal, while the hard Tamboti logs are left to burn through the night to protect the sleeping people from predators. The poisonous smoke from the Tamboti logs also drives away the malarial mosquito. The flowers, leaves and bulbs of the impepho plants, *Helichrysum* (above) are burnt both to kill insects and to invoke the goodwill of ancestors.

zone to the north inhabited by the AmaThonga. Unlike the Zulus, the Thonga clans had no national unity; they had no army and no defence against the invasions and migrations of the Zulu people who dominated their history during the 19th century. The Zulu language became the language of communication throughout Maputaland, although amongst the Thonga women the old dialect still persists. The Thonga people may have submitted, but in the end the conquerors had to adopt their traditional way of life. The Zulus had no choice. The Nguni cattle, which were resistant to many of the fly- and tick-borne diseases of Africa, did not prosper on the fever-ridden coast.

Robert Briggs Struthers, a Scotsman who came to Africa in the 1850s and hunted elephants and buffalo on foot between Kosi Bay, the Pongolo River and Lake St Lucia, wrote that the AmaThonga had goats and fowls but no cattle. They cultivated a great variety of grain – maize, mabele, inyanti, mapila and rice – as well as sweet potatoes, beans, cassava, chillies, bananas, shallots, pumpkins, watermelons and marrows. They supplemented their diet with fish and made a beer rich in vitamins from the ilala palm which grows on the Mkuze flood plain. When the floods receded each winter, the AmaThonga planted their crops. From time to time flash floods swept these away but also ensured prosperity in the next season by filling the pans with fish and renewing the soil. Until their crops were ready for harvesting the AmaThonga fished and collected the bulbs of water lilies and plants such as water chestnuts. On one occasion while living amongst the Thonga people, Paul Dutton provided a dinner for Ian Player in the Thonga style. They ate fried caterpillars and termites, marula nuts and tilapia fish broiled in leaves. Dessert was marula jelly and umdoni berries. One might shudder but Ian Player described it as one of the best meals he has ever eaten.

The Thonga way of life was totally dependent on the pans. They used the reeds and sedges to build their huts and ate figs and other fruit from trees growing close to the water. While the women collected herbs, fruit and berries, the men hunted and traded with their neighbours to the south. Their music, which carried across the coastal plain telling of their prosperity, was played by an orchestra of different instruments: trumpets from antelope horns, gubus or harps with palm-fibre strings, a range of xylophones each with ten hardwood keys, flutes from reeds, drums from hides, and even shells. The AmaThonga lived in balance with their habitat. But it would not always be so.

Although the AmaThonga were to some extent isolated from the Zulu wars later in the 19th century, these conflicts would affect their lives forever. The first major Zulu war was against the Afrikaner Voortrekkers in the late 1830s. The second took place forty years later against the British. In both instances, armed with surprise and superior numbers, the Zulu army initially devastated the enemy. But, in the end, the Zulus, no matter how brave or how numerous, were overwhelmed by the vast superiority of fire-power. Men with guns would be kings.

In his efforts to secure land for the Voortrekkers, Piet Retief had tried to intimidate Dingane, writing to him saying that "kings who conduct themselves as Umsilikazi does are severely punished and it is not granted to them to live or reign long". Retief had then exacerbated his relationship with the Zulu king by refusing to hand over to Dingane the horses and guns he had taken from a neighbouring clan when recovering cattle in what was intended to be a demonstration of goodwill towards the king. When Retief arrived at Dingane's kraal to return the cattle, Retief and his party of one hundred men had no option but to accept Dingane's guarantee of safety and leave their weapons at the entrance. Later two Zulu regiments encircled them in a war dance and dragged them to Execution Hill. Some months later, a letter signed by Dingane giving the Voortrekkers the right to settle south of the Tugela River was found on Retief's body.

In 1838, when Piet Retief led the Voortrekkers over the mountains and into Natal, Dingane, Shaka's successor, found himself in the middle of a tug of war between the Afrikaners and the British missionaries who pioneered contact with the Zulus. Dingane thought he could solve the problem by getting rid of the most persistent and least trustworthy of the suitors for his land. Retief had already shown that he was capable of trickery, so after granting him possession of a large part of Natal (already promised to the British missionary, Captain Allen Gardiner), Dingane's regiments fell on Retief's party of more than one hundred men, killing them without mercy. Ten days later Dingane's impi annihilated the Voortrekkers near Bushman's River at a place that became known as Weenen – the place of weeping. Men, women and children were slaughtered.

On 16th December 1838 the Voortrekkers retaliated, resoundingly defeating the Zulu army at the Battle of Blood River. The Zulus retreated north of the Tugela River and as a result of disagreement between Dingane and his half-brother, Mpande, the nation split. Mpande allied himself with the Voortrekkers and together they attacked and defeated Dingane's army. Dingane himself was killed. For over thirty years Mpande ruled from the Tugela to the Pongolo Rivers, tolerating the white farmers who soon took up the land to the south vacated by the Zulus.

By 1870 South Africa was world-renowned. Fortune hunters flocked to the Kimberley diamond fields and, although the discovery of the Witwatersrand goldfield was sixteen years away, a number of minor gold discoveries attracted a steady stream of prospectors. In 1872, when Mpande died and Cetshwayo, nephew of Shaka and Dingane, took over as king of the Zulu nation, the pressures of annexation and colonialism had grown to frightening proportions. The Zulus were being squeezed from the north by the Transvaal Afrikaners and from the south by the British who were arriving in increasing numbers.

At first Cetshwayo trusted Sir Theophilus Shepstone, the Secretary for Native Affairs in Natal. This trust was eroded as the British policy of land acquisition became increasingly aggressive. In 1875 the President of France, Marshall Macmahon, was appointed arbitrator of the rival claims of Britain and Portugal to Delagoa Bay. Britain lost the bay but the British territorial frontier was drawn just to the south, north of the Kosi lakes, "to everyone's satisfaction". Any claim the Thonga people may have had was dismissed as "they themselves affirmed that they had no power to contract treaty agreements". The AmaThonga were probably handicapped by their inability to understand the system of exclusive land ownership practised in Europe. Henri Junod, the renowned Swiss anthropologist who made a definitive study of the AmaThonga early in the 20th century, explained that these people saw God not so much as a supreme being but rather as a personification of nature. They believed that the land belonged to nature and man had only the right to its use. Thus the new border was drawn with complete disregard for the Thonga people, some of whom found themselves under Portuguese domination while others were under

Right: King Cetshwayo kaMpande ruled the Zulu kingdom from 1872 until his death in 1884. In those tumultuous twelve years he left an indelible mark in history, defeating the British at Isandlwana in 1879. Many people felt that his imprisonment and the subsequent treatment of the Zulu nation was a travesty of justice. After he was permitted to present his case to Queen Victoria in London, he was reinstated as king. His son Dinizulu was exiled to St Helena in 1888 and only allowed to return ten years later on condition that he accepted diminished status as an induna, or chief. In 1970, Chief Mangosuthu Buthelezi was successful in his campaign to have official recognition of the royal kings of KwaZulu restored. King Goodwill Zwelithini is the eighth and current Zulu monarch.

Opposite: In a tradition started by Shaka, Zulu kings award their bravest warriors with the red wing-feathers of the purplecrested lourie.

Lord Chelmsford had made a name for himself in the Crimea in the 1850s. He left Africa 30 years later with his reputation in tatters.

British rule. As time went on, the AmaThonga's sacred sense of place was to be abused again and again.

When Shepstone annexed the Transvaal in 1877 and supported the Transvalers in their land dispute with the Zulus, Cetshwayo felt betrayed. Were they to be next? Cetshwayo was right to be worried. The British viewed the Zulu kingdom as the greatest threat to civilisation on the east coast of South Africa. Cetshwayo was a strong leader: intelligent, popular amongst his people, and courageous. He had revitalised the Zulu army, which had become as powerful as it ever had been under Shaka. He had a formidable army commander, Chief Ntshingwayo kaMahole. Cetshwayo was not a man to be frightened off with words.

In December 1878 Sir Bartle Frere, the British High Commissioner, gave Cetshwayo an ultimatum: disband his army, or the British, under its commander-in-chief Lord Chelmsford, would invade the Zulu kingdom. It was Hobson's choice. Without an army, Cetshwayo would be killed by relatives who had been baying for his blood ever since he had fought a great battle against his half-brother, Mbulazi. If he kept his army, the British with their superior fire-power would, in the end, overrun his kingdom. Bishop Colenso was outspoken in his opposition of the decision to invade Zululand.

Paying no attention to its critics, the British army was well organised and ready. As soon as the ultimatum expired in January 1879, Chelmsford led his troops across the Buffalo River into Zulu territory. Frere and Chelmsford had made their first mistake. They had not waited for approval from Disraeli's government and a nod from Queen Victoria. Disraeli himself was severely criticised by the public and the press in London. Though he tried to extricate his government from responsibility for the actions of the British army's invasion of Zululand, his unpopularity grew as events unfurled. The following year his government was overthrown and Gladstone became Prime Minister of England.

Chelmsford's second mistake was that he underestimated his foe. Chief Ntshingwayo kaMahole had cut his teeth in battle while a young man in Shaka's army. He understood military tactics as well as any commander in history. Now in his early seventies, he was still capable of leading his army of 30 000 at a run, covering more than sixty miles a day.

Lord Chelmsford had no idea that men on foot could move so fast over such long distances, or that 30 000 men could simply disappear in open country. The Zulu discipline was so absolute that not a murmur rose from the ravine where the men crouched waiting for the order to advance. Then fate intervened. A small British patrol stumbled on them and fired the first shots of the battle. The Zulus attacked the British encampment at the foot of Isandlwana, using a traditional military tactic known aptly as 'the horns of the buffalo'. The horns to the left and right moved around to encircle the enemy while the head descended at a run with the terrifying sounds of the rattling of their spears, the thumping of their huge shields and their deafening battle cries carrying across the

Previous page and this page: The men who fought in the Zulu wars had to be both tough to face the hardships of the campaign and also incredibly brave. Many were awarded the Victoria Cross with its understated inscription, 'For valour'. *Below:* The burning of Cetshwayo's house at Ulundi in 1879.

Opposite: After France was defeated by Prussia, the Prince Imperial, great nephew of Napoleon Bonaparte and son of Empress Eugenie, enrolled at the Royal Military Academy. He later volunteered for service in Africa. In June 1879, a month before the final Zulu battle at Ulundi, the Prince died bravely facing a Zulu impi.

open ground to Isandlwana. The British fought valiantly but as the sun disappeared in a partial eclipse at about two o'clock on the afternoon of January 22nd, 1879, the last of the officers and men were annihilated high on the slopes of that Sphinx-like mountain.

It was the worst defeat of a British army in colonial history. Ntshingwayo was to become a legend among the Zulus, but his name does not feature prominently in books written about the battle. David Rattray, who has made a lifelong study of the Zulu wars, and who so vividly reconstructs the Isandlwana battle scene, suggests that he was given so little credit because the British preferred to ascribe the Isandlwana defeat to mistakes on the part of Chelmsford rather than to the brilliant leadership of a Zulu savage.

Later the same day, against the express orders of his half-brother Cetshwayo, Prince Dabulamanzi attacked Chelmsford's base camp at Rorke's Drift where 139 men, including hospital staff and patients, were stationed. British prestige was to some extent salvaged by this valiant group of men, who fought off the Zulus and won more Victoria Crosses than have ever been awarded in a single battle before or since. After further bloody engagements at Hlobane, at Kambula and at Ulundi, where on 4th July 1879 the power of the Martini Henry rifles proved devastating, the Zulu kingdom ceased to exist. The place that the Zulus had called heaven was about to become hell.

Cetshwayo was banished and the British set about destroying the power of the Zulu kings. Sir Garnet Wolseley, governor of Natal, divided Zululand into thirteen separate territories, each under a different chief. Two of the appointed chiefs were cousins of Cetshwayo who had crossed over to the British; the rest were men of little or no standing whom the Zulus contemptuously called the 'abafokazana', the strangers. The most notable of the strangers was John Dunn, a British elephant hunter and confidant of Cetshwayo whom he had deserted before the battle of Isandlwana. Wolseley's division of Zululand – undertaken with advice from Dunn – was regarded by Bishop Colenso as a travesty of justice. He and his two daughters became increasingly outspoken about the fate of the Zulus. Wolseley's policy was certainly enough to set rival upon rival and lead a few years later to civil war. After being permitted to visit Queen Victoria in London in 1883, Cetshwayo was allowed to return to KwaZulu, but by then he was a sick man and without the strength or support to redirect the course of events. He died the following year. Zululand was annexed in 1887. Ten years later Maputaland was also incorporated into the Colony of Natal.

The subjugation of indigenous people by men from Europe was not exclusively a South African phenomenon. In the name of Queen Victoria, armies of soldiers and missionaries had sailed forth to 'civilise' and bring Christianity to the heathen masses. They traded pretty little baubles for land and did so in the belief that it was their destiny to rule the world. Nor were the British alone in the scramble to grab African territory. At a

Left: Prince Dabulamanzi, commander of the forces that crossed the Buffalo River into Natal and attacked Rorke's Drift.

Right: John Dunn, one of the thirteen 'abafokazana', who were appointed to rule Zululand after it was annexed by the British. Earlier in his career Dunn, a handsome, larger-than-life character, had earned the friendship and confidence of Cetshwayo. He had supplied the Zulu king with guns and was lavishly rewarded with cattle and land. He was also made a Zulu chief and was given forty-eight Zulu wives.

conference in Berlin in 1884 and 1885 the European powers agreed on their spheres of influence. By the beginning of the 20th century all of Africa, except for Ethiopia, Liberia and nominally Egypt, was under the 'protection' of one European power or another.

Overshadowing all the political strife, an epidemic of rinderpest swept down from the north in 1896, indiscriminately killing larger antelope and cattle. The Zulu people, who had already lost so much, now lost virtually all their livestock. From being the richest tribe in Africa, they were now amongst the poorest.

There was a brief respite before the final nail was driven into the coffin. For two years the British were at war with the Afrikaner Republics which, with their diamonds and gold, were a much richer prize than the farmlands of Zululand and Natal. In 1902, soon after the Anglo Boer War, a commission was appointed to carve up Zululand. Special areas had already been set aside for game reserves. These included Hluhluwe, Umfolozi and St Lucia. (Mkuze Game Reserve was proclaimed ten years later.) Of the balance of about 12.5 million acres, the Zulu people were left with two million.

The AmaThonga of Maputaland received even less consideration. Virtually the whole of the flood plain between the Pongolo and Mkuze Rivers – the only fertile area in Maputaland – was designated Crown land. The local communities were to be confined to the arid Ubombo mountain range and the infertile coastal area east of the Muzi swamps. Almost immediately two farms on the Pongolo River were occupied by white farmers, but once again nature had the final word. The first cotton-growing experiment failed and for many years no further attempt was made to occupy the Mkuze flood plain.

The door, however, had been left open for others to try their luck.

PAST MISTAKES CAST
LONG SHADOWS

Living close to the earth the AmaThonga had developed a deep understanding of the laws of nature. If those laws were broken they would starve. Maintain the balance, and they would live in paradise. The hippo and the crocodile were both their friends and their enemies. Hippo at times ruined their crops but they also kept open the channels to the pans. Crocodiles kept the barbel, which preyed on tilapia, under control. Destroy either and the tilapia populations of the pans and rivers would be devastated and the people would starve. If the wildlife was annihilated it would take away another important part of their livelihood. And if the natural habitat - on which they depended for their food, their health, their music and their homes - was destroyed, there would be nothing left. This is what happened.

The tsetse fly and the malarial mosquito had kept all but the most intrepid of hunters out of Maputaland during the 19th century. In the next century men arrived hungry for land. They brought cattle that had little resistance to the diseases of Africa. It was not long before war was declared, not on the tsetse fly which was the real culprit, but on the wildlife which was perceived as the carrier of nagana, the deadly cattle disease. Over a period of thirty years the wildlife was systematically slaughtered in a futile effort to rid the land of nagana. If it had not been for the discovery of DDT, there would have been no animals left at all. But no one questioned the effect of DDT on the insect and bird life, or had the foresight to realise that without the agents of pollination, there would be no fruit in the following season.

By the middle of the 20th century nature's merry-go-round was no longer in balance. It was in a vicious downward cycle that nothing could stop. The more white men tried to cultivate the nutrient-poor land, the stronger became nature's resistance. But along the way the land was slowly and inexorably being turned into a desert. The AmaThonga lost their land, and their happy, carefree life. And the Maputaland plain, which had once reverberated with the sound of their music, became silent.

The Zulu people, so proud, so able and so independent, were reduced to poverty both materially and spiritually. It was to be many years before they once again held their heads up high.

THE YEAR WAS 1919 and thousands of young men were returning from war in Europe. Many of them had been schoolboys when they had signed up. Now they were looking to the future, full of hope, enthusiasm and energy.

Many ex-servicemen took up the government offer of allotments of land in northern Zululand, which were given to them provided they had sufficient capital to start farming. Oscar Curry was 20 years old. With the help of a little subterfuge from the local bank manager, who agreed to give him an overdraft facility on condition that he never drew on it, he was able to show that he had a bank balance of £1900. It was enough for him to be granted a piece of dry bushveld to the north of the Umfolozi Game Reserve. For the next 26 years he and a dwindling band of settlers tried to wrest a living from the land. Curry was the last of the original soldier-settlers to give up. His cattle had been destroyed by nagana. Horses, mules, donkeys, dogs and even domestic pigs died. He had tried to grow maize, tobacco and cotton. His first crop of 300 acres of cotton was starting to burst when rain fell in torrents for eight solid weeks. Sixty inches fell between 10th February and 10th April 1925. The next season drought set in. Sometimes hail fell, and if it wasn't the weather, then the insects destroyed his crops. Eventually he was forced to leave Zululand with little to show for his toil except ill health caused by frequent bouts of malaria and other diseases. Curry was a superb farmer, but he could not farm land that was never intended for agriculture. He had learnt one of Africa's harsh rules.

Soon after the turn of the century access to Zulu territory was made easier by a railway line built almost to the Umfolozi River. The clamour to open the area to settlers reached a crescendo. By 1905 the commission appointed to slice up Zululand and give land to settlers had completed its task. The Zulu people had no say in the process and white farmers got the go-ahead to move into Zululand. R.A.L. Brandon, the magistrate for the Ubombo region, summed up the attitude of Natal's white population when he wrote in his annual report for 1914: "Malaria and nagana are the curse of this Division. It is an ideal country for cattle. A few years ago it was heavily stocked but it is now given up entirely to game. There are thousands and thousands of wildebeest roaming about this area, and a large number of game, vermin, carnivora and other wild beasts. It is a shocking waste of excellent country."

Dr D.T. Mitchell, called in by the Veterinary Education and Research Department in 1916 to investigate nagana, reported that there was a definite link between game and cattle disease. He proposed that all game outside the reserves be shot. It was all the farmers needed. The cry went up: "Kill the game." Few people listened to Dr Ernest Warren, director of the Natal Museum in Pietermaritzburg, who repeated over and over again that it was imperative to eliminate the tsetse fly, not the game. In 1917 the whole of Maputaland, except the reserves, was thrown open to hunters. The African communities that lived on the borders of the Hluhluwe,

Previous page: Hinged terrapins take advantage of the heavy rains in Maputaland to move from puddle to puddle searching for safe waters away from crocodiles.

These pages: The nyala, rhino and hippo, protected during the nagana campaign, became the pillars on which the KwaZulu Natal reserves were built.

Umfolozi and Mkuze Game Reserves had been hunter gatherers for generations. Now they were about to lose their livelihood.

Anybody could shoot anything except rhino, hippo and nyala. Frank Vaughan Kirby, the first ranger in charge of the Zululand reserves and a great conservationist, described the proclamation as "a senseless, hysterical piece of legislation". It omitted the rhino because it was close to extinction, the nyala because of its beauty and the hippo probably for no other reason than that they were not easy to reach in the impenetrable wetlands of Maputaland. The farmers and hunters wasted no time in going on the rampage. They killed an estimated 25 000 wildebeest as well as thousands of zebra, impala and other game.

When Curry and his group of ex-servicemen arrived to settle to the north of the Umfolozi Reserve, the first round of slaughter had been completed. The new farmers were invited to make a clean sweep, shooting all that was left of the game on their farms. But it soon became apparent that the wholesale slaughter of wildlife had not stopped their cattle from dying. The farmers should have realised at this point that killing wild animals was not the answer. In fact, the opposite happened. The farmers were adamant that game and cattle could not live together. They demanded the deproclamation of Umfolozi Game Reserve so that all wildlife within the reserve could be killed. Alternatively, they proposed that the government purchase the farms from them and proclaim the whole area as one big game reserve. Eighty years later conservationists are still trying to do just that!

Vaughan Kirby, his anger and frustration showing between the lines, wrote to the Natal Provincial Secretary: "I am debarred by the exigencies of official correspondence from saying what I wish to. But I may at least ask you to put to yourself the question: What has been gained by this slaughter? And I do not hesitate to affirm that you can only find one reply thereto, and that is nothing, absolutely nothing!"

The conservationists had one single trump card in their hands. The white rhino in Umfolozi represented the last of a species that had once roamed all over southern Africa. Now it faced extinction. In 1921 a temporary stay of execution was granted by the Minister of Agriculture who, to placate the farmers, agreed to finance a study of the tsetse fly. The man chosen for the task was Robert Harris, a plant inspector in the Department of Agriculture with no training or qualifications in entomology. He was given three years in which to solve the tsetse fly problem.

Harris tackled the problem with great energy and enthusiasm and soon discovered that the tsetse fly kept to bush country. He thought that if strips of land around these areas were denuded of vegetation, the fly could be localised. The idea was quickly discarded when the cost of keeping vast areas clear of fast-growing indigenous bush was calculated. Then Harris discovered that he could catch thousands of tsetse flies in a trap. He estimated that 30 000 traps would be needed to eradicate the fly. The problem, once again, was who was going to pay? The government

In the 1940s the last free-ranging lion in Maputaland wandered into the old sisal plantations near Hluhluwe, leaving a trail of hunters in its wake. The conservationists tried to help the lion to escape by spreading misinformation through the Hluhluwe party-line telephone system. It seemed that the minute the word 'lion' was heard, there would be twenty ears listening. It was also the signal for every able-bodied farmer to be out with a gun. In the past 60 years there has been a quantum change in attitudes towards wildlife: a far greater consciousness of the importance of all species on earth, not only *Homo sapiens*.

claimed it was the responsibility of the provincial authority, and vice versa. Eventually, when it became clear that the government had no intention of assisting the Zululand farmers, the provincial council agreed to finance a limited number of traps.

Almost immediately it seemed that the problem of nagana had been solved. Flies were caught in their millions, the incidence of nagana disease in cattle diminished, and farmers felt confident enough to restock their farms. But it was an ill-timed decision. Within a year the tsetse flies were back. What had been thought a brilliant eradication programme had been nothing more than a seasonal dip in the number of flies.

General J.C.G. Kemp, newly appointed Minister of Agriculture, had no sympathy for wildlife. In 1925 he stated categorically that the reserves should be abolished and the wildlife exterminated. Although the conservationists were better organised than before, the future of wildlife was poised on a knife-edge for years as pressure to close the reserves mounted. Dr George Campbell, who became chairman of the Natal branch of the Wildlife Society in 1929, played a leading role in the fight. He argued that the slaughter was not based on scientific evidence and proposed a full-scale research programme. But before this could get under way, he lost the first round of the battle.

Between May 1929 and November 1930 an estimated 26 000 animals were killed in the buffer zones around Umfolozi. More were shot on private land and within the reserves. Within the Mkuze Game Reserve, despite the fact that no tsetse fly had been seen for two years, 1400 animals were killed, including nyala which had previously been protected. Dr P.K. Viljoen, acting director of Veterinary Services, stated: "The farmers must come before game. There is only one alternative to the present policy, complete extermination."

As time went on, the battle between farmers and conservationists evolved, as did all major issues in South Africa, into a political struggle between Afrikaners and Englishmen, with no voice at all for black South Africans. And so the battle continued, with General Kemp supporting the farmers and Dr Campbell trying to protect the reserves. Once again the conservationists won a brief respite. Harris was given a second chance to eradicate the fly. He had improved the design of the trap and had greater success than before, catching over seven million flies in the first year with only 487 traps. But once again his fly traps failed. By the end of the decade the fly and nagana were back with a vengeance.

By 1940 scientific knowledge about the tsetse fly had increased. Dr John Henkel had discovered the restricted breeding sites of the fly. This was the key to their eventual eradication, but initially this knowledge was ignored by the farmers. In 1941, with the leading members of the Wildlife Society fighting for their country, the government handed out guns for the final eradication of Natal's wildlife. Within three months an estimated 30 000 head of game had been slaughtered. To the west of Mkuze Game Reserve at a place called Nkonkoni, the Zulu word for wildebeest, the

From 1917 to 1947 the farmers killed about 100 000 head of game in a futile effort to rid the land of the cattle disease carried by tsetse flies. Even the nyala, which were initially protected, succumbed to the insatiable demands of the farmers. Only the animals that lived underground were safe. Below, the aardvark, which is known to have inhabited the earth some 20 million years ago in the Miocene period, managed to survive the 30-year nagana campaign.

Right: The dwarf mongoose was another of the animals that was able to survive because of its instinctive habit of going underground whenever danger appeared. Maputaland's elephants and buffalo had been wiped out in the 19th century. After 1947 few larger mammals and almost none of the predators were left.

antelope had been "as thick as fleas on a dog's back" according to Ian Player. Now there were none.

With the white rhinoceros still protected and warthog, aardvark and other game disappearing underground, the realisation gradually dawned that it was as impossible to eradicate all the wildlife as it was to catch all the flies. Then a new alternative appeared: dichloro-diphenyl-trichloroethane, or DDT. The first tests proved that the chemical was effective against tsetse flies. This time the war against the tsetse fly was waged on scientific lines. For two years the breeding habits of the fly were studied. It was discovered that only three per cent of their feeding area was used for breeding. Oscar Curry, now a member of parliament, persuaded the government to finance the aerial spraying of these breeding areas with DDT. After half a century tsetse fly was brought under control. What little wildlife remained was saved from further slaughter. Sadly, at the same time, DDT did incalculable damage to species diversity. It devastated insect and bird populations and affected pollination processes for years.

During the war against nagana the Department of Veterinary Services removed many Zulu communities from the cool well-watered hills to much harsher low-lying country. The official reason was that the area between the game reserves and the white-owned cattle farms had to be cleared of all animals. The Zulu clans were told that they could move back once the tsetse fly was eliminated. It was a promise that was not honoured. In his book *Zululand Wilderness,* Dr Ian Player tells the story of his lifelong friend, Magqubu Ntombela, whose family had to leave their birthplace in the Ongeni hills. They have never returned.

When the National Party won the election in 1947, it wasted no time in handing out to its supporters the derelict farms abandoned by the First World War settlers who had lost the battle against the tsetse fly. Subsequently the government went to extraordinary lengths to assist them financially through the Land Bank. But once again few of these farmers were successful: one could say none at all in terms of sustainable economic activity. Farming in Maputaland would always be a battle against the elements and the poor soil. In the long run it was usually nature that won.

The Land Bank had come into being to provide cheap credit for farmers in the belief that this would keep food prices down. It was an irresistible argument for any government, but it overlooked the fact that cheap money allowed farmers to neglect sound business management and farming practice. In the 1980s Jane Conyngham, working as an environmental journalist on the *Sunday Tribune* in Durban, brought to light that a farmer was borrowing cheap money to fell the century-old sycamore fig forests and plant bananas on the Mkuze flood plain each summer. The next season's floods would wash away the bananas, giving him the opportunity to claim flood damage. The farmer, who was also a National Party member of parliament, was thus being subsidised twice over while he destroyed the natural environment.

And so in the 1950s with no tsetse fly and no wildlife remaining

Opposite: The Josini Dam built in the 1970s caused the destruction of the wetland system below the dam. Intensive farming in the catchment areas of the Pongolo and Mkuze Rivers has also caused havoc with the river and with ecosystems. In 1853 two sailing ships, the *Haidee* and the *Liverpool,* sailed into the St Lucia estuary. The latter then sailed fifty km up the Mkuze River. Today with the degraded health of the river this is impossible.

South Africa, a semi arid country, has a dearth of natural wetlands. It needs to protect those it has with all its ingenuity. Many habitats such as Kosi, Lake Sibayi, St Lucia and the Muzi Pan are endangered. After years of cattle grazing, the grasslands of Phinda had been destroyed and the pan system running through the reserve had dried up. If the wetlands disappear, so will the herons: the grey (above) and the goliath and greenbacked (right).

except for a few animals that survived within the reserves, Maputaland was ready to be taken over by the farmers. But nature was not to give up that easily. She was ready to go into battle. If the farmers planted cotton, as Curry had done all those years previously, the plants were invaded by insects or destroyed by rain and hail. Attempts at planting rubber trees failed. Sisal was grown for a while until the market collapsed with the development of steel wire ropes. There was a plan to plant rice in the Muzi swamps, a beautiful wetland teeming with bird life. Even that did not succeed. The rice plants hybridised with local grasses or withered away in dry years.

The government then proposed that the best alternative for the ailing economy of Maputaland was sugar. Plans were drawn up to build a dam on the Pongolo River in the Ubombo Mountains and to develop a giant irrigation scheme on the Makhatini flood plain between the Pongolo and Mkuze Rivers. Even the Mkuze Game Reserve was included in the plan. It was to be deproclaimed and pegged out for farmlands.

Despite the controversy that arose when the building of the Josini Dam was announced, the government was prepared neither to listen to the protests nor to commission an environmental impact study. There is no doubt that the motivation for the dam was political: the government saw the project as a wonderful opportunity to attract its supporters to Zululand to compete with the English-speaking farmers who controlled the prosperous sugar industry. It also happened that a government minister closely involved in the project was a large landowner in the catchment area of the dam, giving some credence to speculation that the dam was built to turn the area into a holiday resort. The hugely expensive dam was completed in the early 1970s. Thirty years later it is a massive white elephant. The planned irrigation scheme on the flood plain never materialised. The Mkuze Game Reserve was safe. But ironically, while the dam destroyed ecosystems along the lower reaches of the Pongolo River, the catchment area became a prime game reserve covering 30 000 hectares.

From the start, everything was wrong with the scheme. The site of the dam wall was totally unsuited to the construction of a massive structure built to retain millions of tons of water. The north bank was unstable and had to be drilled and pumped with cement over and over again to strengthen the structure. For many years water was let out as fast as it entered to reduce pressure on the wall. Then in 1984, Cyclone Demoina hit KwaZulu Natal. Over half a metre of rain fell in 24 hours. The engineers held their breath as the dam filled within a few days. Much to their relief, the wall held.

The real problem with the dam lay downstream. The Pongolo River had been the lifeblood of the AmaThonga for more than a thousand years. At the end of summer the floods renewed life on the numerous pans formed as the river meanders across the Maputaland flood plain. As Paul Dutton points out, the dam destroyed far more than their agricultural system, which relied totally on the seasonal ebb and flow of the river. It

destroyed their way of life, their spirit and their will to live. It also came close to destroying the ecology of the region.

When the late summer floods stopped, the access channels to almost a hundred pans closed. This was the death knell for the tilapia and barbel, the water lilies and water chestnuts, the hippos and crocodile and the birds. Everything was endangered – except the precious dam wall. For fourteen years the Thonga people never knew when flood water would destroy their crops. After Cyclone Demoina it was decided to simulate the flooding of the river by periodically opening the sluice gates wide to flood the land downstream. Even this has not worked. The natural rhythm of the land had been destroyed. Paul Dutton remembers how the flood plain was once alive with the sound of the music of the AmaThonga. "Our game guards at Ndumu used to come to work carrying musical instruments," he recalls. "Now, wherever they go there is silence."

The Makhatini irrigation scheme failed for several reasons. Firstly, an estimated 500 000 refugees from war-torn Mozambique poured into the region in the 1970s. Many were AmaThonga who settled easily amongst their own people on the Makhatini Flats. The logistics of moving such a vast number of people to make way for white farmers became unmanageable. As early as 1975 the government changed its mind and decided to reserve the area for black development. And after 1984, the sugar industry entered a lean phase. Export earnings sagged under the weight of international pressure against the government's apartheid policy.

Further south, Cyclone Demoina unleashed another vicious cycle. Man had waged war on nature. This was her retaliation. On the Black Umfolozi River 96 per cent of the riverine forest was destroyed by the massive flood waters. The White Umfolozi fared only slightly better. The canefields were extensively damaged and farmers lost their crops. Erosion caused by cattle grazing and monocultures, largely of cane and exotic forests, had left the land denuded of the thick protective mantle of grasses and shrubs which provided a defence against torrential storms.

Instead of dealing with the cause of the problem, the government built a canal to divert any future floodwaters away from the canefields. A second mouth to the south of the St Lucia estuary was opened, and silt, which should have spread over the flood plain, was dumped into the sea each time the river came down in flood. The inshore current quickly carried the silt a few kilometres north into the mouth of the St Lucia estuary, which has to be regularly dredged to keep it open. Millions of tons of topsoil are lost each year, while the Umfolozi River no longer enters the St Lucia estuary, adding to the serious problem of the high salinity of the lake. The vicious cycle of devastation is now in high gear. Is there any way back? Or are we to continue to lose topsoil until we have created a desert?

The huge Cahora Basa dam on the Zambezi River in Mozambique is another example of man's ability to create white elephants. Paul Dutton remembers the flood plain: "About 50 000 buffalo used to graze on the

Lake Sibayi, which covers 18 sq km, is the largest freshwater lake in South Africa. With its crystal-clear blue water and wonderful fish, hippo and bird life, it is a paradise. All the inflow of water into Sibayi is from seepage from the surrounding wetlands and from direct rainfall. Yet exotic trees, which are notorious for drying the soils and lowering the water table, have been planted within its catchment area.

Previous page:
A spurwing goose takes off from the Mvubu (hippo) Dam not far from the Phinda Mountain Lodge.

Zambezi delta before the dam was built. Then the floods ceased, the grasslands dried out and the animals disappeared. Thousands of Thonga people lost their way of life and their ability to support themselves." The hydro-electric scheme was in mothballs for years. Recently Mozambique has tried to sell the Cahora Basa electricity but has found no buyers among its economically depressed neighbours. Even South Africa had overestimated its requirements.

Despite failure after failure, Maputaland continued to be targeted for agricultural development. Many crops were tried but the summers were far too hot for temperate plants, while the winter nights were too cool for tropical plant species such as vanilla vines and coconut palms. Many of the latter succumbed to a mole rat, which took an immense liking to hearts of palm. The poor soil, haphazard rainfall, gale-force winds and abundant insects added to the problems. Pineapples have been grown successfully, but only the large, established farmers can withstand losing entire crops when freak hailstorms hit the region, as one did in 1998. Granadillas and mangoes have also been tried. An 850-hectare cashew plantation, still in its infancy, is showing promise. Cashews are one of the few crops that replace nitrogen in the soil, but it is doubtful whether even these trees will survive the harsh Maputaland conditions.

Some people have learnt that you cannot tamper with an intricate system – specially one with such a poor resource base – and expect success. People who grow trees are a significant exception. Recently, despite pleas from both the public and private sector, the KwaZulu Natal Department of Forestry planted exotic pines on the wetlands around Lake Sibayi. The reason given to justify this was that the trees would help dry up the wetlands, and prevent the malarial mosquito from breeding in the area. It is the same old story all over again: upset the balance of nature and the repercussions go far beyond man's expectations. In trying to dry up the seepage areas around Sibayi, the lake itself may well be endangered. Like the Pongolo River, the lake is vital to the very existence of the AmaThonga. It is also a magnificent ecotourism venue and has much more potential than a plantation of exotic trees.

More and more, the realisation is dawning that there is an alternative. As Ken Tinley, the outstanding ecologist who had shown Dave and John Varty how to bring Londolozi back to life, pointed out, there are many ways of farming the wilderness. Ecotourism is one. Hunting is another. All the products of the wilderness can be harvested on a sustainable basis, whether animals, reeds, honey, fruit, fish or timber. Ken Tinley advocated an outward creative conservation plan. "There are altogether ninety-one species of wild ungulates in Africa compared to only twenty in South America," he wrote. "Yet more than 90 per cent of Africa's population of 500 million people suffer from a deficiency of protein and calories. This is the African paradox. People are dying amidst plenty." Ken wanted to see the replenishment of wildlife populations over the vast relatively empty areas of Africa, and their sustained use. This does

The African wilderness cannot be replicated – not even billion-dollar Disneyland developments can recreate its perfection. Nowhere else but in Africa can one find the wide open spaces, the sunsets, the clear skies and brilliant stars, the sounds of the wild, the peace and the tranquillity. Or the simple beauty of a herd of baby impala in their natural surroundings.

not automatically imply that hunting should form the basis of the rural economy. On the contrary. The wilderness and its wildlife should form the foundation of an industry that puts money into people's pockets so that they can go to the supermarket and buy food.

The Greater St Lucia Wetland Park could involve the people of Maputaland in adventure tourism, not just as employees but as partners in economic development. It is unimaginative and unjust to blame the AmaThonga and AmaZulu for the damage to the natural forests and the land. Once they lived in harmony with their surroundings and they were fully employed within a productive ecosystem. Now they have become desperate. Almost a century of disaster cannot be put right in a few years, but if the government will work with the private sector, and within a framework that respects the laws of nature, there is a chance that together a solution can be found.

Maputaland needs a single strategy. It needs to use its greatest asset: its wild beauty. Anything that detracts from, or destroys natural systems should be left out of its future plans. Maputaland should let other countries grow cashews and trees and concentrate on its unique attributes.

THE IMPOSSIBLE DREAM

It was South Africa's good fortune in the 1990s that two men took command and steered the country away from the brink of revolution: President F.W. de Klerk before the first democratic elections in 1994, and his successor, President Nelson Mandela. Together they were awarded the Nobel Peace Prize.

Throughout the 1980s the Nationalist government appeared to be blind to the effects of apartheid; inflation escalated, stringent exchange controls were put in place, the tourism industry collapsed, sportsmen were ostracised, products were boycotted and unemployment grew. The government was warned that by the end of the century, 80 per cent of the economically active population of the country would be black. It was trying to hold back a tidal wave.

The world held its breath as South Africa turned away from the brink of civil war. Once reform had been set in motion, there was no turning back. Nelson Mandela was released, the apartheid laws were scrapped and the first democratic elections were scheduled. It was only a matter of time before South Africa would be readmitted to the world stage. When that happened, huge opportunities would be opened, not just for economic gain but, pertinent to this story, for the development and conservation of South Africa's wilderness areas. It was against this background that the story of Phinda began to unfold.

Four men from different parts of South Africa shared a vision for the future of the wilderness. Their common purpose drew them together in 1989, just as the first political prisoners on Robben Island were being released. They were ahead of their time, but confident that together they could make things happen. They wanted to conserve the wilderness they loved. They also wanted to involve the rural communities, which had forgotten how to trust white men, and to borrow from their wisdom and knowledge of the wilderness. They were prepared to overturn established conservation practices and show that there were other ways. They had no idea that it was going to be so tough a ride. But as Dave Varty said, it was the right idea at the right time. And, against all odds, it succeeded.

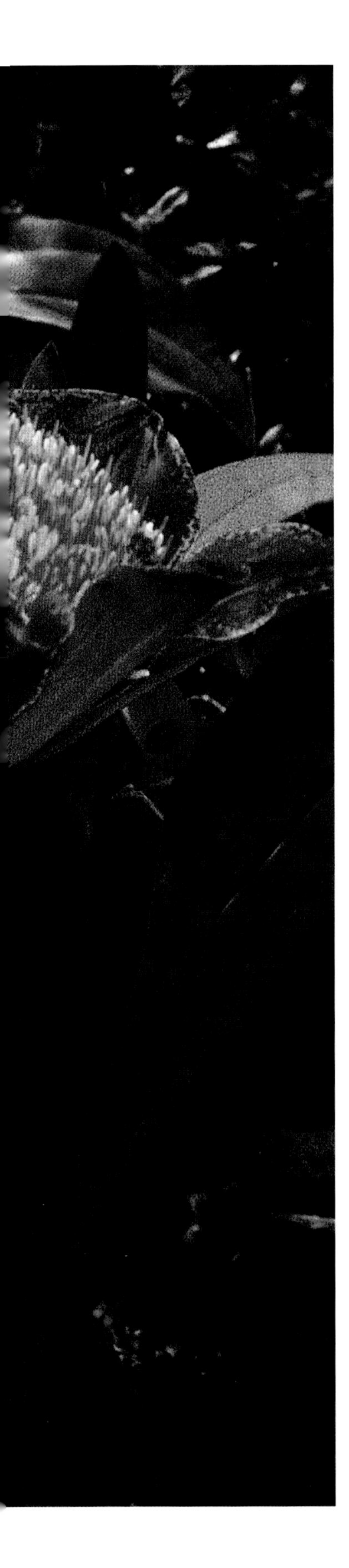

The grasslands and forests that lie between the golden beaches and the Drakensberg escarpment of KwaZulu Natal hold a richness of flora that often defies description. The *Scadoxus puniceus*, snake lily (left), is one of many spectacular flowers found each spring. All year round there are different species in bloom: in winter, flashy red and yellow aloes adorn the dry hillsides, while in late summer exquisite ground orchids hide from view in the forests and grasslands.

MANY PEOPLE REMEMBER the pristine coastline of KwaZulu Natal. The golden beaches. The clear shimmering sea. The coastal forests alive with the sounds of birds. It is hard to believe that in fifty years so much of that wilderness has disappeared. Narrow winding tracks have become dual-carriage highways, and the coastal forests have been hacked down to build houses and make way for canefields. Plantations of exotic trees have replaced the natural beauty of the forests, and years of cattle farming have taken their toll. Fortunately, there were a few who cared enough to say: "Stop! Let's keep something as it was in the beginning."

Trevor Coppen had grown up in Tanzania and loved the wide open spaces of Africa, the birds, the wildlife and the sea. As managing director of a property development company based in Durban, he found himself travelling so frequently to Sodwana, where the company had a major time-share development under way, that he took up flying. The more he explored the beautiful but inaccessible wetlands and the pristine coastal region of Maputaland, the more he became convinced that the area would become the Okavango of South Africa, a prime tourism destination. His dream was that one day, in the not too distant future, all the reserves would be linked together: the Sodwana State Forest, St Lucia, Mkuze, Umfolozi and Hluhluwe. And perhaps he would be involved.

Trevor thought about finding a suitable farm in the area which he could put back to wildlife and develop as a time-share resort. Then out of the blue he read an advertisement for a similar project on a farm outside Pietermaritzburg that was being developed by Agri-Plan Estates. He had never met Kevin Leo-Smith, the managing director, but he knew that Kevin had successfully run his agricultural estate agency business for a number of years. "Principally I called him because I thought he could help me find a suitable farm for a Maputaland time-share project," Trevor remembers. "I asked him what he was doing in the time-share business. 'That's my territory,' I told him. 'You stick to farming. But let's work together.' Kevin's reaction was fast. He said he would leave Pietermaritzburg in five minutes and would be with me in an hour. He wanted to talk to me, not about his time-share advertisement, but about a dream he had for the Mkuze area.

"Kevin arrived at my office with a three-metre-long map of the farms between Mkuze and St Lucia and we identified a group of farms adjoining the Mkuze Game Reserve. The northern section included the farm Zulu Nyala, while further south towards St Lucia there was a maze of small farms mostly under pineapples. We had an idea that once we had secured the options on these farms we would approach the Natal Parks Board and offer to link the farms up with Mkuze. We would retain the rights to develop a time-share scheme on the property.

"Our first job was to visit some of the farmers and establish prices in the area. With so many farms on our schedule we realised our chance of keeping the project under wraps was minimal and it would reduce with

each negotiation. Once the word got out that we were about to start a major ecotourism project, prices would double and even treble."

Trevor and Kevin decided to concentrate initially on Zulu Nyala, a 6000-hectare property owned by Trevor Shaw. The farm had more wildlife on it than any other. Charles Tinley, younger brother of Ken, had seen to that. Thirty years earlier, three experiences had combined to bring him to Zulu Nyala. While working at Mkuze for the Natal Parks Board he had seen the culling of wildebeest and had felt it was wrong that meat was left to rot on the ground rather than given to people starving on the other side of the fence. He had also participated in game capture operations and animal relocation with Jan Oelofse at Mkuze and knew that money could be made out of selling game. Thirdly, Norman Deane, a professional hunter, had taught him the advantages of hunting. Charles was on his way towards the concept of multiple sustainable utilisation of the products of the wilderness and was years ahead of his time as a conservationist.

Charles had always loved Maputaland. One day he heard that a wealthy farmer from the Transvaal was flying to Richards Bay to buy land for cattle ranches. Charles waited at the airport and managed to catch Tinus Bester's attention. He proposed that at least some of the land Bester was buying should be used as a game farm. Bester replied that he knew nothing about game and would not know how to start such a project. Did Charles know? That was the beginning. For nearly a decade Charles and his wife Caroline worked on the Zulu Nyala ranch, bringing in animals and later establishing a sustainable game butchery. By 1975 the butchery was processing 8000 kilograms of meat a week. In the end Charles's success in managing the farm was also to his detriment – he lost his job. Charles had reintroduced white rhinoceros, giraffe and other antelope and had a thriving nyala population. When Bester needed to liquidate some of his assets he sold the farm to Trevor Shaw who closed the butchery.

Zulu Nyala was spectacular. It stretched from the Mzinene River in the south, over the Ubombo foothills and northwards towards the acacia thornveld. The southernmost section in particular, with its sweet grasses, was capable of a high carrying capacity once the invasive bush that had taken over on overgrazed land was removed. Trevor Coppen continues: "Our negotiations had gone so far along the line that we brought in Rand Merchant Bank. Just when we thought we had them in the bag Trevor Shaw changed his mind and wanted more money. Rand Merchant Bank was not prepared to raise their offer.

"In the meantime, Jane Conyngham had joined my company to handle the public relations aspects of our Sodwana development. She knew Maputaland well and, like Kevin and me, was passionate about doing something to save the territory from sliding almost inevitably into destruction. In her previous job as a journalist on the *Sunday Tribune* she had covered environmental issues. She knew more than most of us about the Natal Parks Board's plans for the area. I asked her to look at our map and give us her ideas. Jane immediately made another suggestion. 'Why

Previous page: A darter on the Mzinene River hangs its wings out to dry after an underwater swim to catch a fish.

Nyala (from the Zulu name inxala) never stray far from the security of riverine forests of fig (below) and fever trees.

not abandon going south and look northwards?' We stopped, had another look and drew a new outline. This time there were fewer farms. One was particularly big – Zinave, named after the Zinave National Park in Mozambique. South of Zinave were two farms of over 2000 hectares, Bumbeni and Lulubush. If we included Zulu Nyala we had everything we could have wished for within that pencil outline – mountains with glorious views, sand forests, rivers lined with wonderful fig and fever tree forests, the flood plain, the sea to the east, and not least of all, a common boundary with Mkuze Game Reserve to the west. There and then we decided to switch our focus. Instinctively Jane had extended the proposed reserve from wetland to wetland: from the Mkuze River in the north to the Mzinene River in the south. She had brought in a far greater diversity of habitats and consequently of wildlife.

"Kevin Leo-Smith had an ideal background for the project. He was an experienced agricultural economist and a game farm owner as well as having wide experience in property. His task was to secure options on all the farms within the area we had identified. He quickly established that most of the farmers weren't making money. Some were close to bankruptcy. That did not make his job any easier. There were some keen sellers and others, who were running hunting safaris, who weren't interested.

"One of the first people we talked to was Dr Alan Heydoorn, chief executive of the SA Nature Foundation, an associate of WWF, the World Wide Fund for Nature. Alan was excited about the project. If South Africa was going to maintain its wonderful biodiversity, it desperately needed more land under conservation. Already many migratory birds were on the red data list of endangered species – a sure sign that there was not enough natural habitat for them. Alan suggested that we needed an established conservationist with a high profile to get the project off the ground. Jane proposed that we approach John Varty who, with his brother Dave, had founded the Londolozi Game Reserve. John had started film-making because he felt it was the most powerful way to tell Africa's story.

"Kevin had met Alan Bernstein, managing director of JHI International, which he had formed specifically to unlock the potential for development in sub-Saharan Africa. He knew Alan had identified ecotourism as a major investment opportunity once the apartheid regime collapsed. One call from Kevin was all it took for Alan to swing into action. He went to the UK and invited David Jones, director of the Zoological Society, London to come to South Africa and listen to our dreams. He then asked John Varty if they could bring a party along to hear the Londolozi story. With those two calls, Alan had a team that could provide international conservation credibility and wide experience in animal relocation, habitat rehabilitation and rural community involvement. We also had our first meeting with the Natal Parks Board. Although there were no commitments made on either side, we left feeling that if we were able to arrange the finance, they would be interested in taking the project further. We were wrong.

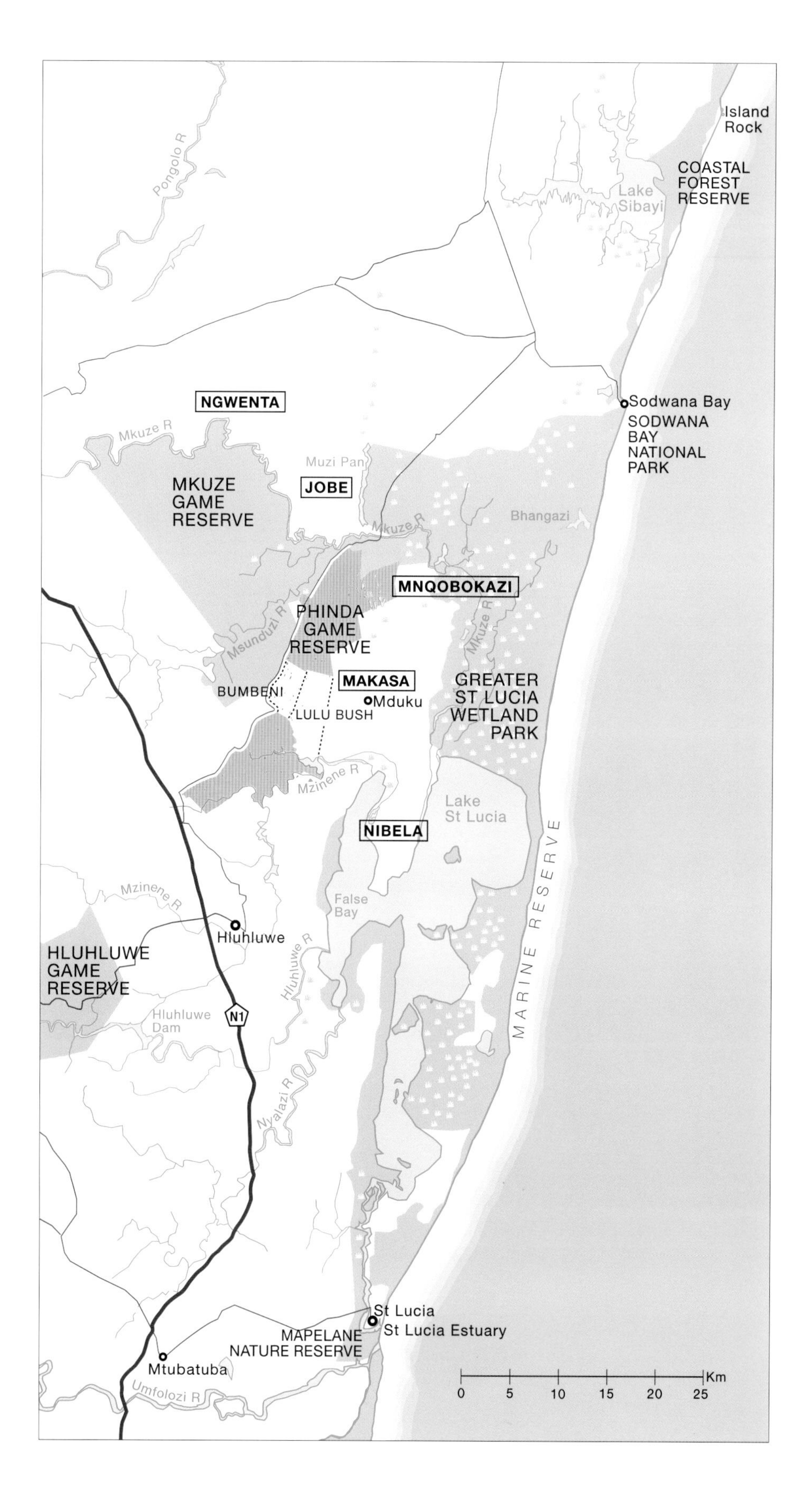

Right: Southern Maputaland stretches along the coastal plain from Lake St Lucia to Lake Sibayi, and inland to the Mkuze Game Reserve and the Ubombo Mountains. At the start of 1991 Phinda Game Reserve consisted of two properties: in the north the farm Zinave, and in the south, Zulu Nyala. The two properties were separated by the farms Bumbeni and Lulubush, while the main Sodwana road ran between Phinda and the Mkuze Game Reserve.

For five years Phinda enjoyed traversing rights over Lulubush but the lease over the farm was not renewed in 1997. Long before that, however, Bumbeni had become part of the Munyawana Game Reserve (see page 110). The most significant change to the map has been the building of a new road through to Mozambique, which, for the first time, provides all-weather access for the Nibela, Makasa and Mnqobokazi communities that live to the east of Phinda.

Next page: In KwaZulu Natal a sangoma (centre), imparts knowledge of her skills to her apprentice (left). The inyanga, or traditional healer (right), uses nearly 1000 different plants to treat ailments.

There is much to learn about these people; from the uncanny powers of the sangoma to the healing qualities of the herbs and plants that are used by two-thirds of the people of Africa.

"On the surface everything was better than we could have believed possible. Then a bombshell hit us. The Minister of Environmental Affairs announced that he was going to expropriate all the farms over which we had options. The public perception – and that of the Natal Parks Board – was that we had used inside information to acquire the options. Nothing could have been further from the truth. We decided to tackle the problem at the very highest level. Alan managed to set up a meeting with the Minister of Environmental Affairs, Mr Gert Kotze, in Cape Town. He confirmed that there was no way we could have known of any expropriations. The announcement had been premature, he told us. And, in any event, the government did not have the budget. He asked us to back off the farms on the southern bank of the Mkuze River as the Parks Board hoped to raise funds to buy a corridor of land linking the Mkuze and St Lucia Reserves. We readily agreed. He promised to advise the Natal Parks Board of our discussion. What we did not realise then was that the incident would leave a legacy of distrust that would prove to be a great stumbling block when Phinda sought partnership with the Natal Parks Board towards constructive developments in the area.

"It was an enormously exciting time. Although we had no capital, we had consolidated options over quite a large area. We had even bought our first farm. After our meeting with the Minister, we celebrated with a bottle of champagne. Over dinner we began to talk about a name for our project. Kevin suggested that we should look for the Zulu words meaning the return of the wildlife. *Phinda Izilwane*. That was where the name was born. In a little restaurant in Cape Town.

"Our next trip was to Londolozi where John Varty was to present the Londolozi 'model' showing how they had taken land damaged by years of mismanagement and turned it into one of South Africa's premier game reserves. David Jones arrived from London and joined Alan, Kevin and me. At the last moment John opted out. He had malaria and couldn't even stand on his feet. Then Dave Varty took over. For everyone it was enormously exciting. Dave talked about what they had achieved at Londolozi. About his ambitions to spread the Londolozi model throughout southern Africa. I was especially keen to learn more about the work they had initiated in the neighbouring rural communities. It was one of my basic concepts that the rural people living close to Phinda had to be very much part of our project from the beginning. They had been cut off from the benefits of the KwaZulu Natal reserves for far too long. I had started working with the community on the Nibela Peninsula on the northern shore of St Lucia and their poverty had convinced me that someone had to give them a hand."

Dave Varty was equally excited. "Although both John and I had studied commerce at university, Alan Bernstein was in a different league when it came to his breadth of understanding of international financial structures. I wrote to Alan soon afterwards and said that if he could bring real funding to Africa I could show him how to wake up the wilderness.

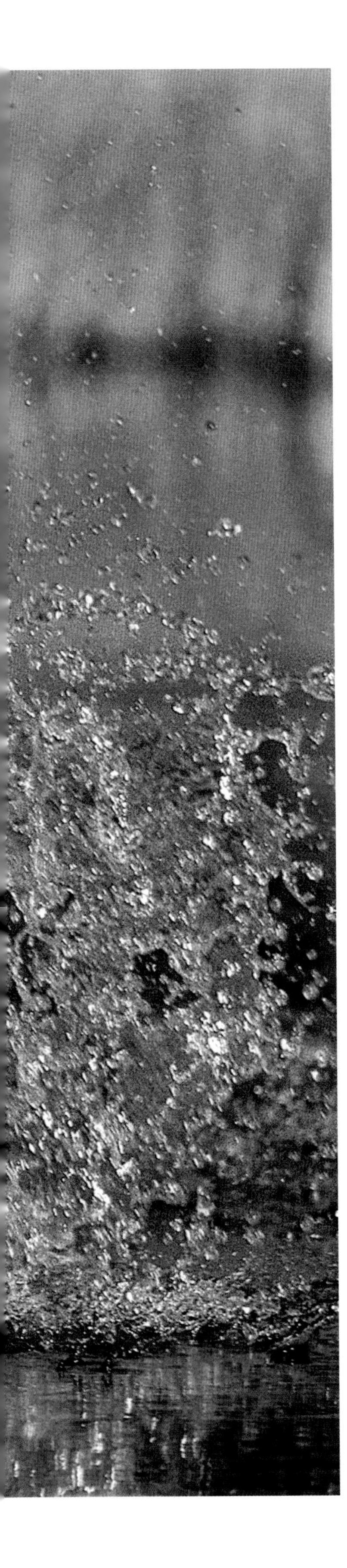

St Lucia is the largest marine lake in Africa and the only stretch of water in the world shared by sharks, crocodile and hippo. The huge demands made on the upper catchments of the Mkuze, Mzinene, Nyalazi and Hluhluwe Rivers have placed St Lucia's ecology under threat: proof of the fragile link between ecosystems.

We decided to form a company, which we would name Conservation Corporation, to bring a businesslike approach to conservation; the four of us, Alan, Kevin, Trevor and myself, would have equal shares. We knew we needed a strong financial partner and decided to approach Derek Keys, chief executive of Gencor, one of South Africa's 'big five' mining financial institutions."

At the time Gencor had a major row on its hands. Richards Bay Minerals, a Gencor group company, had applied for permission to extend its heavy mineral mining operation northwards, from Richards Bay to the eastern shores of St Lucia. The conservationists, strongly supported by the press, began a 'Save St Lucia' campaign which turned into a head-on confrontation between big business and conservationists worldwide. The problem was that RBM would need water in vast quantities, which would have to be drawn either from the St Lucia catchment area or from the lake itself. There was also a strong possibility that once RBM mined below sea level it would break through the impervious layers of compacted sand and calcium chlorides that formed a barrier between the lake and the sea.

"Once again our hope to have a major South African institution financially involved was stillborn," Trevor said. "Alan and Dave were given the go-ahead. We were told that Gencor was prepared to invest R100 million. It was time to celebrate and once again the champagne corks popped. Again prematurely. The next day we flew a party of Gencor executives to Phinda and had a wonderful visit starting with breakfast in the hills overlooking the flood plain. On the return trip Alan and Dave were told that a meeting had been set up for the next morning with Marinus Daling, chairman of Gencor's holding company, Sanlam. We were given to understand that once he had rubber-stamped the proposal we would be able to go ahead and exercise our options. We still felt no threat of impending disaster. The meeting, we were told, was a formality. However, that was not so. The following day Marinus Daling decided that there was no advantage to Gencor in investing in ecotourism in Maputaland.

"We were devastated. Time was running out. Only three weeks were left in which to exercise the options on the farms. We had already discovered just how difficult it was to raise money from South African investors, all of whom wanted security. We could not put up guarantees, only ideas. A grassroots project such as ours would not show profits for years. I was up at Sodwana telling our sad tale to an insurance broker from Sanlam. He suggested that we talk to Koos Jonker, chairman of Masterbond. I immediately went to the nearest phone box, put in the coins and dialled Koos. Within three weeks we had the guarantees in place."

Koos Jonker was an enthusiastic supporter of their dream. Masterbond had already identified Maputaland as a prime area for development. Plans had been drawn up for the building of airports, yacht marinas and major resort infrastructure at Kosi Bay and Lake Sibayi. At that stage Masterbond was flying high. Money was pouring into its business. Trevor

Coppen says: "Koos backed us to the hilt and suggested that we go back to our original plan and include Zulu Nyala in the scheme. Trevor Shaw had started an ecotourism development on the farm, building a massive structure on the top of the hill. He had also put his price up to R12.4 million. This was when my involvement started to wane. I felt we could not justify that amount straight away. I was outvoted. Conservation Corporation bought Zulu Nyala in March 1991. We now owned two fairly large pieces of land and had an outstanding loan of R30 million. I felt that I could not handle a debt of that magnitude. I also had another problem.

"I had run up against a major hurdle with the Natal Parks Board. I had been invited to the University of Natal to participate in a debate on resource utilisation. My opponents were the Natal Parks Board with which I had already had some disagreements. As a counsellor for the Nibela people, I had been fighting on their behalf with the conservationists. Soon after what became a rather heated debate, I decided it was time for me to bale out. The project was bigger than one person and it needed all the goodwill of the Parks Board it could get. Phinda was still my dream. It embodied everything I believed in."

The next stage was not the stuff dreams are made of. Alan Bernstein was waking up to a nightmare. Masterbond had provided a line of credit of R60 million in short-term funding of which more than R30 million had already been drawn. CCAfrica was running up a heavy interest bill, paying two per cent over prime which, at that time, stood at 18 per cent. They had to find more cash to develop the lodges, reintroduce game, restore grasslands, and install adequate water and power supplies and fencing. Although Nelson Mandela had been released from prison, he was still calling for sanctions and international investment markets were unsympathetic. The local market was also unresponsive. Alan had to roll up his shirt sleeves and get down to work.

One of the first things he did was go back to London. He knew Jan Newman, a fellow South African at Hambros Bank, and hoped to interest him in an investment in Phinda. "Jan introduced us to his two colleagues, Jonathan Klein, also a South African, and Mark Getty," says Dave. "These three professional financiers made a huge difference to us. Jonathan Klein proposed that Hambros convert the short-term loan from Masterbond into long-term equity. While they were drawing up a prospectus, Hambros also arranged for a due diligence investigation on Masterbond. The results they came up with were far from satisfactory." Dave recalls the timing of the events over the next few weeks vividly.

"Alan and I were on the 21st floor of the Ford Foundation, making heavy weather of our first attempt to raise equity in the United States. Our presentation to a group of rather bored high financiers went something like this: 'Yes, we are aware that Nelson Mandela is calling for sanctions. And, yes, we have bought derelict farms in the middle of northern KwaZulu Natal where the Zulu leader Mangosuthu Buthelezi is trying to go to war with the ANC. And yes, we plan to turn these farms into a

Right: Maputaland's biodiversity includes many reptiles. Top: an African rock python, *Python sebae*, which grows to about five metres in length, and a mole snake, *Pseudaspis cana*. Centre: a crocodile and a tortoise, and below, a water monitor, the largest of the African lizards, searching for birds' nests in the trees on the banks of the Mzinene River.

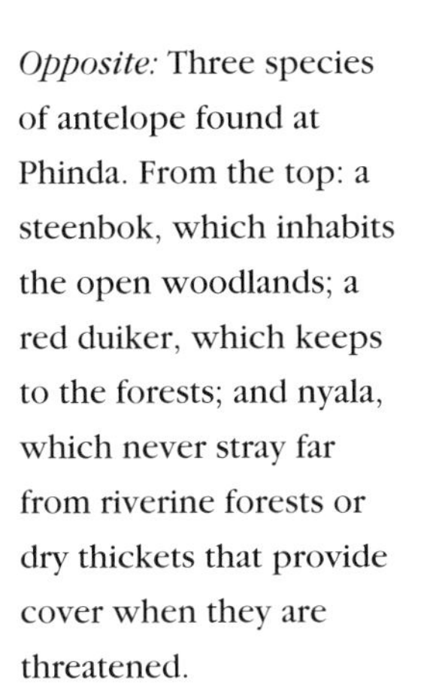

Opposite: Three species of antelope found at Phinda. From the top: a steenbok, which inhabits the open woodlands; a red duiker, which keeps to the forests; and nyala, which never stray far from riverine forests or dry thickets that provide cover when they are threatened.

A hundred years ago ivory was being exported to Britain at the rate of 500 000 kilograms a year and the African elephant was on its way to extinction. In more recent decades the combination of poaching, internecine wars, failed ideologies and a reduced range have put further pressure on the elephants. By the end of the 1980s elephant populations over the African continent had reduced from many millions to less than 600 000. The Cites ban on the ivory trade in 1989 resulted in a dramatic decrease in poaching. Fortunately modern capture techniques have made it feasible to restock the vast tracks of land left denuded of wildlife, particularly in countries such as Zambia and Mozambique.

pristine wilderness. Well, almost pristine. We would remove fifty years of rusted debris, string a fence around, reintroduce the wildlife and build luxury lodges which would attract people from all over the world. Some of the foreign currency we earned would be used to help the surrounding communities, some to improve the badly damaged habitat. There would even be a little left for shareholders.' I told them that Phinda would one day prove to be a better investment than gold! They must have thought we were lunatics. There were certainly many sceptical comments as we went off to lunch. Mark suggested that I should drop the reference to gold in future presentations. I still think that time will prove wildlife to be a much better investment.

"Later that day we received a message from South Africa that Masterbond had gone bust. If Hambros had not alerted us to the looming disaster Phinda would have had a very short life. The first lodge at Phinda was well on the way. It opened a few months later. There were construction companies and material suppliers to pay. Staff to pay. Suddenly at the end of the month there was no money. Masterbond had stopped functioning. Subsequently it would be recorded as South Africa's largest fraud case. Hambros came to our rescue and provided the bridging finance to keep us going. Because they had anticipated the disaster it took them less than 48 hours to get us organised – and we lived for yet another day. Once we had raised the equity finance we were also able to repay Masterbond in full."

Mark Getty also chalked up the miles, accompanying Alan and Dave to the major cities of the United States in their quest to raise equity. Dave was never quite sure whether he shared their dreams from the beginning or whether, after listening to over 200 presentations, any doubts he had were simply worn away! The turning point in their fortunes came when Mark decided that he would try to interest his entire family in an investment in Conservation Corporation. It had been years since the family had split up, and their major investment in Getty Oil had been sold and divided among four trust companies. Mark, grandson of J. Paul Getty, felt that perhaps Phinda would provide the means to heal old wounds and reunite the family in a fascinating conservation project with a strong social component. His younger brother, Tara, agreed with him. It might prove to be a costly adventure. On the other hand, given the time, it might one day provide them with a good return on their investment. They were prepared to take that risk.

It certainly was a visionary move for one of the great United States dynasties and set a trend that was followed more and more frequently a decade later. Today we often hear of men of great wealth, amassed largely during the information age, who are looking at ways to put something back into the natural world. Perhaps it is because these people of enormous ability and intellect have achieved so much in finite terms that they look beyond their busy lives towards the natural world and to what is infinite. There is no doubt that the wildlife and the sparse areas of

The greatest threat to cheetahs is not lions, nor is it hyenas or leopards. Ever since men from Europe arrived in Africa, man has proved to be the greatest enemy of these timid cats. Cheetahs need space in which to hunt and to establish their own territories away from the heavier, more aggressive predators. Man has systematically reduced their range and forced them into close proximity with their natural enemies.

pristine wilderness that remain on this planet need all the help they can get. There is just so much that can be done.

Mark had a sympathetic adviser on his side: Judge Bill Newsom, a trustee of three of the four Getty trusts and an old family friend. Bill's involvement in conservation seemed far more than any one man could handle. He was a trustee of the Environmental Defense Fund and the Sierra Club Legal Defense Fund (Earth Justice), which represents the environmental movement in the United States. He was also president of the Mountain Lion Foundation in California, a state that is rapidly losing its wilderness areas as its population expands to over 50 million. Bill was someone who understood CCAfrica's goals.

The geography of our planet has always been dynamic, much more so in its early history, less so today. But even now the changes continue. These are usually imperceptible until one day a river starts flowing west instead of east, an earthquake shakes buildings to the ground, a volcano erupts, or an island disappears into the sea.

Millions of years ago Gondwanaland, the ancient super-continent of the southern hemisphere, began to split into the land masses that are now Africa, Madagascar, India, South America, Australia and Antarctica. Huge blocks of land were thrust high above the plains while others collapsed into deep valleys or into the sea. Some 140 million years ago, as a result of the pressure of the continual westerly continental drift, the east coast of Africa fractured almost from top to bottom, forming the Red Sea in the north, the Great Rift Valley of East Africa, and the Ubombo and Lebombo mountain ranges in the south.

Over millions of years the southern African subcontinent continued to heave while sea levels worldwide rose and fell. During all this geological activity the ocean periodically advanced to the foot of the Ubombo Mountains, while at other times the sea receded, revealing a low coastal plain. These marine inundations changed the topography and the ecology of the region. Sedimentary and sandy marine deposits were laid down, the courses of rivers changed, and lakes and depressions were gouged out. Even today the high range of dunes along the coastline continues to form. Centuries of wind and water erosion have uncovered beds rich in marine fossils that tell the story of this turbulent geological history.

Maputaland lies between the coastal sand dunes in the east and the Ubombo Mountains in the west. To the north is Mozambique and to the south Lake St Lucia, the largest estuary in Africa. Phinda covers an area of 15 000 hectares in the south of this region and is within sight of the coastal dunes and the northern shores of Lake St Lucia to the east and the Ubombo Mountains in the west. It lies between the Mkuze River in the north and the Mzinene River in the south; wetland to wetland.

It is a wilderness made for wildlife.

Maputaland had a long history of harmony. Of man and animals living together. Of man respecting nature and never taking more than could be replenished in the next season. Was it possible that at least some parts of the coastal plain could stay the same forever?

DAVE VARTY AND ALAN BERNSTEIN were the last to climb into the helicopter. They paused for a moment. Ahead of them were five men who could make a difference, not only for the fledgling company: it was just possible that their combined influence would set the ball rolling and bring change to this part of the world which for so many years had been devastated by man's unwitting activities. Christopher Sporborg, deputy chairman of Hambros Bank, London, had underwritten the prospectus for a private placement of Conservation Corporation's shares. Neale Axelson, chairman of the AECI pension fund, had taken a keen interest in their ideas. Mark Getty had brought his uncle, Gordon Getty, head of one of the largest financial dynasties in the United States. Judge Bill Newsom, a trusted adviser to Gordon, completed the party. Dave thought that he could not have been more fortunate. It was a remarkable group. All were responsible men who wanted to make the world a better place. Nonetheless, the black clouds that had threatened Alan and Dave for a year had not yet rolled away. It was imperative that every aspect of this trip to Phinda was perfect.

It was an early November morning. A few puffy white clouds sat on the horizon to the south. Otherwise, the sky was clear and there was no sign of the change in the weather forecast for later that day. There was still an enormous amount of work to be done even though the first lodge had been opened a few months previously. The executive team had been so busy raising funds that getting the reserve going had taken second place on their agenda. But that was changing fast. If the day went well they would have the time to concentrate on Phinda's operations. They would be busy listening to reports from key staff members, visiting tribal chiefs and meeting neighbours. There were some vital land consolidations outstanding and that would take much of their time.

Dave had a vision of extending the green frontiers and in time joining together with their neighbours to form another Sabi Sand Wildtuin, the community of private reserves adjacent to the Kruger National Park. Already a name for the new reserve had been chosen: Munyawana, the river of salt, named after the river that flowed through the centre of the reserve. But that was still in the future. They first had to prove that multi-use conservation development in Maputaland could better any other form of economic activity; that it could prove to be both ecologically sustainable and economically viable. After a year of anxiety everything had come together. Now there was hope.

Maputaland is a unique combination of beautiful wetlands and lakes, meandering rivers and magical riverine forests interspersed with dry sand forests, acacia bush and palmveld. The coastal dune forests, the golden beaches and a marine reserve add to the beauty of Maputaland. This intricate web of ecosystems just south of the tropics supports a wide diversity of life; it is a paradise for mammals, birds, reptiles, butterflies and thousands of insects. The mosquito and the tsetse fly had provided a last

This page: The dense coastal forests are the home of samango monkeys and leopards which are seen on the beach on rare occasions.

Opposite: A giant marine turtle, like some prehistoric monster from millions of years ago, emerges from the sea to lay eggs on the beach.

line of defence protecting the land from an invasion of farmers and developers. But men had come. And they had destroyed.

Flying across the northern shore of Lake St Lucia, the helicopter crossed a line of pinkbacked pelicans. On the other side of the bay flamingo took off in a pink flurry. A flock of woollynecked storks flew close below them – too close for comfort. The lake, almost 100 kilometres in length, is home to more than 500 bird species. As the helicopter flew over, hundreds of hippo ducked below the surface, treading the shallow floor of the lake, while the crocodiles sunning themselves on the sandy banks, moved into the water with remarkable agility. From the air the lake looked as beautiful as ever. But with silting and reduced water flowing from the catchment areas it had changed significantly. Today the depth of the lake ranges between one and three metres and the salinity has sometimes risen to three times that of sea water, causing a massive number of aquatic plants and animals to die out. If ever there was a need for conservation, Dave thought, it was here.

The helicopter crossed the 200-metre-high sand dunes and a few seconds later was over the sparkling Indian Ocean. On the inland side the dunes were covered with dense forests of trees up to twenty metres in height. Below the canopy, the bushes and shrubs were interlaced with lianas and the large, spiked creeper, the thorny rope. On the sea-facing slopes of the dunes the vegetation was stunted by the salt-laden winds. The forests were home to the pretty little samango monkeys and hundreds of birds, from noisy trumpeter hornbills to brilliant narina trogons and louries. When night descended the owls and nightjars would begin their calls.

They turned again, flying north along the pristine beach. Here and there were turtle tracks which had not yet been covered by the incoming tide. The previous night a few giant leatherback turtles had left the sea in the moonlight and headed up the beach to build nests and lay eggs. Before dawn the 900-kilogram marine reptiles had completed their task and returned to the ocean. Nature has been generous in planning for the survival of this species. Each leatherback lays up to a thousand eggs during the early summer season. But from the moment of hatching the little turtles live a precarious life. An army of sea birds and crabs lies in wait as they make their way down to the sea. Once in the water their troubles are not over. They may survive the turbulent surf zone only to swim into the jaws of barracuda, tuna or some other tropical fish. Those that reach the Agulhas current are swept south until they reach the southern tip of Africa. Then the Benguela current of the Atlantic Ocean carries them more slowly northwards. Only one in a thousand hatchlings is likely to find its way back to Maputaland to begin the cycle again. It was impossible not to marvel at nature's unique and vibrant system at work – a system that has developed with little interference from man since the beginning of time.

The helicopter deviated again, turning west over the line of dunes separating Lake Sibayi from the sea. They flew over Thonga villages with

In some past age Lake Sibayi was an estuary open to the sea and to the tides. As the chain of high dunes along the coast formed, the lake became landlocked, the salinity disappeared and crocodiles and fresh-water fish replaced the marine species.

Right: A spoonbill flies over Lake Sibayi.

In a silent world of beauty, a scuba diver has a thrilling encounter with a whale shark, *Rhinocodon typicus*, the largest of all fishes. This species has been measured up to sixteen metres in length but is harmless, feeding mainly on small fish.

Above: A powder-blue surgeon, *Acanthurus leucosternon*, on the Maputaland coral reef. *Below:* A lemon shark, *Negaprion brevirostris*, is one of about forty different species of sharks found off KwaZulu Natal.

Opposite: From top left: A few of Maputaland's waterbirds: whitefaced ducks, Egyptian geese with a flotilla of goslings, redbilled teal, a pygmy goose amongst the water lilies, a darter and a black crake.

their thatched beehive huts and then over the largest fresh-water lake in South Africa. Most of Sibayi's water seeps in from the surrounding wetlands which act as a filter, releasing water that is crystal clear. Sibayi hippo have a special role to play in bringing nutrients into the lake and thus helping to feed the lake's fish population. In the shallows fishermen were intent on spearing fish caught in one of their traps.

Then they were back above the beach, flying north. Off Black Rock, a headland jutting into the Indian Ocean, they saw a school of whale sharks, the biggest of all fish species. Although they reach between 15 and 20 metres in length, whale sharks are harmless and have frequently been approached by scuba divers. The coast and the estuaries are also the home of the notorious Zambezi river shark, *Carcharinus leucas*, one of the most vicious shark species, which is responsible for many of the shark attacks on the southern and east coast of Africa, and as far afield as the Persian Gulf and the coast of South America.

They were now flying over a marine reserve. Offshore were Africa's southernmost coral reefs. No river of any significance enters the sea between the St Lucia and Kosi estuaries, with the result that the sea on this stretch of coast is wonderfully clear and the offshore coral reefs are a kaleidoscope of colour. At low tide the rocky pools along the beach also provide sanctuary for thousands of tropical and subtropical aquatic species. It is a paradise for scuba divers and snorkellers.

A little further on they reached the entrance to the Kosi lakes. This was as far north as they would go. It seemed inconceivable that a place so beautiful had had to fight so hard for its survival. At the end of the 19th century the lakes had been the subject of a tug of war between the South African Republic and Britain. Both had wanted to use the lakes for a harbour. The British quickly annexed the territory, cutting off the ambitions of the Afrikaners. But the tiny malarial mosquito did more than a Boer or Zulu army in persuading the British not to develop the area. Then, in 1982, the landlocked country of Swaziland negotiated with South Africa to buy a corridor of land through to the Kosi lakes and the sea. At the eleventh hour the KwaZulu government's objection won the day and the lakes remain as beautiful and unspoilt as ever.

As with Lake Sibayi, the Kosi lakes are separated from the sea by a line of high dunes and, apart from the Sihadla River, most of the water seeps into the lakes from the surrounding wetlands. The Kosi system consists of four lakes which are linked by narrow channels rather like a string of pearls, and a tidal estuary. Lake Nhlange, the largest of the lakes, covers about thirty square kilometres. As one progresses south from the estuary, the salinity of the lakes decreases and the vegetation changes from mangrove trees to giant *Raphia* palms and blue water lilies. Kosi has been described as an aviary and an aquarium. The fish population of the entire lake system is spawned on a wall of coral just inside the mouth of the lagoon. Even from the air one can see the surface rippling with the leaping of thousands of fish.

The helicopter landed at the mouth of the estuary for a short break before turning west to overfly the Tembe Elephant Park. Thirty years ago elephants migrated freely between the ecologically linked Tembe Park and the Reserva d'Elefantas d'Maputa. A military fence erected by South Africa during the civil war in Mozambique now divides this area. By the time the war ended in the late 1980s, most of the elephants in the war zone had been killed. Ivory bought guns. A few elephants escaped south and continued to live in the sand forests of Tembe. From the helicopter they saw a large male elephant with one tusk moving as fast as he could away from them. Elephants have memories.

The massive ecosystem across the border had been made inaccessible by the bush war in Mozambique. Dave wondered whether the new order in South Africa, as it grew in stature, would see the wisdom of removing the fence. Whether all the follies of a colonial and apartheid past could be wiped out and another wilderness reserve could be created, one that would be even bigger than the Kruger National Park. Whether the elephants would ever have their right-of-way restored to them. And, most of all, whether the people would ever be reconnected to the land.

The helicopter now headed south, across the Muzi swamps with their hippo and teeming birdlife, to the Mziki marsh, the most northerly of Phinda's seven ecosystems. With his years of experience at Londolozi, Dave was well aware of the amount of work that had to be done. Removing the debris of farming. Erecting fences. Bringing in power and water. Building roads and runways. Constructing dams big enough to ensure that there would be sufficient water during drought years.

They had already started removing the invasive bush just as they had done at Londolozi. Once there were fewer trees drawing on underground water, the water table would rise and it would not take long for the grasslands to come back. Only then would the land be capable of carrying an optimum number of animals. The bright green patches of cleared grassland contrasted dramatically with the darker greens of the dense forest. But wherever they looked they could still see uniform patches of *Acacia nilotica* which had invaded areas damaged by cattle farming. Pineapples, cotton and other crops had also taken their toll. Most of the Phinda property lay between forty and sixty metres above sea level on nutrient-poor soil. Once there had been a chain of pans through the reserve but these had all dried up. It was small wonder that farming had been a failure.

The helicopter settled down on the edge of a vlei in the middle of the reserve. In traditional style, a breakfast was laid out under the trees in the sand forest and Kevin Leo-Smith and Les Carlisle joined the party. It was time to start talking. There were many questions, and not all the answers were going to be satisfactory. They knew they had an uphill battle selling a dream, but that was all they had to offer. Except, perhaps, that nature had woven its own magic. Was it possible that the morning's flight had set in motion an exciting journey? Would these men from

A purple gallinule pauses for a second before disappearing into the reeds that line the Mzinene River. Gallinules feed on water lilies and other aquatic plants which they systematically destroy to get at the soft edible pith or seeds. Their strong beaks are also used to break open eggs which they will steal from any vacated nest.

Europe and America join with the South Africans in their quest to turn back the clock and save a piece of Africa? Dave felt that the fundamentals were there. It was a wild land of remarkable beauty. Nonetheless, it was going to be a long day.

* * *

Before Christmas, CCAfrica's executive team was able to put the year of stress and strain behind them. Neale Axelson brought in the AECI Pension Fund, and was their first South African investor. Other South African investors followed, amongst which were Anglo American, De Beers, Ernest Oppenheimer & Sons, Southern Life, Metropolitan Life and Federated Life. Christopher Sporborg of Hambros Bank continued to give them his full support and became chairman of CCAfrica's main board. However, the most significant investment came from America. Judge Bill Newsom, a man of enormous intellect and compassion, fully endorsed Mark Getty's proposals. All four of the Getty Trusts invested in CCAfrica. Bill went one step further. He personally became a shareholder in the young company and has been a generous supporter and, as a director, a wise and able guide to the executive team. But without Mark Getty there would have been no Phinda and no Conservation Corporation. He believed the dream and he made Phinda a reality.

That Christmas the team celebrated what had been a very difficult birth. They did not foresee then that it would be years before the toddler would be capable of standing on its own two feet.

THE HARD REALITY

The 20th century has seen the development of extraordinarily sophisticated lifestyles which are dependent on oil and paper, metals and minerals and plastics and chemicals. It is a life of mobility, instant communication and luxury. But it has problems. It is a hungry giant that can never be assuaged. None of today's first-world countries have sufficient raw materials to continue to feed the monster they have created. So they have had to find the materials elsewhere. The demand has played havoc with the natural resources of the world and has left a trail of destruction and pollution in its wake.

The problem is who is going to pay to repair the damage already done and find new ways of achieving the high standards that we take for granted. For the most part governments are not going to do so. They have other priorities. It is ironic that the people who hold the solution to conserving the natural resources of the world are the executives and owners of those same industrial giants that caused the damage in the first place. At the same time, the undeveloped world desperately needs to find alternative and sustainable sources of income for its people.

The CCAfrica model, which operates on the principle that private enterprise, in partnership with the public sector and the rural communities, can combine to develop Africa as the adventure continent of the world, is one solution to the problems facing rural Africa. It recognises that the continent's future depends on the 'haves' reaching out to the 'have nots' and that the mistakes of the past must be redressed. In a way, Phinda is a modern-day Robin Hood, acting as a conduit for the transfer of wealth from the rich to the poor. But at the same time, Phinda and the other CCAfrica reserves ensure that both sides benefit from the exchange; those that give, receiving a unique experience of the African wilderness in return.

Phinda, developed without the aid of the public sector, was a hard learning curve. But in less than a decade it has shown what is possible, never wavering from three bottom-line priorities: environmental sustainability, social opportunity and dignity, and economic prosperity. The latter has been a long time in coming.

Green pigeons take a shortcut across Phinda's different ecosystems, traversing from the Mkuze River wetlands in the north to the Mzinene River in the south where they will find another sycamore fig forest and ripening fruit. On the way they stop for a rest in an acacia thicket.

AT THE FIRST COMMUNITY MEETING, Kevin, Les and Dave had told the local community leaders what they planned to do. How they would bring back the lions and elephants. The dangers that were involved. How they would compensate their neighbours if a lion took any of their cattle. What they hoped to achieve. And how they would be able to provide jobs and help their neighbours through a fund which would be set up for that purpose. They were breaking new ground. The reaction of the people was spontaneous. They were astounded. Few white people had ever before bothered to discuss anything with them. And any promises that had been made had not been kept. Simon Gumede, the leader of the Mduku community and a member of the KwaZulu parliament, was sceptical. He wondered if these young men had any idea what was involved. It was not going to be easy.

They had promised to give people jobs. But finding people with skills was like looking for needles in a haystack. Jobs in the district were few and far between. Anyone who acquired skills moved to the cities. Phinda Mountain Lodge, and later Forest Lodge, were built using an 'all hands on deck' approach. Rangers and reserve managers learnt brick-making and bricklaying. They learnt carpentry, tiling and plumbing. They learnt landscaping and how to build swimming pools. And then they set about teaching their teams of raw recruits. It was not ideal. Things seldom are in the bush. Phinda had one big advantage. It was able to draw key people from Londolozi. Whoever could be spared from the Eastern Transvaal was sent to Phinda: Hugh Marshall, expert game ranger and lodge manager; Yvonne Short, with her imagination and flair, a creator of dreams and romance and one of the best hospitality managers in South Africa; Tony and Dee Adams who took the Phinda game rangers through an intensive training course; and Shan Varty and her sister BJ Watson, who had hands-on experience in lodge construction and interior decorating. Shan in particular carried a heavy load. She was the operations, marketing and human resources director for CCAfrica during those early years when Dave and Alan were on the road looking for funds.

After a short delay while the finances were rearranged, the race was on to meet the deadline for the official opening of Mountain Lodge, which stayed as scheduled for 16th October 1991. A million rand had already been spent on the central complex before they bought the property. Dave nicknamed the incomplete concrete monolith on the top of the hill 'the gorilla': it was totally out of keeping with their style of building small secluded camps. And it was in the wrong place. But they could not waste the money already spent on the building and decided to do their best to turn the 'gorilla' into a princess. Eventually, after many alterations, it started to come right. The secluded suites, tucked neatly into the hillside, the spectacular views over the coastal plain and the lovely acacia trees which have grown up around the lodge, have completed the transformation of the lodge into the princess it is today.

Keeping to the launch date meant that everyone had to work twice as hard for twice as long. Kevin Leo-Smith sold his real estate business in Pietermaritzburg and moved to Phinda. When they had their backs to the wall they pulled in Les Carlisle. Yvonne Short recalls that everyone was under pressure. After Masterbond collapsed the stresses and strains got worse. It was tough for everyone, and often the construction site resembled a battle zone; there was major rivalry between the old Londolozi people and the new Phinda team. It was a collection of extremely capable, energetic individuals, who came from many different backgrounds: the family business versus the corporate culture, developers versus operators, autocratic management versus empowerment. Fortunately, there was Yvonne Short. No one could resist her irreverent approach to problems and her mischievous sense of fun. After a few sherries (it was winter), Yvonne suggested that they form a single team which they would call PhindaLozi. That broke the ice and got things going.

Yvonne collected a team of trainee kitchen staff selected from the neighbouring communities. Out of the whole group only Sam Nguni had any kitchen experience. He had taught himself English by buying two bibles, one in Zulu and the other in English. At one time in his life he had been an ice-cream vendor. Then he had landed a job washing dishes in the kitchen at the hunting camp on Zinave, the farm in the north taken over by Phinda. He watched and he learnt. He was to become Yvonne's right-hand man at Phinda. Yvonne took her recruits back to Londolozi. Each man was assigned to one of the experienced staff and instructed to become a shadow, following exactly what the other man was doing. Eight weeks later Yvonne returned to Phinda with an incredibly proud team. She then spent a further two months working with them at Phinda. It was an amazing challenge for her, turning the group, some of whom spoke hardly any English, into five-star cooks.

Halfway through the training programme Yvonne received a call from Dave to say he was bringing a party of a hundred people to Phinda. Would she arrange lunch? Although ill-prepared, Yvonne had been brought up in the Londolozi culture in which no was not an answer. She was starting with nothing: the kitchen was being used as a dormitory for staff and she would have to prepare lunch on a wood fire 'out the back'. There was also no food except the basics for the construction camp. First she had to buy groceries on her own credit card. A hasty call to her bank manager the next morning covered the deficit. Then, after a splendid lunch, one of Dave's visitors asked to see her new 'modern' kitchen! Yvonne had some very fast talking to do. But she is capable of cooking or talking her way out of any situation. Well, almost! One night she was returning to her room rather late when she was chased by an ostrich. On the basis that there was no time to knock but she would answer questions later, she dived through an open window to land in a bed, *ménage à trois*. The two already there were much embarrassed. They were both married, but not to each other!

Among the special features at Phinda are the bush dinners, originally developed by the late Ian Sibiya, who is remembered with much affection. A clearing under a giant umbrella tree, *Acacia tortilis* (left), lit with hundreds of flickering lanterns, would often be the setting for a romantic evening in the bush. Eric Buthelezi, recently promoted to assistant manager at Rock Lodge from his position as food and beverage manager at Mountain Lodge, watches over the evening. Perhaps a spotted eagle owl may also watch from the security of a high branch in an overhanging tree?

Right: Sam Nguni gives his expert attention to a bush dinner at Mountain Lodge.

The summer storms in Maputaland are often sudden and spectacular. The clouds gather in the Mozambique channel and then sweep inland towards the mountains. Baboons have learnt to make the most of a very wet situation!

While Yvonne was teaching the kitchen team, Shan and BJ supervised the interior decoration of the lodge and interviewed people; they needed to employ more than a hundred people before they opened. Eric Buthelezi, nephew of Chief Mangosuthu Buthelezi, heard that Phinda was looking for staff. He was ambitious and prepared to start anywhere. His first job was as a porter. He has moved up the ranks to food and beverage manager at Mountain Lodge, and to assistant manager at Rock Lodge.

Les and Kevin were still working on the plumbing in one of the hillside suites when the first guests arrived on the morning of the launch. Armed with monkey wrenches, they made a hasty exit from the bathroom as the guests were ushered through the front door. Timing was critical!

The launch itself was spectacular. The press and key people in the travel industry arrived. All went well. The luxurious split-level suites were praised. The panoramic views were admired. The cheetah obliged. A bateleur soared overhead. The weather was perfect. Yvonne Short cooked a sumptuous banquet. It was the culmination of months of extraordinarily hard work for everyone. Yvonne was one of the last to leave. She was content that her staff knew what to do, whether it was an impala kebab, roast pheasant, seafood soup or a chocolate soufflé. By that time she was also six months pregnant with twins and wanted to get back to her husband and home at Londolozi. As her plane took off from Phinda storm clouds gathered and lighting flashed across the skies.

Typically of Maputaland, two weather patterns were converging on a very tired team. Soon after sunset a major storm erupted. Over 100mm of rain fell that night. Once again it was a case of all hands on deck – very weary hands. Water poured through the incomplete thatched roof of the lodge. The staff shunted furniture around and tried to save a huge painting by Keith Joubert that had been borrowed from the Everard Read Gallery in Johannesburg. It looked as if it had been hung under a waterfall. At dawn the next day they assessed the damage. Hardly a suite had escaped from a mud slide that had swept down the newly landscaped hillside. The insurance claim ran into hundreds of thousands of rands. But Phinda had opened and it was vital that it kept going.

Dave had anticipated that the early years would be difficult. KwaZulu Natal was one of the hot spots on the planet. While the Mozambique war on its northern border was coming to an end, a civil war had broken out on its doorstep. The rivalry between followers of the Inkatha Freedom Party, led by the Zulu leader Dr Mangosuthu Buthelezi, and the African National Congress, Nelson Mandela's party, would heat up until the elections in April 1994. Thereafter it continued to simmer throughout KwaZulu Natal. It meant that they would have an uphill job selling Phinda as a prime ecotourism destination. Their longer-term plan was to build more lodges on the reserve. More beds would spread the start-up costs and put profitability within reach. Their initial forecasts were that Phinda would run at a loss for five years and thereafter start to move into the black. They were wrong. There were just too many hurdles.

Phinda's warthogs come in many sizes and colours! The different soil types on the reserve, which support a diversity of habitats, are the cause: white and pale brown sandy soils in the sand forests, brown, black and red clays close to water courses, and, in the hills, the hard red soils are often interspersed with patches of stony ground. When the warthogs take a mudbath they may come out red, white, brown or black.

Above: Tony Adams has been overwhelmed by the support and genuine kindness of the Zulu people. Every day he learns about their culture, their hopes and ambitions and the problems they face. People like Gladys Zikhali, who started as a maid and is now assisting Isaac Tembe with the RIF, Benson Ngubane who is a ranger at Phinda, and Octavia Ngobese, who started out as a waitress and is now receptionist at Forest Lodge, are amongst the many he has helped in their careers.

When Phinda Mountain Lodge opened its doors, the reserve consisted of two separate properties: 7235 hectares in the north and 5779 hectares in the south, separated by about five kilometres. Visitors were taken from Mountain Lodge in the south, along the main Sodwana road by kombi, and then transferred into a Land Rover for a game drive in the north where most of the animals had been released. It was cumbersome but no one complained, perhaps because guests were made to feel that they were participating in a hugely exciting grass-roots project. One of Phinda's first priorities was to buy, or at the very least acquire traversing rights over, the intervening farms. Lulubush to the east consisted of 2300 hectares and was owned by Tinky van Rensburg. To the west another farm, Bumbeni, owned by Hans and Siegfried Schutte, also covering about 2000 hectares, was being run as a hunting lodge. Neither were keen sellers. With the inclusion of these farms they would have their wetland-to-wetland reserve. It took about a year before Tinky van Rensburg agreed to a five-year lease of his property. Although the Schutte brothers were initially reticent about becoming involved with the newcomers, it was not long before the changes on the Phinda land began to influence their thinking. Today Dr Hans Schutte is chairman of the Munyawana Game Reserve and an enthusiastic supporter of their aims. Dave anticipates that Munyawana, with Phinda at its core, will grow to 30 000 hectares, almost double its present size. When it is linked with Mkuze Game Reserve and the wetlands belonging to their rural neighbours, there will be a continuous wilderness of over 65 000 hectares.

Mountain Lodge had not only looked like an ugly gorilla it also started out life behaving like one. With 40 beds, it was too big for a ranger, accustomed to operating a 12-bed camp, to handle without first going through a steep learning curve. Bringing in an hotelier was not the answer. They would lose the special skills acquired by a manager who had spent a decade or more learning and improvising in the African bush. They would lose his or her ability to open the door to what is a new world for many people, and to keep visitors fascinated and uncomplaining despite the heat, the insects, the rain storms and the breakdowns. In the end Dave Varty gave Phinda to Londolozi's best man, Tony Adams. Both Tony and his wife Dee had joined Londolozi as rangers. After a few years Tony took over Londolozi's community development programme and was later promoted to general manager.

He arrived at Phinda to find that operations were very different from the smooth flow at Londolozi. A party had been taken out on a beach adventure. Their Land Rover had broken down and when they eventually returned there was not even a grain of rice for them to eat. The kitchen staff had locked up the storeroom and gone home. Even if they had the keys, Tony, who has enormous talents in many fields, openly admits that he is the original 'hambone in the kitchen'. "Phinda staff had not yet learnt how to create harmony out of disorder," he says. "You have to be on your toes all the time. We could not do a thing except open a

In the early days Phinda had numerous problems. The Mzinene River on its southern boundary separated the reserve from a number of cattle farms. Something had to be done about these properties. Phinda could hardly sell an Okavango-type river cruise, only to have the peace disturbed by the mooing of cows, the buzzing of motor boats and the shooting of waterfowl. The long-term plan was to persuade these farmers to join the Munyawana Reserve. Not only would this secure the south bank of the river for game, it would also link Phinda directly into the St Lucia Reserve. Only in 1999 was this problem solved with a long-term lease of all the farms, now back under wildlife, along the south bank of the river.

bottle of champagne and hope that our guests would prefer drinking to eating." Tony, who is now the senior CCAfrica director based at Phinda, says: "It's not just a case of putting things right when they go wrong. In the bush things go wrong all the time. It's how you put them right that counts. And usually the only person who can put things right is the person on the spot. It is unlike almost any other business. We have to train people at every level to take decisions on their own. They have to have the ability to make an adventure out of a disaster."

At the beginning of 1992 CCAfrica was approached by Frans Stroebel of the WWF, the World Wide Fund for Nature, and Dr Robbie Robinson, the National Parks Board's chief executive: "Would CCAfrica be interested in operating the Ngala Game Reserve which had recently been donated to the WWF by Hans Hoheisen?" The 14 000-hectare property, on the western edge of the Kruger Park, was valued at about R100 million. The fence between the reserves had been taken down and, although it had been ceded to the Park, Dr Robinson felt that private-sector skills were needed to run an up-market lodge at Ngala.

The timing of the proposal could not have been better. It was going to be years before Phinda would stand on its own two feet. A partnership with the public sector would be immensely valuable, adding to CCAfrica's credibility. Ngala would have none of the huge start-up costs that had made Phinda such a tough project. The Kruger Park would look after the land. CCAfrica would only have to finance the rebuilding of the lodge. At about the same time Dave decided to realign his interests by bringing Londolozi under the CCAfrica umbrella. Marketing three reserves would spread their overheads. Londolozi guests might also be tempted to visit the new reserves.

Phinda's occupancies rose slowly. Their problems, however, were far from over. The 40-bed reserve had a balance sheet showing a capital outlay of over R40 million, while their turnover was far too low. This was not a healthy situation and would never enable CCAfrica to live up to its promise of a sustainable ecotourism development. Even at full capacity they would never be able to show a reasonable return on capital outlay. The solution was more beds. But this was South Africa in 1992. The war between the ANC and the Inkatha Freedom Party in KwaZulu was getting into full swing. If people wanted to see Africa's big game, there were many other places to go rather than to the middle of war-torn Maputaland.

Building the roads and dams, upgrading the landing strip, bringing in water and power, putting up the fences, removing the debris left after 50 years of bad farming and returning the wildlife had cost too much. They had removed 175 tons of scrap metal, 22 kilometres of power lines and 250 kilometres of fencing, and flattened many derelict farm buildings. They also had to budget another R500 000 to clear the bush which had grown so thick over most of the reserve that it was almost impossible to spot game. In retrospect, Dave felt that it had been just too big a bite for a grass-roots company to swallow. They had to find a solution.

When game viewing started at Phinda the bush was so thick that unless you were lucky the only animals you could see were the giraffe. But there were many compensations. The bird life was superb. The orangebreasted bush shrikes (left) were amongst the rich rewards.

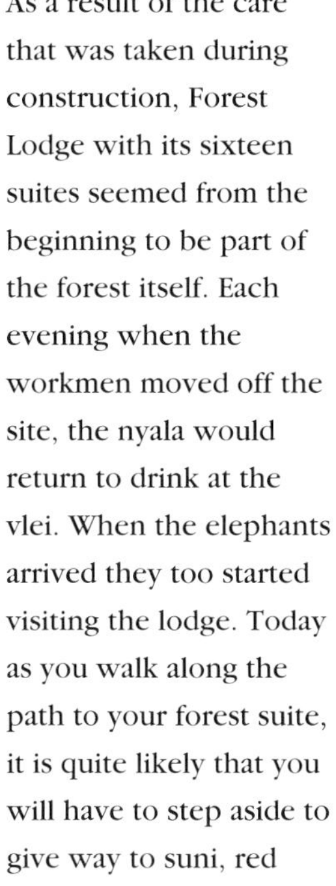

As a result of the care that was taken during construction, Forest Lodge with its sixteen suites seemed from the beginning to be part of the forest itself. Each evening when the workmen moved off the site, the nyala would return to drink at the vlei. When the elephants arrived they too started visiting the lodge. Today as you walk along the path to your forest suite, it is quite likely that you will have to step aside to give way to suni, red duiker or nyala (below).

In 1992 Dave and Alan went back to their shareholders. The country was rapidly emerging from the apartheid era. They were brimful of confidence that after the 1994 elections the ecotourism industry in South Africa would flourish. They had more than enough space on the Phinda reserve for a hundred beds. Would their shareholders back them to build a second 32-bed lodge? Despite the negligible short-term prospects of success, the board showed their faith in Phinda and gave CCAfrica their full support. Dave and Alan then had the task of simultaneously building the Ngala Lodge and the Forest Lodge in the Phinda sand forest.

Ngala was about 100 kilometres to the north of Londolozi. The fence between the private reserve and the Kruger Park had been removed and there was plenty of game. Elephants came down to the lodge waterhole to drink. Impala and kudu wandered through the camp. The original camp had been ranger-built. Dave was familiar with the style. All his life he had been involved in building camps – drawing in the sand and getting on with the job. He suggested that Alan and Kevin Leo-Smith handle the design and building of the new Forest Lodge at Phinda while he sorted out Ngala Lodge. "It was a case of taking a hammer and chisel, knocking out a few windows, changing doors around and building bathrooms. Watching for the sunrise and the moon. Seeing which way the wind blew. Making use of a tree. And there it was. We fixed the whole of Ngala, a 42-bed lodge, for R4.2 million."

At Phinda, Kevin and Alan had briefed their architect, Jonathan Ridler, who came up with a great design for Forest Lodge, keeping to his brief of not interfering with the forest habitat. The chalets were to be built on stilts just above the forest floor. Glass walls would give the impression of being enclosed by the forest, not by man-made walls. The low pitch of the roof would not compete with the lacy canopy of the trees. The design was simple and elegant. Because so much attention is given to space, it appears to have an Oriental influence, rather like Chinese paintings which derive much of their beauty from their clean, uncluttered lines.

Martin Rickleton and Colin Bennett, who were both part of the original development team, were given the job of building the lodge. They were told to use local labour and had very little machinery to help them. They had to learn quickly and then train men from the local community. They were not to damage or remove a single tree during construction. If necessary, the chalets had to be built around the trees. No vehicles would be driven to the construction sites in the forest. Everything would be carried by hand or on a wheelbarrow following a narrow path marked out with string for up to 500 metres from the road. Concrete was mixed by hand and a relay of 100 wheelbarrows kept the concrete pouring. At the height of construction Martin and Colin had about 200 people working on site. No one was allowed off the path. It was a statement on how to build in a sensitive ecological area.

Forest Lodge opened in November 1993, six months before South Africa's first democratic elections. The doors were open but visitors from

A number of epiphytic orchids have been discovered in the Phinda sand forest. Amongst the orchids which flower in early summer in the area is *Mystacidium capense*, a flower that is used by the Zulu people as a love potion and by Europeans as a token of love.

Opposite:
Flowers of the KwaZulu Natal grasslands: *Eulophia cucullata*, used as a love charm, *Ruttya ovata*, a scrambling shrub, and *Dicerocaryum senecioides*, which is used as a soap substitute.

overseas stayed away. Slowly, local people started to drift towards the lovely lodge in the forest. Everything about it was superb. Tara Getty, who had started work in Johannesburg for CCAfrica, suggested to his beautiful English girlfriend, Jessica Kelly, that she take a job at Forest Lodge. She sent her CV, which showed that she had trained at the Pru Leith School of Cookery in London and had experience in France and Switzerland. Not surprisingly, she was offered a job immediately. She hardly knew what she was letting herself in for; she found the walk through the forest from her room to the kitchen especially daunting. But it was not long before her influence became evident. The food was outstanding.

In the meantime, Tara worked at CCAfrica's head office in Johannesburg and then at various lodges learning the ropes. A year later he came to Phinda and directed the development of the two satellite lodges and the upgrading of Mountain Lodge. After they married, they showed their love of Phinda by building a magnificent thatched house just outside the reserve at Mziki from where they could continue to watch over Phinda and involve themselves in the reserve's activities. Jessica, along with Les Carlisle's wife Lynette and Tony Adams's wife Dee, are role models of what a woman can achieve despite being uprooted from her familiar background to follow the man she loves into the African wilderness. Today Jessica is organising training programmes for Phinda staff so that they can work towards a nationally recognised qualification in their chosen field of hospitality service. Lynette, after training as a teacher, taught herself bookkeeping and took over the accounts wherever Les managed new projects. In the early days at Phinda she kept track of their spending, which ran at over a million rand a month. Dee Adams became a game ranger herself until her family arrived. She now takes an active interest in Phinda's progress.

The next stage in CCAfrica's development came with their decision to extend operations to all the high spots of Africa: to the legendary Ngorongoro Crater, the Masai Mara and the Serengeti, the Zambezi and the Victoria Falls and the Okavango Delta. While operating losses piled up and up at Phinda, CCAfrica went on a spectacular development phase. There was no lack of opportunity. Geoffrey Kent of Abercrombie & Kent saw little future in owning and operating lodges in East Africa. He was agreeable to selling his interests and getting on with his far more profitable business as a tour operator. CCAfrica acquired some superb and some indifferent properties in Kenya and Tanzania. Fortunately the good far outweighed the bad and properties that did not fit into their style were sold. They entered into partnership with the Zimbabwean government to establish lodges at the Matetsi Private Game Reserve on the Zambezi, 40 kilometres upstream from the Victoria Falls. They linked up with other lodges in South Africa: Makalali in Mpumalanga near the Kruger Park and Tswalu in the Kalahari.

The decision was also taken to build two 12-bed satellite camps at Phinda: Vlei Lodge close to Forest Lodge, and Rock Lodge a kilometre

Above: Vlei Lodge chalets are set out on the edge of a grassy vlei which is a continual hive of activity. *Below:* A Forest Lodge suite set in the shade of the sand forest trees.

Opposite: Looking across from Leopard Rock to Rock Lodge with its chalets set into the hillside, and beyond, to Mountain Lodge at the top of the hill.

from Mountain Lodge. These small camps were relatively inexpensive to build as they utilised many of the facilities of the main camp – kitchen, laundry, administration, shop and stores. It meant that they would have 96 beds at Phinda, and provided they could fill the beds they would, at last, be on track to making a reasonable return on their investment. At the height of this development phase CCAfrica was operating nearly 30 lodges and camps. Some, like Londolozi, were extremely profitable, but on balance they were not healthy. Eventually Jan Moehl, a director of CCAfrica and trustee of the Cheyne Walk Trust representing Mark and Tara Getty, was the first shareholder to object. He told Dave that they could not go on pouring money into development. CCAfrica had first to get its house in order.

In the middle of all this, Dave and Alan had been advised that they needed a professional to manage their operations. Dave's first choice was an old friend with an outstanding track record in the Cape, Steve Fitzgerald. He and his wife Nicky had turned the Arniston Hotel on the southern tip of Africa, and later The Bay Hotel on the Cape Peninsula, into magical hotels, both with five-star status. They were enthusiastic about taking on a new challenge. Steve, like Dave, was an operator. He understood the need to consolidate and he tipped the scales in this direction. The two other members of the executive team, Alan Bernstein and Kevin Leo-Smith, had led CCAfrica through the development phase. They had flair and imagination. They also had the courage to go ahead despite all the negatives. Without their input Phinda would never have got off the drawing board and the wildlife would never have been returned. But now, sadly, the time had come for a parting of the ways. There would be no more development. It was time for the operators to take over the reins.

Almost immediately there were perceptible changes. CCAfrica decided that any camp that did not fit in with its self-imposed discipline of operating only at the top end of the market had to go. Within a year the number of operations had been reduced to twenty-two camps in fifteen locations spread over five countries. CCAfrica designed all its camps to meet the requirements of discerning travellers who do not want to be herded in large groups. Who do not want to queue for tea at an urn. Or jostle for a window seat in a bus. That is not the CCAfrica style. Little by little all its operations have been brought into line. They know that visitors prefer smaller camps where they can sit down to dinner with their own small party or with a few like-minded people. Perhaps with strangers from half a world away with whom they can compare conservation issues. Or where they can learn from camp managers and rangers who are outstanding naturalists and passionate about wildlife. And they come to recharge their batteries in the peace and quiet of the African wilderness.

Phinda had capitalised very nearly R85 million in development costs and operating losses. In 1999 Steve Fitzgerald was able to report that Phinda would show a profit of over R8 million on a turnover of almost R25 million. Added to that, long-term reservations looked good. It was

Above: Some of the birds seen at the lodges. Top left, a whitefronted bee-eater at Mountain Lodge; right, a scimitar-billed woodhoopoe which had made its nest above the Rock Lodge deck; and right, hoopoes are frequent visitors.

Opposite: Above left, a blue waxbill and right, a redheaded weaver busy building its nest. Below, mocking chats have made Rock Lodge their home, flying to and fro while imitating many other bird songs. Left, the handsome male, and right, the less striking female.

In 1998 Tony Adams watched as occupancies rose. They were starting to become known. The previous year, against stiff competition from Kenya, the Seychelles, India and the Middle East, Phinda had won the British Airways "Tourism for Tomorrow" award for the southern region. The award recognises efforts to reduce any destructive impact of tourism, either geographically or culturally, and to ensure that the "product is kept safe, unsullied and fresh, not only for the next day but for every tomorrow". Weekend after weekend, Phinda was full. The wildlife experience had come of age. Even Phinda's leopards were becoming accustomed to Land Rovers.

champagne stuff. As Steve, who is far more pragmatic than Dave, says: "Ultimately the measure of our success and our credibility is in that bottom-line profit." Dave, on the other hand, looks at the earth. He sees their success in the changes that have taken place. The higher water table. The grasslands that have been reinstated. The flourishing vegetation. And the diversity of wildlife. And then he looks across the fence to the neighbouring communities. How much has changed there in a decade! Now people have hope where before there was none. This is his reward.

The vision shown by CCAfrica's principal shareholders – the four Getty Trusts, the AECI Pension Fund and Hambros Bank, whose shareholding has recently been taken over by Investec – was extraordinary. Many would have called the investment foolhardy. No one does now. In 1999 CCAfrica received an offer of R200 million for Phinda. But it is not for sale. There is still too much to be done.

* * *

Since CCAfrica was founded almost a decade ago there have been few changes to the short but important list of shareholders. In 1995, The Wellcome Trust and SA Breweries became shareholders; the latter when its subsidiary, Southern Sun, sold CCAfrica two lodges bordering state-owned parks. The following year Capricorn Ventures, under its chairman, Dick Enthoven, gave CCAfrica the added financial strength to carry out its consolidation programme. The one other significant change was that Christopher Sporborg resigned as chairman when Hambros Bank's South African investments were acquired by Investec, one of South Africa's most successful investment banking operations. Tony Williamson, a South African businessman well-known for his chairmanship of Wooltru, has taken over as non-executive chairman of CCAfrica.

A CATALYST FOR CHANGE

Londolozi Game Reserve, with its simple philosophy of care of the land, the wildlife and the people, became a blueprint for the development of Phinda. John and Dave Varty had learnt there just how important it was to care for their rural neighbours; they found it was impossible to prosper as an island of wildlife amid a sea of poverty. Helping people in the neighbouring communities was not just a philanthropic gesture: those same people ensured the success of Londolozi.

At Phinda this strategy has been taken one stage further. The Rural Investment Fund (RIF), set up in 1992 with an initial donation from an anonymous Swiss trust, became a catalyst for change, not only in the areas around Phinda, but wherever CCAfrica's commercial operations and management presence provide a platform from which RIF initiatives can be launched to help rural people.

After decades of neglect, the 30 000 people in the communities on Phinda's eastern boundary were in desperate need: there were no hospitals, school classes were held under trees, training facilities were non-existent and there were few job opportunities. Phinda, which created jobs for some 400 to 500 people but made losses throughout its developing years, had a mammoth task on its hands. It was like a David trying to support an ailing Goliath. But with the help of guests from all over the world, the building of clinics, classrooms and other basic facilities was made possible.

Phinda has become a model for all CCAfrica's operations. Lodge managers, as part of their duties, undertake not-for-profit community projects amongst remote communities in Botswana, Namibia, South Africa, Tanzania, Kenya and Zimbabwe. The work is funded by contributions to the RIF which are tax deductible and under good governance, managed in the United States by a board of trustees that includes Getty trustees. The weakness of the RIF is that it can be perceived to be furthering the aims of the commercial lodges. And yet this weakness is also its strength. Not only are the aims of the lodges and the RIF on a parallel course. The lodges are in a unique position to manage and carry the administrative costs of RIF operations. There can be no better way to reach these remote and impoverished people.

"TODAY THE BIGGEST SINGLE THREAT to the wildlife of Africa, apart from internecine wars and rogue armies, is the diminishing free range of the animals and its misuse through inappropriate farming and an obsession with cattle," says Les Carlisle. Since his arrival at Phinda in 1991, Les has developed boundless empathy with Phinda's neighbouring communities, which have been disconnected from their natural heritage for so long. He has also become deeply involved in working towards the establishment of the Greater St Lucia Wetland Park and bringing together the private reserves, the government parks, the communities and the farmers. World Heritage Site status, which is now in the pipeline, will give Maputaland's unique wilderness the protection it desperately needs. But achieving the full potential of this magical place will be neither simple nor straightforward.

For a land that is totally unsuitable for farming and has even less industrial or mining potential, the future, if it is to have one, must lie in the sustainable utilisation of its natural wealth. For millions of years, nature has seen to it that there is co-operation between species for its limited resource base. Man must also learn to adhere to nature's laws. To fight over what little there is will lead very quickly to extinction of all species. Ecotourism is one of the least damaging of all industries. But it is a double-edged sword. Huge developments damage ecosystems, and the peace and tranquillity that are the hallmark of the African wilderness can all too easily be destroyed. There are so few places left in the world today where one can see the horizon stretching from east to west without a man-made structure to interrupt the natural beauty. Low-impact, small-volume facilities that take cognisance of the environment and provide for rural people can be made to be sustainable, both ecologically and financially. The example that Phinda has set, of turning derelict farms into prime big game country, could be repeated many times over in Maputaland to bring a better way of life to the Zulu and Thonga people who have been impoverished through no fault of their own.

"People need to learn that in this part of the world we are all going to be winners or we will all be losers," says Les Carlisle. "One of our first targets when we started Phinda was to reduce the potential impact of the communities on our wildlife. To achieve this we had to reduce their dependence on the land and increase their dependence on the rand. In the cities you get an automatic reduction in the size of families, because to feed people you need money, and money, as we know too well, does not stretch. In rural communities, if they have more people to feed they hoe another row of mealies. It is a flexible system – that is, until the drought years hit and the ecosystem collapses. The development of the regional economy is crucial to maintaining Phinda's wildlife. If the communities have no alternative, they will eventually be forced to consume the animals. That is why we have to go so far beyond elementary help to the poor. Giving people food is not the answer. We have to help with their

Ten years after the dream of Phinda was born, the Greater St Lucia Wetland Park has been prioritised as a lead project for the economic recovery of Maputaland. The Spatial Development Initiative (SDI), established by President Nelson Mandela to kick-start the economy and encourage private-sector investment, has set a target of 100 000 new sustainable jobs, created on the back of the emergence of the Lebombo region as a world-class tourism destination.

education and health and then create opportunities for employment and small businesses so that in the end they will be integrated into a sustainable economic system.

"Starting the Rural Investment Fund was the key to solving many of our own problems. That, without any doubt, was part of our motivation. But it went far beyond self-interest. We had the huge advantage of being able to utilise an established infrastructure at the Phinda lodges to support a non-profit organisation. This is a highly efficient scenario in the remote areas of Africa that are not only difficult to reach, but also difficult to live in without organised support. It's hard to imagine living in the conditions of rural Africa where every drop of water has to be carried over long distances and, more often than not, has to be boiled, where there is no electricity and no shops to purchase even basic needs. That is why non-profit organisations need support. A few individuals working on their own amongst these remote communities will eventually find it too difficult. Giving our lodge managers the job is a sustainable solution. They start off by trying to identify the most pressing needs of the people. This can take many months and even years, specially in places such as Phinda where three communities' requirements had to be considered. Then they co-ordinate and implement new developments. Finally, they are right there to monitor results and provide feedback to donors. This is all essential to the good management and governance of the RIF."

At the start of the new millennium, there are still many mistakes of the past to put right. The land claims courts will help settle grievances. But some of the claims go back a long way, to the aftermath of the Zulu War when Britain appointed thirteen chiefs, the Abafokazana or strangers, to take over Cetshwayo's kingdom. Other claims arise from a history of forced evictions, which started soon after the turn of the century. The claims are being handled sympathetically, but too slowly. Many people feel they should return to the land which a century ago belonged to their families. Mkuze Game Reserve is a typical example. When it was proclaimed as a reserve in 1912, the Zulu communities living within the reserve were moved to the north of the Mkuze River. This policy was repeated in 1953 when the AmaThonga in the Ndumu Reserve were moved, and again in the 1970s when the Tembe Elephant Park was proclaimed. After the first democratic election in South Africa in 1994, the communities were given the opportunity of reclaiming the land or receiving compensation. Many of their grievances have not yet been addressed and the people remain impoverished. This could be a disaster for the game reserves.

"No reserve can keep wildlife unless they do something about the needs of their neighbours," says Les Carlisle. "When Phinda started, in the worst month we collected about 160 snares on the property. That is about sixteen freshly placed lines with ten snares to a line – a snare line every second day. That is serious activity. The impact on the predators was appalling. Probably at the most only two or three snares on a line would

Opposite: A young Zulu woman wears a head-band with money pinned onto it and carries a miniature spear. These are symbolic of her engagement. Below: a young Zulu boy at the entrance to the family kraal.

The Thonga people lived in complete harmony with their surroundings for thousands of years. They fished and hunted, collected fruit and herbs and planted crops when the floods receded. With population pressures and the introduction of cattle, their habitat is under threat. Maputaland is drying out and even the grass the Thonga women use to make mats may disappear.

Of the 11 000 commercial beds in the Lebombo region, fewer than 300 are owned by blacks, or by groups with black shareholders. It is small wonder that the Zulu people, who understood the laws governing sustainable utilisation of natural resources, were poaching wildlife.

catch small antelope. Two or three out of ten. That would leave seven or eight snares open to hook the predators that would come to investigate the baying and crying of strangled antelope. We lost many lions, cheetahs, leopards and hyena.

"In the early days we had a large force of game guards. Once we started the RIF programme we reduced this force substantially, expecting the snaring to fall off immediately. What we didn't allow for was the time lag between when we started to deliver benefits and when individual people began to feel that their lives had improved. It took a long time. So the lesson for new and old game reserves is, don't slacken off on your patrolling and anti-poaching units until you've got tangible benefits flowing out of your community development programme.

"Today we have built strong relationships with the communities. Phinda employs about 330 people and has created jobs directly linked to its operations for several hundreds more. In the past ten years the per capita income of the district has more than doubled from an average of just over R400 per annum. But until there are more opportunities for people through economic growth, we must continue with our community development programmes. They are crucial to our future. We also have to maintain a game guard force. Otherwise it will be the end of the wildlife and our business. Recently we have reduced the size of our force and it is more effective, specially as we have a much better network of trained and motivated informants. All this makes for a very secure reserve."

Lameck Sibanda, manager of Phinda's game protection unit, has over forty women helping him. "For the most part poachers are not community members," he says. "They are intruders from Mozambique. They are also often in poaching syndicates backed by unscrupulous foreign businessmen with a single objective: making money. Our team of local women can quickly identify the poachers. In return for their help, we take them into selected areas of the reserve to collect wood and cut grass for their thatching and craft needs. From time to time we take them on game drives so that they understand what Phinda is all about. It is a mutually beneficial exchange."

"We now have a total of twenty-two men in the force," says Les. "They have two reaction vehicles and two reaction teams, five men in each vehicle. The rest of the guys are on rosters patrolling the boundaries. If they pick up tracks coming into the reserve they radio in and track until they find the snare lines, which are usually set during the night. We aim to find them the next morning. This system has meant that the benefits from setting snare lines have been reduced while the effort and risk involved have been greatly enhanced. In the last three months we have not uncovered any new snare lines. This is unusual at the end of the winter months, specially as we haven't had a good start to summer. With the rains late, crops have not been planted and the pressures from hunger are mounting. But our programme of community involvement is becoming really effective and people aren't seeing us as a resource that should be

Above: Lameck Sibanda, manager of Phinda's game protection unit. *Below*: Manderfosi Mnomisia and Samson Sithole (front), and Wisdom Ndlovu, Lameck Sibanda and Simon Dube (behind): Phinda's frontline custodians of the wilderness.

exploited. They know that the benefits they get from Phinda and the Rural Investment Fund far outweigh any short-term gain from poaching.

"We use the tribal courts to punish subsistence poachers unless there is an assault or weapons involved and then we call in the South African Police," Les explains. "Tribal courts are likely to provide a much more sensible solution to the problem than paying for his full board and lodging. When he is released from jail his circumstances are unchanged. He has no food for himself or his family. So he climbs straight off the police van and back into the reserve, sets his snares, catches his animal and walks down the main road with it so you can catch him again. Then he can go back for another three months in jail. Once again he has shelter and free food. By then it has rained and his land will be ready to be planted. So he goes home. It is completely ineffective and inappropriate to use a first-world judicial system in a third-world developing community. It amazes me that our government still hasn't cottoned on to this fact."

The Zulu people have paid taxes since 1905 when a poll tax of £1 a head was enacted by the Natal parliament, but received little in return. In an area of over 12 000 square kilometres, only 300 kilometres of road were tarred, while sanitation, electricity and water infrastructure were almost totally absent in rural areas. The apartheid government deliberately kept African education inadequate, both in quality and quantity. It considered education a weapon vital to the maintenance of white supremacy. "To train the Bantu … means that you train him to come into competition with the European," announced the Minister of Bantu Education in 1959. The Nationalist government proposed moving education facilities for blacks from urban to rural areas, but little money was spent. A few universities were established, including one in Zululand, but technical educational facilities were conspicuous by their absence. The government believed that there was no need for them as skilled jobs were reserved for whites. Hospitals and clinics provided by the government in rural areas were also seriously inadequate. If it had not been for the mission hospitals, the health of rural people would have been much worse.

Despite early financial difficulties, CCAfrica has, since its inception, paid the administrative costs of the Rural Investment Fund. Nicole Young, RIF's first administrator, was well equipped to manage the fledgling fund, having obtained a postgraduate degree in economic development in the United States. Robin James, an old friend of Londolozi, arranged RIF's first major donation of $160 000 from an anonymous Swiss trust, which has been followed up each year with some smaller, but often very much larger gifts. Two community liaison officers, Walter Zulu and later Isaac Tembe, have worked in the field and, as soon as Les Carlisle's work on relocating the wildlife was completed, he too became involved as regional development manager.

There are three communities on Phinda's eastern boundary: Nibela on the shores of Lake St Lucia to the south-east, Makasa to the east, north of the Mzinene River, and Mnqobokazi to the north-east. The population

Left: Nyala, which have inhabited the Maputaland coastal forests for many centuries, and the relocated elephants share a waterhole not far from Forest Lodge.

Right: During the drought of 1992, Zibane Mazibuko was caught poaching nyala on Phinda property. He was found guilty by the tribal court and sent to do three months community service at Phinda where he was given a job making bricks. While there he realised he had found an opportunity for a small business venture. With the backing of the Rural Investment Fund, Zibane started his own brick-making business. Soon afterwards he won the contract to supply the 300 000 bricks for the building of Forest Lodge. He has not looked back.

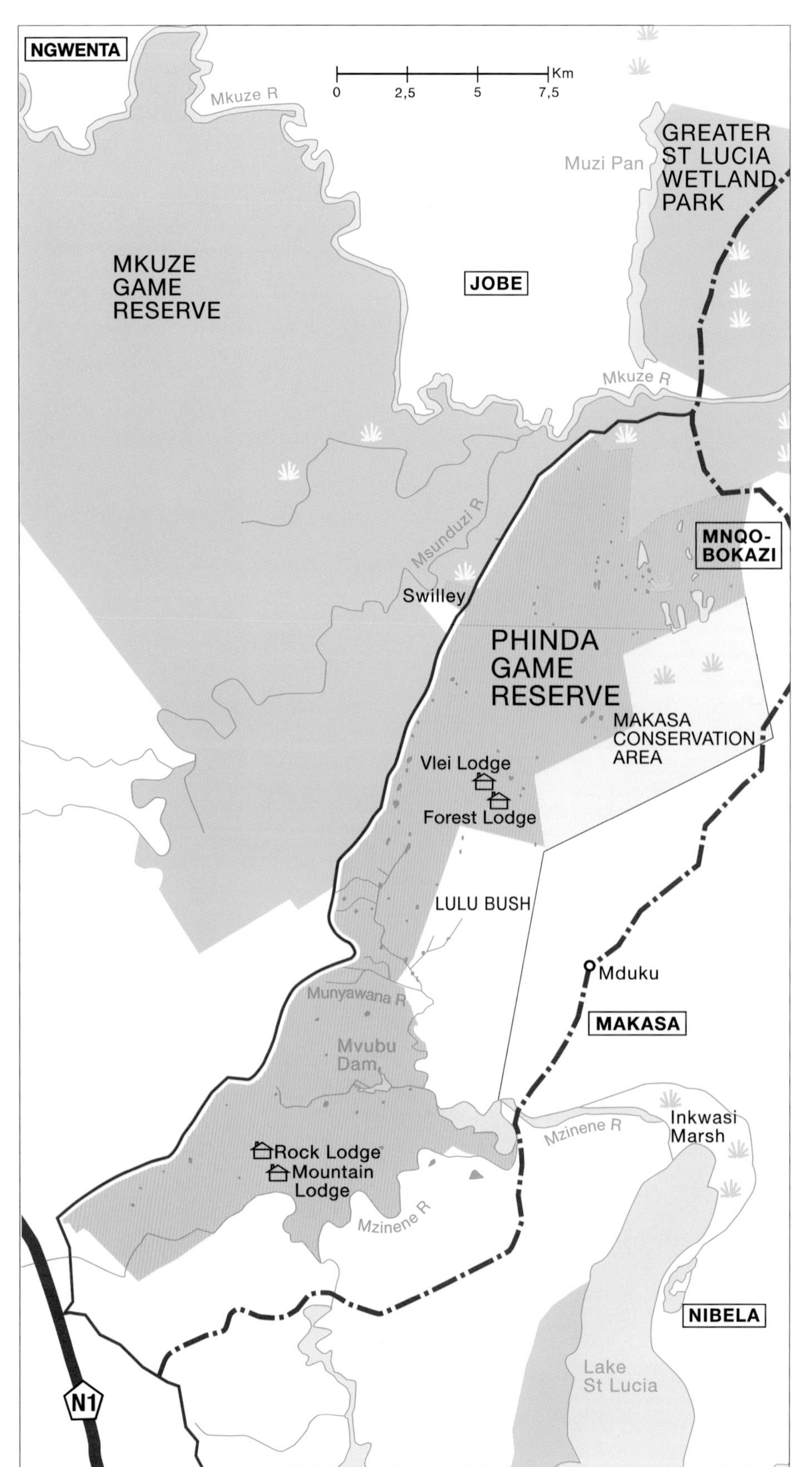

The new road to the east of Phinda will provide access to many prime areas of natural beauty along the KwaZulu Natal coast. It will also bring about 160 000 people within five kilometres of an all-weather road and will open the way for no fewer than seventy-seven small and medium-sized enterprises directly linked to the road.

Below: The unspoilt estuaries, lakes and wetlands of Maputaland have made it one of the wonderlands of the world. Maputaland bird life is extraordinary and nowhere more so than at St Lucia where flamingo forage in the shallows.

Above: Walter Zulu and Alan Bernstein discuss the start of the Rural Investment Fund. Walter was instrumental in establishing communications with Phinda's rural neighbours and setting up a framework for rural development.

Below: Dr Ian Player, one of Natal's most visionary conservationists, congratulates Isaac Tembe on winning an award for his work amongst the rural communities on behalf of the Rural Investment Fund.

of about 30 000 is largely of mixed Zulu and Thonga heritage. Isaac Tembe keeps in close touch with the schools, clinics and students that are benefiting from RIF funding, spending much of his time meeting tribal committees, parent-teacher associations and a range of people from Nkosi Simon Gumede, leader of the Makasa community, to the schoolchildren. They all know him well. His job is to identify their needs, arrange for education, health and sports facilities to be built, set up women's forums and sewing classes, and give talks on health, environmental awareness, and on the many opportunities that will open to them when the new road is completed.

Early on Les Carlisle saw the need to move the main Sodwana road from Phinda's western boundary where it would always be an impediment to the consolidation of Mkuze and Phinda. He had a staunch ally in Nkosi Simon Gumede, who recognised that a road through the centre of the communities to the east of Phinda would do much to stimulate economic development. With these motivations, building a new road became a major goal of both Phinda and the RIF. Aerial surveys were done at the Fund's expense, the communities were consulted and a plan was drawn up to which each of the three tribal chiefs agreed.

They had a bit of unforeseen luck. Prior to the elections in 1994 provincial development had come to a standstill. Les was able to persuade the Natal Provincial Authority to use the slack time to design the road. After several years of lobbying, the central government took up the plans and, under the guidance of the the Spatial Development Initiative, a 156-kilometre coastal road was built through to Mozambique. The R180-million road is making an enormous social and economic impact: altogether about 160 000 people live within five kilometres of the new road, which will facilitate access to many existing and proposed tourism projects. On the back of the growth of the tourism industry, many secondary developments are being planned, from garages and shops to a craft centre which has been donated by Tara and Mark Getty. To help the rural people further, the RIF is setting up educational programmes to develop craft skills and teach basic business practices.

Initially the RIF focused on the essential needs of the communities, that is, on providing classrooms for schools, bursaries for advanced education, health-care facilities, community centres and training. Pre-primary education did not exist prior to 1992. Today nearly 2000 children in the three communities have the opportunity to attend pre-primary schools and prepare for formal education. Much more is involved than building classrooms or finding suitable accommodation for the pre-primaries. The RIF ensures that each of the sixteen pre-primary schools it has helped establish is financially self-sustaining, that teachers receive pre-school instruction and that school committees are formed to support the teachers. The RIF also liaises with provincial and government educational authorities on their behalf, ensuring that 'rand for rand' subsidies are efficiently processed.

Below: A Zulu dancer brings the rich history of his people to life while entertaining guests at a Phinda Mountain Lodge dinner. Zulu game rangers also tell stories of their customs and the respect owed to their ancestral spirits, which govern tribal life from the cradle to the grave.

Opposite: Top left, Elias Ntombeni greets guests at the main gate and radios through to the lodge so that their arrival is anticipated. Top right, Jerry S'khosana brings centuries of accumulated knowledge of the wilderness to his job as a tracker at Phinda. Below, Kevin Oxley and Zulu Ndhlovu service a Phinda Land Rover.

School facilities were hopelessly inadequate at the beginning of the 1990s. Many schools had more than 100 pupils in a class and lessons were frequently given under a tree. When it rained the children stayed at home. There were no school buses and pupils had to walk up to ten kilometres a day to get to school. The RIF set about changing this. It has built over twenty classrooms and built and stocked four libraries and laboratories. To help with the shortage of teachers, a community leadership education fund has been established which has been overwhelmed with applications, particularly for teaching diplomas.

Nine years ago the Mavuso High School in the Makasa tribal area consisted of two classrooms and a storeroom. The headmaster appeared to be disinterested in improving the school. Then a new headmaster was appointed. "We were delighted," says Les Carlisle. "Muzi Nzama was a man we could work with; his energy made a huge difference. We funded two classrooms. Then Mr Nzama raised money for more." When Getty Images executives attended the opening of the new classrooms they were so impressed that they pledged a computer to the school – and a generator. Later they donated shares in their company (today worth R500 000). In rural Africa, the computer is extraordinarily significant: the Internet puts information and skilled teaching programmes within reach of even the most remote communities, bringing them into the 21st century. Today, the RIF is redirecting more and more discarded computers received from the first world, where the fastest and the best is part of the big business survival kit, to the rural communities of Africa where they are already making an impact.

The problems facing Maputaland are encapsulated in these schools. The Mnqobokazi Primary School has 1200 pupils, the two high schools at Nibela and Mduku together nearly 2000 students. When these students leave school their future is far from secure. The rural economy cannot cope with the rapid population growth that has taken place since the 1970s when the population swelled with refugees fleeing from the war in Mozambique. Better medical care and the high birth rate did the rest.

At present the students have little alternative but to leave their homes and go to the cities to look for work. There the competition for available jobs is fierce. South Africa's population has been increasing by over two per cent annually, while its real economic growth has been negative. In the 1930s the population of the Ubombo region was just over 20 000. By 1980 it had increased to 148 000. Today the population has doubled to 280 000. Maputaland has plenty of space. The problem is that it has virtually no arable land, no industry and no mineral resources, while many of its existing tourism facilities are underutilised because of lack of planning and marketing, poor quality and poor service.

The problems of unemployment and poverty are compounded by the tragedy of Aids. Statistics on the incidence of the virus are conflicting, but clinics and hospitals in Maputaland generally report that between 50 and 60 per cent of babies are born HIV-positive. A statistic like this masks

ELIAS

Above: Even the most remote KwaZulu village is threatened by the tragedy of Aids. *Below:* A sangoma or diviner throws down a handful of bones and interprets messages received from restless ancestors who are thought to be the cause of many of the problems of daily life.

volumes of human suffering and sadness – as well as utter helplessness. So far there has been no hope for the people of Africa who have contracted the virus. However, recently a leading US pharmaceutical company, Bristol-Myers Squibb, committed $100 million to fighting Aids in southern Africa and challenged other pharmaceutical companies to do the same. The United Nations Health Organisation is also looking at establishing a base in southern Africa to fight Aids.

One of the greatest problems in Maputaland is that tuberculosis has been endemic in the region for years. Once the immune system is destroyed, the myco-bacterium tuberculosis quickly gets out of control. The result is that thousands of HIV-infected people are dying of TB annually. The immediate repercussion of Aids is a huge drain on the already over-burdened financial resources of the country. In the next decade this is going to become worse.

CCAfrica has tackled the problem in a unique way. It recognised that throughout Africa, Aids educational programmes have had little effect and that it is often only when every family has experienced at least one HIV-related death, as has happened in Uganda, that the rate of infection appears to slow down. There had to be another way. What CCAfrica set out to do was firstly, to change people's attitudes towards the use of condoms, secondly, to encourage a more sympathetic approach towards those who had contracted Aids, and thirdly, and the most difficult of all in a polygamous society, to change sexual behaviour patterns.

The HIV-intervention team took a circuitous route. It set up interactive workshops to provide life-skills training for all CCAfrica staff. During these workshops, conducted by peer educators who are also role-models, staff members were taught how to negotiate: not a skill one would initially equate with Aids prevention. But if one was trying to persuade one's partner to use a condom, it could make the difference between life and death. Isaac Tembe, representing the Rural Investment Fund, has taken the life-skills training programme into the neighbouring communities where positive shifts in behaviour have already become evident. For instance, at the last workshop not one person acknowledged more than five partners. Two years ago a quarter of the group did.

Malaria is also endemic in Maputaland and has been identified as a major deterrent to development. For the local people, it is not as serious a threat as one might imagine. Through years of exposure to malaria, they have built up an immunity to the disease and the only manifestation of malaria may be a headache. This resistance seems to continue as long as they are in contact with the malarial mosquito. However, a plan to clear the whole of Maputaland of malaria is being implemented.

The RIF also tries to bring in other organisations to help with the financing of larger projects. The first residential clinic at Mduku in the Makasa district, which was completed in 1995, was financed jointly by the RIF and the Independent Development Trust, an autonomous organisation founded in 1990 with an initial government grant of R2 billion to help

A Zulu herbalist, or inyanga, with the barks and herbs he sells. Traditionally, plants have been collected in the wild and there has been no need for cultivation. In recent years, because of the huge demand for them from urban businessmen and international pharmaceutical companies, a number of species have been driven close to extinction. The pepperbark tree, *Warburgia salutaris*, which is used to treat headaches, flu and malaria, has almost disappeared in Maputaland, although it is still found at Phinda. Increasingly, traditional healers are recognising the long-term advantages of propagation and sustainable harvesting.

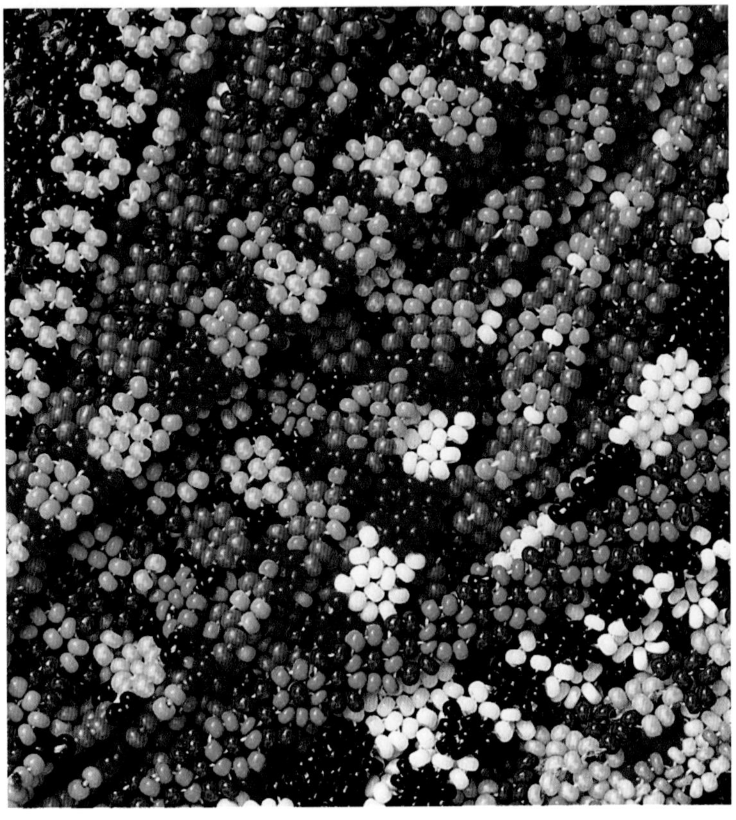

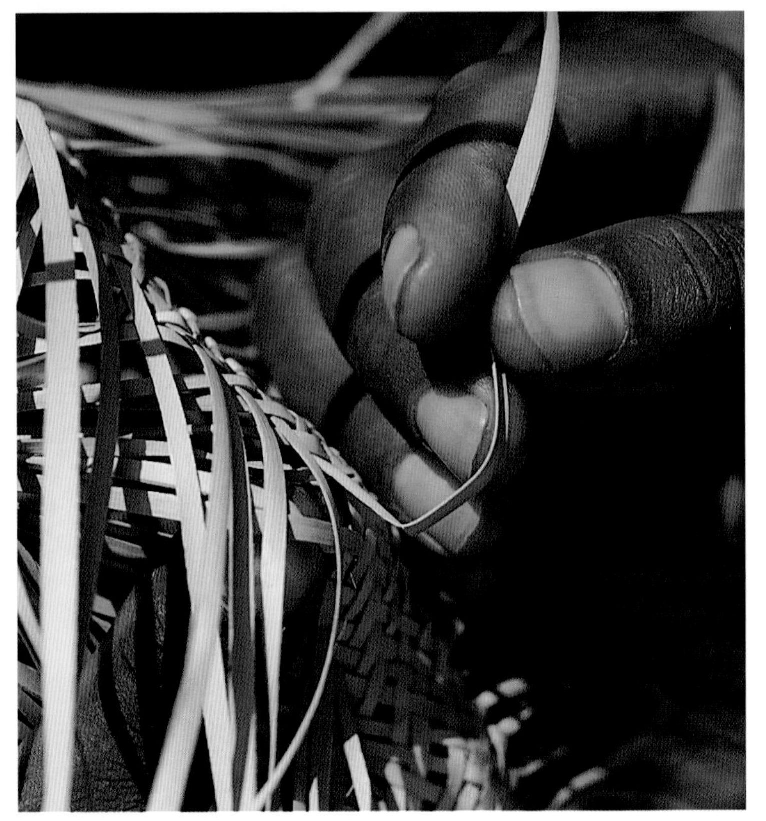

Phinda is a ready market for the beadwork, basketwork and pottery made by the Zulu people. To help the communities the RIF is building training and production centres and, as a primary component of this development, will provide entrepreneurial training. This will help offset the lack of business skills in the communities, which has often resulted in goods being sold at less than cost.

The rural people have learned that the ilala palms (above), from which a nutritious wine is made, are tall and healthy across the fence at Phinda while theirs, on land that has been grazed by cattle, are inferior. It is an illustration of how correct land use adds nutrition to the soil. The RIF has the infrastructure to help the communities move away from cattle and into sustainable wildlife farming.

poor communities. Two years later the RIF added a pre-natal facility. A doctor flies in twice a week to attend to serious cases. A number of doctors and dentists vacationing at Phinda have also offered their services to the clinic free of charge during their stay.

The RIF plans to develop two projects aimed at environmental awareness. The first is an ambitious "Footprints Across Africa" programme which will give rural children the opportunity to explore the natural world around them. By funding a visit to a "Bush School", normally the preserve of children whose parents can afford to pay, the programme will help the children to develop an environmental consciousness and also give them the opportunity to meet youngsters of other cultures and have a great adventure. The second project is designed to give teachers and children lessons in conservation which will eventually assist a new generation in making informed decisions about land-use and conservation projects.

The RIF has also acted as a catalyst in developing small business operations, particularly where Phinda can give ongoing support. For instance, Phinda's bush-clearing operations have provided opportunities for a number of highly successful charcoal businesses. John Raw, another pioneering member of Les Carlisle's team, co-ordinated a scheme in which a dozen local entrepreneurs employ community members to collect wood on Phinda. No payment is made when the wood is removed, but John has set up a central marketing depot to sell charcoal on their behalf. More than 100 people have improved their incomes five- and tenfold through this project. Other industries that have developed are recycled paper, candles, uniforms, baskets and local curios.

The third phase of community development – and the most vital – is to ensure that the people benefit from the wilderness. The first scheme that Phinda and the RIF investigated, the Makasa Environmental Education Centre on Phinda's eastern boundary, was part of a broader plan by the KwaZulu Natal Conservation Service to re-establish tribal conservation areas. A few years ago Phinda hoped to participate in developing the Makasa Tribal Reserve. Regrettably, the property was put out to public tender, not as a Big Five reserve, which it had every potential to become within the Munyawana Reserve, but as a stand-alone reserve, too small for development into a significant area of biodiversity. Despite Phinda's obvious advantages, its proposal to take down the adjoining fence and incorporate the tribal land into the Munyawana Reserve was turned down. The company that was awarded the Makasa project has, however, recently made contact with Phinda, so that in a rather convoluted way Makasa may yet become part of a larger, more sustainable area, to the advantage of both the community and conservation.

A second ecotourism scheme, on Phinda's western boundary, is presently the subject of discussion between the RIF and the KwaZulu Natal Conservation Service and could directly involve the KwaJobe and Mnqobokazi communities which own the wetlands, including the Muzi Pan, to the north of Phinda. This co-operative conservation project could

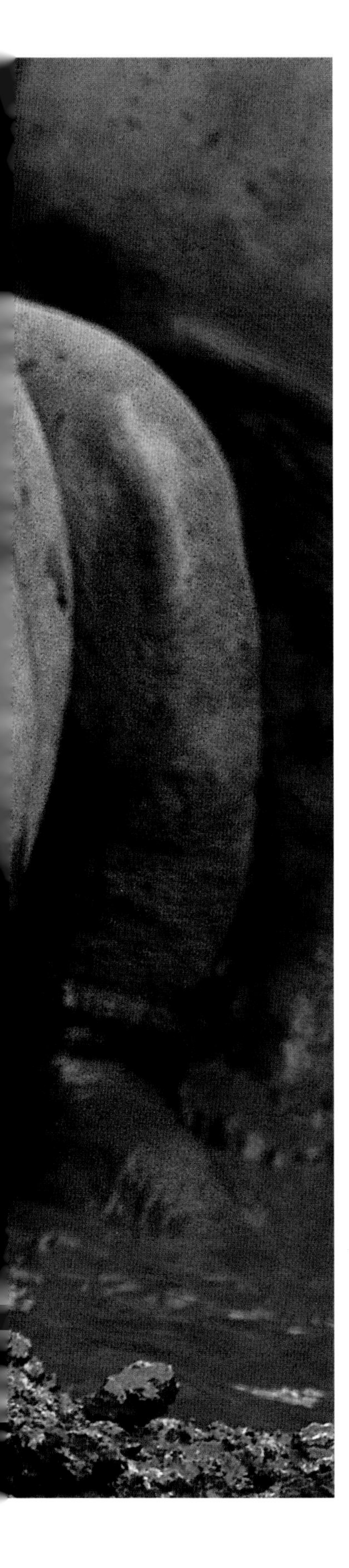

By 1920 it was feared that the white rhino would become extinct: it was reported that the total population in southern Africa had dwindled to about twenty. Today, as a result of the work of the Natal Parks Board, white rhino number in the thousands and form one of the major attractions in many reserves in South Africa. CCAfrica has a vision to relocate white rhino from the safe haven of Phinda, which has not lost a single white rhino to poachers in ten years, and re-establish them elsewhere in Africa.

be the first step in unlocking the door to future equity-based community involvement in ecotourism.

This is what conservation is all about: linking the benefits from the reserves back into the community. The RIF cut its teeth at Phinda, CCAfrica's first project. As the group has grown, so too has the number of communities that benefit from its involvement. Each of CCAfrica's twenty-two lodges has appointed community officers to reach out to their neighbours. The RIF has a well-established base at Ngala and at Londolozi in Mpumalanga, where two communities, amongst the poorest in South Africa, were relocated during the apartheid years. The Fund is also working with the Masai in the Serengeti region of Tanzania and in Kenya from the Kichwa Tembo Lodge. Few, if any, other fund-raising conservation organisations have CCAfrica's on-the-spot infrastructure which is needed to manage projects.

One of the problems that Les Carlisle, Nicole Young and later Anthea McGregor, who was persuaded to give up her own human resources business to join CCAfrica and the RIF, have had to face is that they are not working with developed societies in which meetings are held and decisions taken immediately. "Some of the projects have taken years," says Nicole. "In part, this is because the people we work with lack the infrastructure for communication that we take for granted. There are often no telephones, no faxes and no computers. The roads are bad and vehicles frequently break down."

The efforts to establish a Greater St Lucia Wetland Park that will include the communities and the public and private sectors, have been slow to show tangible results. A feasibility study was undertaken by Les and Nicole in 1996 with financing from the Caisse Francaise de Développement and the French Bank of Southern Africa. The project involved eight tribal authorities, the KwaZulu Natal Conservation Service, agricultural associations, local government departments and private landowners. As a start, eight small pilot projects were identified, one in each of the tribal authority areas. These were aimed at providing evidence to government and local people of the benefits that can flow from community projects. The RIF hopes to raise sufficient finance to take these pilot projects off the drawing boards.

Anthea has never had any doubt that she did the right thing in giving up her own business to join CCAfrica and take over the RIF portfolio. There is never a spare moment in her life, between establishing links with governments in southern Africa, managing operations and fund raising. As the work of the Fund has progressed, so too has its ability to attract help. Anthea has discovered how generous many of the visitors to Phinda are: "One visitor from America sent us dentist's chairs and dental equipment. Several have gone back to America and packed up tons of books for the school libraries," she says. Her job has increased in volume and in excitement in the past year with the arrival of Tara Getty and Judge Bill Newsom on the board of RIF International. Their goal is to raise at least

Left: Petros Jobe, a tracker at Phinda, uses his expert knowledge to show guests the beauty of the wilderness and to explain the interaction between different species.

$10 million and to establish an international foundation from which RIF's operations in Tanzania, Kenya, South Africa, Zimbabwe and Botswana can draw funds. They have already made a good start towards this target.

Tara spends quite a bit of his time at Phinda taking overseas guests to meet community leaders. "When we are in America and England it is hard to put across the scope of what we are trying to do," he says. "It is so vast. But if we interest people sufficiently to come on safari and see for themselves, we have succeeded. Once they are here we can take a back seat. Africa speaks for itself. Many of our guests come on a holiday and go away as ambassadors for the RIF cause."

"Most of the $2 million we raised in the first seven years has been spent at Phinda," says Anthea. "What is thrilling is that more and more we are seeing that our initial help is motivating people within the communities. In the end it is not going to be the millions that we pour into the rural communities that make a difference. It is that each and every rand or dollar acts as a catalyst. We can show people a path away from poverty and the past. We could not ask for more."

NATURE - AN ENDURING PARTNER

Southern Africa has been identified as one of the richest areas of the world in terms of biodiversity. It has more than 24 000 species of flowering plants, thousands of grasses and ferns, 337 mammals, over 280 reptiles, 130 frogs, 900 birds, 100 000 butterflies, spiders, scorpions and other insects, and 245 freshwater fish, while around its shores, the variety of sea fish rivals the Great Barrier Reef of Australia.

Like the spring flowers of Namaqualand and the migrations across the Serengeti grasslands, the biodiversity of Maputaland can best be described as one of the natural wonders of the world. Except for the Cape floral kingdom, the species concentration is higher there than anywhere else in southern Africa. One only has to stop for a few minutes and look and listen to discover another world: a spider building its web, a snake basking in the sun, chameleons watching for the opportunity to catch insects with their long tongues, frogs setting up orchestras, butterflies preparing to migrate and hundreds of different birds. Every living species has its part to play. Even the legendary droughts are important in helping to maintain the balance in nature.

After a century of destruction of one species of mammal after another, Phinda has shown just how quickly nature responds to co-operation. It was no simple matter returning the most dangerous of animals to Phinda. But prey species, and elephants, buffalo and rhinoceros, are as much a part of nature's rich tapestry as are the smallest and most insignificant of insects. With the return of the wildlife and the rehabilitation of the land, nature once again has the upper hand. We see it in the health of the natural vegetation, the way birds, which have been absent from the area, suddenly reappear, and in the productivity of the mammals which sense the change in atmosphere.

Surely this is a paradise worth saving.

Les Carlisle is quick to point out that the relocation projects were always a joint effort: "The total commitment from everyone epitomised what Phinda is for me," he says. "Everyone was prepared to give their unstinting energy – the guys and the girls – and we were backed to the hilt by a team of professionals from the KwaZulu Natal Conservation Service and the Veterinary Department." Last, but not least, Les gives credit to his wife Lynette, who kept his life in order and took over much of the administration of the projects he worked on.

LES CARLISLE was as inquisitive as it is possible for a small boy to be. Every toy had to be taken apart to find out how it worked. When no more toys were forthcoming he discovered other interests: snakes, frogs and lizards – much to the horror of his mother, who found it almost impossible to keep a servant with frogs jumping about and snakes appearing in the strangest places. Banished from the house by his mother, he soon set up a 'laboratory' in the garage, using a dissecting knife to find out how the reptiles and 'jumpers' worked.

By the time he was at high school, he was spending all his spare hours working with Dr Blackie Swart, the local vet in Nelspruit near the Kruger National Park. He was sure that he would go to Onderstepoort to study veterinary medicine, but first he had to complete two years of military service. While at the South African military base at Hoedspruit he was able to continue his veterinary work as a cheetah research project was underway there. He looked after injured animals and helped with their rehabilitation. Soon after that, Blackie Swart started a professional game capture company and asked Les to work with him. That was the turning point in his life.

Several years later, Les was well on the way to success with his own game capture unit. Then, to the advantage of Phinda, he and his partner, Keith Coppen, had what Les calls 'a bad day'. They were called in to dispatch a rogue elephant that was causing havoc in the Hoedspruit area. The elephant had severe AK47 wounds and had probably crossed into the Kruger Park from Mozambique. There was nothing they could do for the poor animal except relieve it of its suffering. Keith agreed to meet the conservation and military people near Hoedspruit, where the elephant had pulled up the Kruger Park electric fence the day before. He was to fly in at dawn with his heavy-bore rifle, suitable for stopping an elephant on the rampage. The reconnaissance party was to make a fire so that he could both find them quickly and judge wind direction from the smoke. Unfortunately, with the wind blowing straight out of the east, and with the sun in his eyes, Keith could not see the power lines directly in his path. He hit them and flipped, crashing into the Olifants River upside-down and almost on top of a hippo bull. Keith lost consciousness but one of the army officers managed to drag him out of the crocodile-infested river while the irate hippo watched ominously. When Keith came to, he had a very sore back and they agreed to abandon the elephant hunt and get him to hospital as fast as they could.

Before they had gone very far, the road ahead was blocked by the angry rogue elephant, trumpeting and aggressively flapping its ears. It gave a mock charge but then backed off. The conservation officer decided to shoot the distressed animal there and then. He picked up Keith's rifle and followed the elephant on foot into the thick bush. Keith followed: he felt safer behind the rifle. When they got to within 40 metres of the elephant, the conservation officer raised his rifle for the shot. The

"If things aren't going well, think of Keith: a wrecked helicopter, a severe back injury, a charging elephant and no gun. Now that's a bad day!" says Les.

next second, Keith saw the elephant turn on them. But no shot was fired. The officer had collapsed with a heart attack. Despite his painful back, Keith moved like lightning. He picked up the rifle, shot the elephant and called for help. "If I have a particularly bad day, I think of Keith facing that rogue elephant," says Les Carlisle.

After six years in game capture, and with marriage to Lynette a major goal in his life, Les decided to change the direction of his career. He took up the challenge of building the Karkloof Falls Game Reserve and moved to Pietermaritzburg in Natal. He also got to know his next-door neighbour, Kevin Leo-Smith, who was destined to become one of Phinda's founders. It could not have been a more fortuitous move for Phinda.

On the other side of the planet, Luke Hunter began a love affair with African cats when, at the age of four, his grandmother gave him a toy lion. His fascination with carnivores took Luke from his home in Australia to Phinda – a place he had never heard of until Professor John Skinner of the Mammal Research Institute at the University of Pretoria proposed an interesting line of study to him. Les Carlisle could not believe his luck when he received a phone call from John Skinner. He had an Australian biology student who was keen to do his PhD thesis on the behaviour of large cats. John knew that Phinda had reintroduced lions and cheetahs. Did Les have a place for him? The answer was immediate and enthusiastic.

Les had the predator reintroduction programme up and running when Luke arrived, but he knew he needed help. With a thousand-and-one other things to do he could not monitor the cats around the clock. Little scientific study had been done on the post-release behaviour of carnivores despite the high level of interest and often emotional response from the public. Phinda proved to be an ideal opportunity to break new ground. In the forty months during which Luke studied the predators at Phinda he was able to define many of the parameters for the successful relocation of lions and cheetahs. The two men, one academic, the other brimful of practical experience, complemented each other perfectly. Phinda could use the interaction between the two.

Luke quickly discovered that the 'soft release' practice, in which animals are kept in captivity for limited periods, worked well. "Most animals have a strong homing instinct," he said. "There are staggering examples of leopards being released at Etosha and then making their way back to their home range 800 kilometres away. In Kenya a study was done in an area where nearly 100 leopards had been released. Only one of the tagged leopards was located. Many probably found their way back to the farming areas where they had been captured and were shot.

"The Phinda holding bomas give the animals time to get accustomed to the sounds and smells of their new territory and to become conditioned to electric fences. Most animals learn quickly that fences are nasty. I watched lions stalking calves on the other side of the fence. Being rather silly animals, the calves would come to within five metres of the lions, which would crouch down looking for all the world as though they were

During his research, Luke Hunter used microchips to identify the lions and cheetahs, and radio collars and receivers to keep track of them. He also used a satellite geographical positioning system (GPS) with which he could pinpoint an animal's location to within forty or fifty metres. Luke's work earned him a doctorate. It also had a practical side. Keeping track of the cats was part of Phinda's agreement with its neighbours, and it enabled the rangers to find the cats far more easily in the dense bush which had not been cleared in the early days. Today all such devices have been removed and Phinda's wildness has been returned.

about to attack. But despite the temptation they would not attempt to break through the fence." On another occasion Luke watched lions chase a zebra which ran right through the fence. The lions were so conditioned that they stopped at the gaping hole and would go no further.

Phinda's long narrow territory with 115 kilometres of boundary fencing is not ideal, but everyone hopes that in the not too distant future the fences between Mkuze, Phinda and St Lucia will be dropped. If adventure tourism is to bring prosperity to the region, fences between wildlife and wildlife no longer have a purpose, no matter what the jurisdiction. Meanwhile, what is important, specially with lions, is to recognise that when males reach sexual maturity they want territories of their own. Lions are a highly successful species. In perfect conditions they multiply rapidly, but if there is a shortage of food or they are contained in too small a territory, they regulate their numbers themselves. It's a case of competing for available resources and the victor taking all.

"There have been about 55 cubs born at Phinda in the seven years since lions were reintroduced," says Les. "A very small percentage died naturally, about 30 have been shifted to other reserves and some have died as a result of human activities. For instance, when the dominant male was snared by poachers, five cubs were killed by the two males that formed a coalition and took over the pride. Phinda's objective is to create a good balance. If the numbers were higher there would be a lot more pressure on animals inside the reserve and they would try to get under the fence. We monitor the lion population and remove males as they reach sexual maturity. This makes for a very easy life for those left behind. They look as though they have not had too many fights – which they haven't. The lions provide a useful source of revenue for Phinda, which is also able to trade the cats for other species."

The second major problem of keeping lions in a relatively small area is inbreeding, which reduces their resistance to disease and eventually their ability to breed. This has happened at the Umfolozi and Hluhluwe Reserves where the lion population, which originated from five lions introduced to the reserve, is suffering from an immuno-deficiency syndrome as a result of inbreeding. There is already a generation of inbred cubs at Phinda but Les is trying to mimic natural processes through exchanges and removals. The plan is to swop males with those at another game reserve. Two new lions will immediately wipe out the inbreeding problem. There will be some upset to the population, and the new males may kill some of the younger cubs. But that is normal. The advantages of bringing in new blood far outweigh the disadvantages.

Of the original fifteen cheetahs reintroduced, ten survived for 600 days or more. Most of the losses occurred as a result of conflict with lions, some through snares and others through territorial clashes during the early settling-in period. Over the past six years the cheetahs have given birth to 48 cubs which have been particularly successful when compared with the cheetahs of the open grasslands of the Serengeti, where cub

Wildebeest prefer the short open grasslands of the Mkuze Marsh where they can see the approach of predators, rather than the forests and thickets to the south of Phinda where there is plenty of cover for lions on the hunt.

Next page:
Dave Varty describes leopards as a barometer measuring energies in nature: "When they show themselves this is an indication that nature has renewed her partnership with man," he says.

mortality is as high as 95 per cent. The Phinda cubs have a major advantage in the many hiding places they can find amongst the rocky outcrops and dense forest areas on Phinda. On ten occasions Luke watched cubs scatter into the bush, evading a persistent search for them while the mother distracted the lions.

Of the thirteen lions reintroduced, five were caught in poachers' snares and three were destroyed after one of the group killed a guest walking alone at Phinda Mountain Lodge just 55 days after they had been released in 1993. The aggressive reaction of the lioness resulted in part from her being cornered between the boma fence on one side and the swimming pool wall on the other: circumstances which combined to bring about the tragedy. Visitors are constantly reminded that the camps are open to wild animals. If anything, a fence gives a false sense of security to those on the inside. It has been proved over and over that lions can get under fences. The rule adopted at all CCAfrica camps and lodges is that after dark guests must not leave their chalets unescorted. It is all too easy to dash out spontaneously to collect a camera or some other item left behind in one's chalet. But the chances of slipping out unnoticed are minimal, as a posse of rangers and guards has been trained to watch out for guests who forget the rules.

Gavin Hulett, who manages Forest Lodge, reinforces the need for vigilance in the vicinity of the lodges. "It seems that we built our satellite camp on a wildlife highway," he says. "Vlei Lodge is less than a kilometre from Forest Lodge but, possibly because it is more open, it has an extraordinary traffic. Just after the lodge opened in 1997, our manager had to stay in a guest chalet as her accommodation was not ready. That night a lion chose to drag a wildebeest kill under the room. If guests had been there, they would have suffered a sleepless night listening to the gnawing of bones. On another occasion two guests at Vlei Lodge decided they did not want to go on a game drive. They had it all on their doorstep! Since first light they had been riveted at the big glass window watching a lion on a kill."

In the dry season elephants come to Vlei Lodge to drink out of the plunge pools on the chalet verandahs. One guest photographed an elephant from the sliding door of his bedroom. Only two or three metres away he had caught the animal in the act of breaking down a tree. Rock Lodge, the small camp close to Mountain Lodge, also has its share of nocturnal visitors. The steep, rocky hillside, overlooking a ravine, is ideal habitat for leopards which often prowl through the camp at night leaving their spoor behind as a reminder of their presence.

Ten years ago there was a limited number of animals on Phinda and the biodiversity of the area had been devastated by farming and hunting. Only a few predators had survived the onslaught. Because there were no lions or cheetahs and few leopards, the nyala had thrived. In the early days there was so little big game to see that the rangers learnt to give a 15-minute discourse on the behaviour of frogs. Or they would talk at

length about dung beetles, spiders and snakes. Since the return of the wildlife so much has changed. Birds and insects have reappeared and even the flowers bloom again. In spring Phinda is quite beautiful with the orchids in the sand forest and the many other flowering plants and trees. The biodiversity at Phinda is one of the reasons why it has been declared a National Heritage Site and could earn its place within an internationally recognised Greater St Lucia Wetland Park.

When Phinda started there were few leopards seen. They would disappear into the forest as soon as man appeared. It was not surprising. They had often been shot by farmers and much worse, they had been baited. Carl Walker, a Phinda ranger, spent all his spare time following leopards and habituating them to the presence of men. The result is that the leopards at Phinda are again showing themselves to humans and day after day guests have the excitement of seeing these beautiful cats.

During his studies of the lions and cheetahs at Phinda, Luke Hunter discovered that predators have distinct preferences in their selection of prey species. "The lions favoured wildebeest, while cheetahs killed reed-buck at almost eight times their relative availability. Warthogs were also killed by lions in high numbers. Unless the lion population was controlled, the effects of predators, particularly on wildebeest and zebra, would be far greater at Phinda than would be found in much larger areas such as the Serengeti and the Kruger Park where the antelope have the opportunity to move away." On Phinda's western boundary, Mkuze Game Reserve has no lions and, as a result, had to cull wildebeest in fairly large numbers before live sales kept wildebeest numbers under control.

Les has had to do quite a bit of juggling to make up for the excessive pressure placed on prey species at Phinda. In 1998, with zebra numbers down to 350, relocation was resumed in an effort to bring the numbers up and balance natural population increases with prey offtake. Without the injection of new animals it appeared likely that the zebra numbers would dwindle to a critical level when extinction in a small reserve would be inevitable.

Les Carlisle visualises that it will not be long before the reserve will be able to sustain itself: "We have to balance the need to have predators at Phinda with the cost in terms of our prey species. Lions, leopards, cheetahs and hyena are interesting. Often totally fascinating. I can hardly think of anything that is more special than watching a cheetah teaching her cubs to hunt, lion cubs playing hide and seek, or a mother leopard indulging her cubs as they romp about her, chasing anything from a butterfly to a lizard. These experiences are among the many reasons people come to the African wilderness again and again.

"We have to be objective in maintaining that natural world while balancing our budget. If we are able to sell a hundred nyala each year together with a few rhino, cheetahs and lions, we are able to recover between 60 and 70 per cent of our land costs. This makes a huge difference to our overall operating budget. The 1999 summer has been very dry.

This page: Top left; a fire-ball lily, *Scadoxus multiflorus*, is grazed by antelope in the bushveld. Centre left; *Stapelia gigantea*, called the giant carrion flower because of its fetid smell, is one of the largest flowers in the plant kingdom. The plant is used in traditional medicines.
Below; the flame lily, *Gloriosa superba*. The roots of this lily are used in traditional medicines to treat impotency and barrenness.
Right, the flowers of the Sausage tree, *Kigelia africana,* are seldom seen on the ground. Any that fall are quickly eaten by antelope.

Opposite: Some of the multitude of insects to be found at Phinda: Top, a long-horn, wood-boring beetle, *Ceroplesis sp.*, with its long antennae; centre: a dung beetle of the Scarabaeidae family rolls a ball of dung many times its own weight; and below; newly-hatched locusts, (family Acrididae), provide a rich food source for birds.

In nature, longevity is closely linked to reproduction. For instance, elephants live between 60 and 70 years, have a 22-month gestation period and reach sexual maturity at about ten years. Rhinos, which live for about 35 years, have a gestation period of 16 to 18 months. Each only produces a single calf. On the other hand, lions and cheetahs, which seldom live for more than 15 to 20 years, often produce litters of up to six cubs after a gestation period of 90 to 100 days.

The rhinos and elephants are thriving under the ideal conditions at Phinda. But there will come a time when they will need more space to roam. There will be just too many animals to be carried on the reserve's 15 000 hectares. Interlinked ecosystems ensure greater carrying capacity, which in turn provide more excitement for visitors and more jobs for rural people.

There is every chance that there will not be enough grass or vegetation for the number of animals we carry. Wild animals react very quickly to poor veld conditions. Before you know it, you can have lost hundreds of animals. So we plan to sell off several herds of nyala before winter sets in. This gives us extra revenue and reduces the pressure on the veld. Selling nyala may also help us to bring in rare species such as the beautiful sable and roan antelopes."

The biggest single threat to game during droughts is not a shortage of water but a shortage of food. When animals do not have enough food they soon lose condition and become susceptible to tick and other parasitic infections. As soon as he could, Les started clearing the bush and re-establishing the grasslands which had disappeared as a result of years of overgrazing. Andrew Lewis, who had learnt the techniques of land management at Londolozi from Dave and John Varty, moved to Phinda to work with Les on the mammoth task. Their first priority was to clear the invasive acacia species close to the roads. It was not long before the animals were congregating on the open grasslands and the pans were filling with water. Andrew was thrilled to watch elephants and bulldozers working side by side clearing the thick bush in the south: "Not long ago this area still had the fences used for the old cattle camps," he said. "In another year it will be sufficiently cleared to start game drives. The old roads went straight up and down the hills and were a major cause of topsoil run-off and erosion. We will put our roads on the contour line and then start the long job of opening up the invasive bush for game viewing."

Andrew also set up a programme to maintain the grasslands at optimum productive levels. Particularly in the north, the land is marginal, and without a plan to create a green flush each spring, the wildlife utilisation of the area would be minimal. Once again, much of what is being done at Phinda is experimental. Without elephants and buffalo to do the work for them, Andrew tried various options and eventually settled on a programme of burning and mowing in alternate years. "As Phinda's populations of buffalo, elephants and rhino increase, the need for these operations will be reduced," he says. In the meantime bush clearing is essential to restore the moisture balance of the soil and encourage the grasslands which are the key to a healthy herbivore population. Without impala, nyala, wildebeest, zebra and other smaller antelope, the predator reintroduction programme would stand little chance of success.

Nothing can be more descriptive of the change that has taken place at Phinda than comments in the visitors' books at the camps. For instance, in March 1998, Mark Houston from Ohio, who stayed at Rock Lodge, recorded his experiences:

"We left the Land Rover to do a warm-up hike in preparation for tomorrow's black rhino tracking. This time we were tracking five giraffe. Along the way we learnt about the trees, the biodiversity of insects and birds – not what you would consider big game but spectacular within itself and of immense interest. For example, the strength of the golden

Giraffe proved to be the most difficult of all animals to relocate. Their circulatory system, designed to pump blood up their long necks, is just too powerful for them to lie down. And when standing in a vehicle, any jolt could result in a broken neck. The solution was slow but sure - to provide a secure habitat in which they could breed.

spider's web, the butterflies, dragonflies, the bugs and beetles, chameleons and scorpions. As we neared the giraffe every little move and every sound we made seemed to be magnified. The giraffe kept a keen eye on us and the closest we managed to get was 20 metres or so, just enough to get great photographs.

"On the way back to the Land Rover we were distracted by a rhino and its mate. The dam between us, which was first seen as a barrier, became the setting for the highlight of my trip. The two rhino came to the water's edge for a drink. It was very hot and the male soon climbed in and waded around. The female was so intrigued that she soon followed. Eventually they waded across to our side of the dam. Now we were to have some hands-on practice at tracking rhino. To make things more effective for us they met up with two more so now we had four to work with. They gradually moved towards us while we crouched down and watched, holding our breath. As they neared, Anton instructed us to climb a tree if they charged.

"When they were about ten metres away we began to fall back and that is when they were first aware of us. Much to our relief, they retreated. Words will never do justice to the excitement of what we saw this evening. The past four days have been an unforgettable and unsurpassable experience. From terrapins and barn owls and all the in-between, our stalking elephants on foot in thick forest vegetation, a rhino calf suckling, a porcupine, crocodiles, wildebeest, impala, nyala, zebra, nine giraffe, kudu, pelicans, various kingfishers, bushbabies, a genet, and oops, I nearly forgot. We saw a pride of lions. Two females stalked zebra and we became almost part of the chase, because the baby zebra crashed into our Land Rover. Fortunately the lioness veered off. She made the kill and we saw and heard the lioness devour her prey. The other highlight was an hour-long territorial fight between two huge male leopards which entertained us royally. It was an awesome experience." Few guests can believe that less than ten years ago, this was a derelict cattle farm!

The question is often asked: "Is walking in the wilderness dangerous?" Hugh Marshall, who has spent more than fifteen years working in Big Five game country and is in charge of the 130 rangers in the CCAfrica group, answered the question with a 'yes' and a 'no'. "You can't ever get away from the fact that wild animals should be treated with respect," he said. "There are times when they can be dangerous. It's something we should never forget. If we do, it is at our peril.

"People have been walking at Londolozi since 1926, and have frequently encountered elephants, lions, white rhinoceros and leopards. Never once has there been an incident, although there have been many exciting times. The tragedy at Phinda in 1998, when an elephant killed a professional photographer, was unusual. We have already accumulated a great deal of knowledge about the signals wild animals make, but there is still so much happening that we do not yet understand. Our rangers have been trained to use all their senses: to watch and listen to the animals –

"What is so wonderful about all the animals in the African bush, except perhaps for the lone buffalo, is that they tell us what they are going to do," says Hugh Marshall. "You only have to read their signals. You also must listen to the birds. The Natal francolin greets the dawn with raucous calls which change dramatically if a predator is about. All wildlife watches and listens. Monkeys and baboons chattering excitedly in the forest tell of leopards. The cackling of crested guineafowl is a sure sign that lions are not far away. Elephants watch the spoonbills in the shallows busily collecting crabs and frogs, and the stilts and sandpipers foraging quietly on the shoreline. The atmosphere of harmony, of grazing animals and feeding birds, can change instantly to one of tension and alarm calls as predators get on the move. It is increasingly becoming apparent that frequencies and energy forces unknown to man, are at play in these great interlinked webs of life."

On the vast plains of the Serengeti, zebras and wildebeest move in great numbers in their endless search for food - known as the East African migration. Can we dare to believe that a similar movement of animals, from Lake St Lucia in the south, through the foothills of the Lebombo Mountains and into game reserves in Mozambique, can be recreated in our life times?

not always to the guests. When a dangerous animal indicates 'That's close enough,' and a guest asks if he can get a little closer to get that great shot, it is just not possible to please him."

With the first priority of stocking the reserve well under control, Les and Andrew are now looking to the future when they are likely to have too many animals rather than too few. Ian Player provided a solution for this long-term problem. He said: "I can think of no valid reason why the fence between Mkuze and Phinda should not be dropped." What a difference it would make. There would be an overwhelming response from neighbours, to the east the Zulu and Thonga communities and to the south, the private landowners who have farmed cattle for generations and have watched Phinda – at first with curiosity – and with some cynicism. Many have already been converted and are now farming wildlife themselves. If all the fences were removed, the animals would be able to move freely over an area of 65 000 hectares. Taking the removal of fences one stage further, the Greater St Lucia Wetland Park, with the inclusion of Phinda and Mkuze, would cover over 300 000 hectares.

Maputaland could become one of the great ecological playgrounds of the world. The first step needs people with vision to facilitate co-operation between private enterprise, public-sector conservation bodies and the AmaThonga and AmaZulu who were there first. The road ahead is full of obstacles. The first stage is to get onto that road.

PHINDA ADVENTURES

The day starts at Phinda with an early morning call. This is not always the persistent ring of a telephone. At Forest Lodge guests wake to the frog-like call of the African broadbill - *brrrrup, brrrup* - or the tinkling song of the gorgeous bush shrike. Greenspotted doves feed under the trees giving their call, *some birds have three eggs, some, one, but I have tu-tu-tu-tu-tu*. In the canopy of the sand forest a series of high-pitched calls and the conspicuous flash of red wings may give away the presence of purplecrested louries. At Vlei Lodge narina trogons with their colourful red and green feathers hoot in the trees while little waxbills twitter amongst the vlei grasses.

At Mountain Lodge the Natal robin's melodious song starts the day. In winter the flowering aloes attract eastern blackheaded orioles and starlings, while excited chatter announces the arrival of a bevy of colourful sunbirds; collared, whitebellied, purplebanded, African black and scarletchested compete for the sweet nectar of the flowers. Bulbuls call to one another *wake-up, wake-up* as they hunt for insects in the trees of the boma. A bateleur, so distinctive with its upturned wings and crimson beak and feet, rides a thermal while watching for carrion. In summer European bee-eaters are regular visitors. Not far away at Rock Lodge, mocking chats run and flit from rock to rock while attempting to mimic the songs of other birds. In the ravine below, a colony of lesser masked weavers has been busy since dawn noisily building their nests in a fever tree. Scimitarbilled woodhoopoes sound the alarm when guests arrive for early morning coffee on the patio where they have built their nests. From there one may also see crowned eagles flying around Leopard Rock, which towers over the Lodge from the opposite side of the ravine.

There is hardly time to feel the spirit of the land, which is embodied in the magical African dawn, before the curtain goes up on a great African adventure; the forest and bushveld, the wetlands and rivers, the beach and the warm Indian Ocean are all within reach. This is what is so uniquely different about Phinda. There is so much to see and so much to do. From early morning until the sun dips below the horizon and the fierynecked nightjars and owls call over the deafening buzz of thousands of cicadas, the days are filled with excitement, fascination and fun.

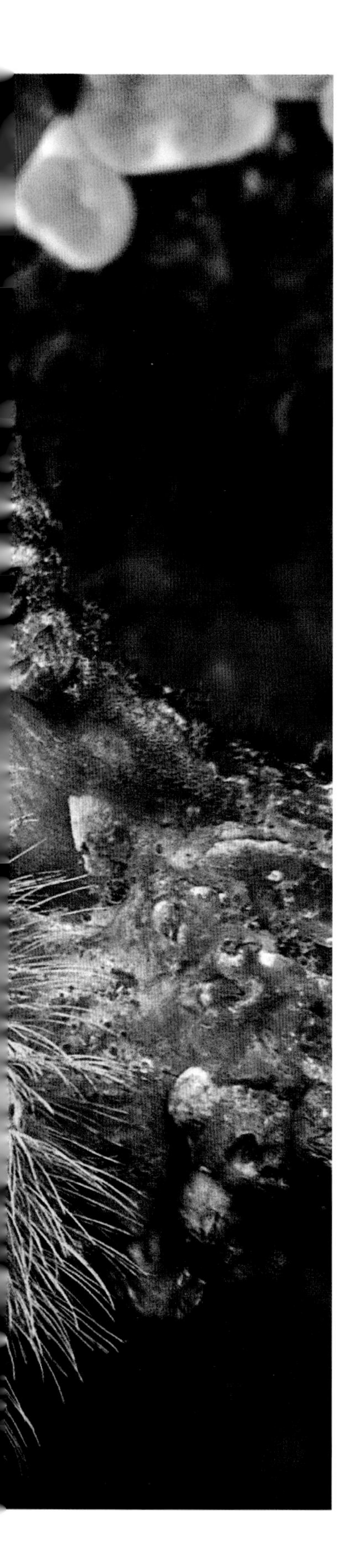

Maputaland's offshore coral reef, the southernmost reef on the African coast, is ideal for a scuba safari. In the crystal-clear water, the corals, the sea anemones, the fish and the crustaceans, like the hermit crab (left), provide a spectacle of colour and fascination.

PHINDA'S FIRST ADVERTISING CAMPAIGN, designed by Hunt Lascaris, one of South Africa's leading advertising agencies, was superb. It promoted the unique 'Big Six' at Phinda: the five most dangerous mammals – lions, leopards, elephants, rhino and buffalo – plus dolphin. The coastal forest zone and the marine reserve, which stretch from St Lucia to the Kosi lagoon on the border of South Africa and Mozambique, lie within easy reach of Phinda, yet they are not easily accessible, particularly for overseas visitors who do not come equipped with 4x4s, tents, battery-operated fridges and self-catering equipment. Phinda provides visitors with another option. It makes it possible to explore Maputaland using Phinda as a base camp.

Most game reserves have a simple formula for entertaining their guests: dinner in a boma under the stars, an early morning game drive, a walk after breakfast, leisure during the heat of the day, and a late afternoon drive, stopping for sundowners and returning to camp long after the sun has set, using a spotlight to catch sight of nocturnal animals.

Phinda planned to break away from this routine. But it was no easy matter. A long list of equipment was required: boats and canoes, additional Land Rovers fitted with special tyres for beach driving, spotlights, ski boats, scuba diving and fishing gear, snorkels and fins. As well as an extensive knowledge of wildlife and the wilderness, Phinda rangers had to qualify to track black rhino and needed to learn more about the habits and breeding activities of the birds of Maputaland and about the marine life, the tides and the currents along the coast. They also had to qualify in sea rescue and scuba diving. Phinda would need a small aircraft for 'the flight of the fish eagle', a regional flight over the southern Maputaland wetlands arranged for guests. They also thought they would need a helicopter although this has proved to be low on the list of priorities, partly because of the expense, but also because helicopters are not allowed to land on the Maputaland beach. Most of all, they would need organisation – and a crystal ball to tell them about the weather.

A visitor to Phinda wrote: "Whilst on the river cruise we got hit by the biggest hailstones we've ever seen in the first storm of spring. There followed a rapid drive through lightning strikes and crashing thunder to arrive back soaked but relieved. For the first time on this trip the weather was more spectacular than the wildlife. Jim and Heather, Hampshire, England. P.S. You might have guessed that the English would comment on the weather."

In the early days there were simply not enough visitors at Phinda to warrant organising adventures in the style originally envisaged. Helicopter beach safaris were cancelled, others had to be amended. Then, as the number of visitors increased, there were not enough qualified rangers, and for a while off-reserve trips were doubly difficult. Now that occupancies are high, Bibi van Tienhoven has taken up the challenge of reorganising the adventure programme.

Bibi exchanged the concrete of Johannesburg for the wide open spaces of Maputaland, leaving behind a career in merchant banking. But, accustomed as she was to working to tight deadlines, it has been no easy matter arranging the daily Phinda adventure programme. She describes it as trying to complete three jigsaw puzzles at the same time, working against the clock and with all the pieces muddled together in one heap. The reserve may be full; that means 96 guests, all requesting different adventures which have to be organised at the last minute taking into account the tides, the vagaries of the weather and the availability of specialist rangers and vehicles.

Often it is only when guests sit down to dinner that the next day's schedule can be finalised. Behind the scenes is a hive of activity: bush breakfasts and picnic lunches to be prepared and packed, flight schedules co-ordinated and pilots alerted, beach rangers organised with equipment for scuba diving and snorkelling, and Mkuze rangers advised.

Bibi arranges visits to the neighbouring communities to see the work of the Rural Investment Fund and to a Zulu cultural village as well as co-ordinating about ten different eco-programmes. Guests are offered a choice of staying on the reserve for game drives, walking through the different ecosystems or cruising or canoeing on the Mzinene River. The off-reserve alternatives are Mkuze black rhino tracking, birding excursions throughout Maputaland, a flight over the spectacular Maputaland wetlands, the coastal zone and the offshore coral reef, or participating in one of the beach adventures.

The twice-daily game drives, early morning and late afternoon, are very much part of the Phinda experience. In one outing it is almost impossible to cover all seven of the different ecosystems on the reserve. There will always be something left over for another day or another visit. And there's always the unexpected, when there is so much activity in one area that you never move to another. The interaction between lions and cheetahs can keep one riveted for hours. On the other hand, a stop to view game can be abruptly terminated. Recently John and Jill Koch from Durban watched elephants confront a pride of lions. "The female elephant had two youngsters with her and she was very angry when the lions walked into her territory," said Jill. "We were in a primeval war zone! Our ranger, Mike Karantonis, wasted no time in moving us away from what he described as a potentially dangerous situation. Mike has a wonderful knowledge and understanding of the wild and is passionate about Phinda and Maputaland. We felt safe with him and thought it most interesting that the local community at Mduku has recognised his affinity with the earth. It is very much part of their culture. For a small sum, they have allocated him a piece of ground at their village. He is building his home there."

Waterbuck and kudu are often found on the edge of the riverine forest against a backdrop of fever and fig trees. Elephants prefer the deep forests of the south in summer but move north to the ilala palm veld in winter. The open plain is also favoured by wildebeest whose keen

Left: A darter appears amongst the riverbank foliage. Canoeing on the Mzinene River at dawn is a wonderful way to see the birds. A pygmy goose dances on the water. *Right:* Forest prey and predator: leopard cubs will soon be on the prowl. At the first sign of danger, suni, a rare antelope found at Phinda, will freeze, only the twitch of its tail giving away its presence.

A Diederik Cuckoo (which takes its name from its song, *dee, dee, dee-de-rik)* catches a caterpillar in the canopy of a tree on the banks of the Mzinene River.

eyesight gives them warning of predators. Leopards, red duiker, nyala, suni and crested guineafowl find secret places in the sand forest. Nyala also hide in the thickets dotted about the montane grasslands. Giraffe and impala feed both in the broad-leaved woodland and the acacia thornveld. White rhino and zebra graze on the open savannah, while cheetahs like to have the space to watch and to hunt. Lastly, the wetlands are the scene of a continual to and fro of wildlife, and often this is where the lions will wait.

Mark Tennant, a ranger at Phinda for three years, says that even the Okavango cannot compare with the magic of the Mzinene River. The KwaZulu river cruise takes you through reeds and grasslands, dense riverine forest, steep banks with overhanging vegetation and acacia and broad-leafed woodlands. Sometimes the river has long open stretches of deep water, at others it has quiet backwaters and mudflats. A crocodile slithers silently off the bank. Terrapins scurry into the water. Nile monitors look for nests to raid. Vervet monkeys clamber in the trees and only disappear from sight when an eagle flies overhead.

The river has a wonderful diversity of bird life and is a continual hive of activity. When the fruit of the fig trees ripens this activity reaches a crescendo. The reeds provide both hiding places and perches for many birds. Malachite kingfishers sway on thin reeds as they hunt in the shallows for small fish. Greenbacked, squacco, grey and goliath herons watch from within the reeds. Purple gallinules with their brilliant red beaks and eyes scurry quickly away at one's approach. Thickbilled weavers build nests between two reeds while whitebellied sunbirds hang their nests on a single stem. The rare African finfoot, with their brilliant orange beaks and webbed feet, swim in the shadows of the riverbank. African jacana hop daintily from lilypad to lilypad searching for insects in the cups of flowers. Both species of night heron – the whitebacked and the blackcrowned – nest in the bushes overhanging the river. During the day they seldom leave their nests but at dusk, when the activity of the day slows and they are safe from eagles, they emerge to catch crabs and other aquatic species. At sunset whitefaced ducks will often leave the river and fly to a nearby wetland, whistling in unison as they go.

Giant and halfcollared kingfishers fly up and down the river looking for fish. A pied kingfisher hovers over the water and then turns, tail up and beak pointing down, in a swift dive towards an unsuspecting fish. Cormorants wait on half-submerged logs for fish to appear, while darters hang out their wings to dry after a swift underwater swim to spear a fish. In the canopy of the trees on the riverbanks, another group of birds waits to be identified. A Wahlberg's eagle has built a nest in a fig tree. Steppe buzzards and African goshawks watch from their perches for the opportunity to hunt. And right on the top of one of the tallest trees on the riverbank an African fish eagle calls to its mate.

Many of the rangers at Phinda have become birding specialists and will take guests on bird adventures both within the reserve and throughout the Maputaland wilderness. Key off-reserve areas are Lake St Lucia

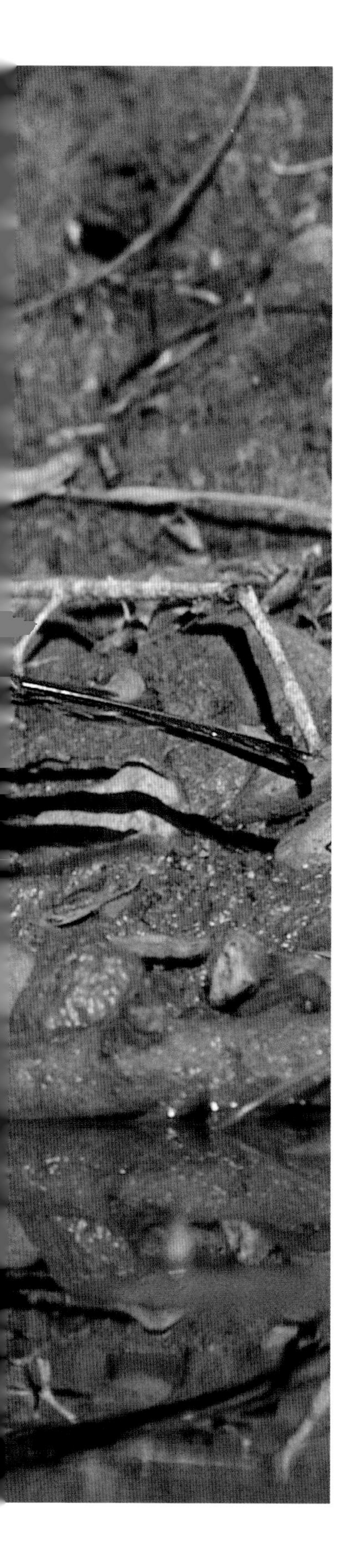

An African finfoot (left) on the banks of the Mzinene River and a pink-throated twinspot (right) in the forests at Phinda, add to the richness of the reserve's biodiversity. Their colour and form, habits and idiosyncrasies, hunting and nesting skills, flight patterns and songs, freedom and vulnerability, are all part of nature's great interdependent plan.

Left: Six kingfishers at Phinda. From left to right: A pied kingfisher, a giant kingfisher, a malachite kingfisher, a halfcollared kingfisher, a brownhooded and a pygmy kingfisher. Contrary to their name, not all kingfishers eat fish. Of these six, three are fish-eaters. The pygmy, brownhooded and malachite kingfishers will take crabs and crustaceans at the water's edge, but their main source of food is insects.

Right: The female snipe (below) is far more attractive than her mate (above). Like the female jacana, she is polyandrous, leaving the incubation of her eggs and the care of her hatchlings to her mate while she goes in search of another mate: an efficient system for a rare species.

and Lake Sibayi, the Muzi pan, Mkuze Game Reserve and, further afield, the Kosi lakes and Ndumu Reserve. Five birds are endemic to the region: the lemonbreasted canary, pinkthroated twinspot, Neergaard's sunbird, Rudd's apalis and Woodward's batis. The latter requires more effort than most to locate. To find this elusive bird, Mark Tennant would wake his guests at three o'clock in the morning and take off thirty minutes later to arrive at the St Lucia coastal dune forest just as the sun started to light the sky. He then played the call and the batis responded. After a breakfast picnic there would be many other bird species to see on Lake St Lucia; flamingo, pinkbacked pelicans, southernbanded snake eagles, olive bush shrikes and rufousbellied herons are amongst the specials. And then there are the crocodiles and hippo.

As well as being able to identify individual lions, leopards and cheetahs and recognising relationships, rangers need to observe the feeding preferences of herbivores and detect subtle changes in the health of ecosystems. Part of their job is care of the wilderness and the wildlife. Another part of the job of the head ranger at Phinda is to be always on the lookout for ways to improve the wilderness experience for guests. Leading experts are invited to Phinda, both to help rangers with their interpretation and to give talks to guests. Among those who have visited Phinda are Vincent Carruthers, a specialist on frogs, Dr Peter Taylor on bats, Professor Gordon McLean, Geoff Lockwood and Aldo Berruti on birds, David Rattray on Zulu history, Mark Read on grasses and trees, Elsa Pooley on flowers and Dr Mario Dinagio on the stars.

There is so much to learn about nature and there is no better way than by walking. Almost every step is one of discovery. You learn to read the history of the earth at your feet; to see the fossil remains of giant mollusc shells laid down when the Maputaland plain was beneath the sea. At St Lucia you can see the fossil teeth of a 25-metre sea monster, an ancestor of the great white shark. You learn to recognise the bird calls and know where to look for the more elusive species. You watch the patience and ingenuity of spiders as they weave gossamer-light webs between trees. And the dung beetles, one of thousands of species belonging to the Scarabaeidae family, which will attempt to roll a ball of dung many times its own size over seemingly insurmountable barriers until a suitable site for reproduction is found.

There is an extraordinary link between fig trees and the tiny wasps of the family Agaonidae. Each of the five different fig species on Phinda plays host to a specific wasp, the wingless males never leaving the figs in which they are born and bred. When the female wasp emerges from the fruit she begins her task of flying from one tree to another to find a mate. In doing so she pollinates the tiny flowers within the figs which are inaccessible to the usual array of birds, bees and butterflies. Destroy the wasps with DDT or other chemicals and the chances are that the forests of fig trees will eventually be destroyed, and a chain reaction involving birds, animals and man will be set in motion.

Guests at Phinda are reminded that according to the dictionary an adventure is 'a risky undertaking of unknown outcome'. There is no guarantee that you will not end up a tree, possibly one with thorns, when tracking a black rhino (left). Or that when you spend a night on the beach watching and waiting for a giant leatherback turtle, you won't get stuck in the sand, the weather will not change or the giant reptiles will fail to appear. Fortunately, in this wonderful world, we have learnt to live by a simple philosophy: the greater the risk, the greater the reward. Phinda heaps rewards on you: excitement, thrills. But be warned!

There is so much to learn from animals. Watch the elephants when they walk down to the water's edge to drink with all the apparent nonchalance in the world. But while they walk, they gather information from the bird songs and their activity. The repetitive song of the redfronted tinker barbet (above) would stop suddenly if danger was around. When walking, one needs to use all one's senses: a sense of smell, of sight and sound, and even of touch and taste. Feel the velvety smoothness of young leaves and flower petals. One must also listen to one's sixth sense which, without logic, can give early warning of danger.

Walking is an opportunity to watch nature at work, to understand the intricate patterns of life on this planet and learn how every living species has a special role to play. It also provides the time to feed the inner spirit; to wonder at nature and watch, as if an outsider, the course of your life. As if from the wrong side of a pair of binoculars, you gain another perspective on man's role in the universe. It is a lesson in humility. It is also a lesson in love and interdependence.

Mark Tennant established a 25-kilometre walk through Phinda's seven different ecosystems. Starting in the predawn silence his party would set off from Mountain Lodge, walking the first 10-kilometre leg through the hills and down to the Munyawana riverbed for a light breakfast and plenty of fluids. The second leg of the journey would take them through the woodlands to a second stop for a leisurely lunch under a shady tree. Once the heat of the day was past they would set out on the last leg of the walk to Forest Lodge where they would arrive at dusk. A long day, but full of interest and adventure.

Mark always started the walk by picking wild basil, which he asked his guests to roll into balls and put into their nostrils. Within a few minutes their sinuses would be cleared and their sense of smell enhanced. He learnt the remedy from Zulu herbalists. Then he would teach the city dwellers how to listen and to be in tune with nature. The redfronted tinker barbet would be a good starting point; its monotonous call, *clink-clink-clink*, repeated 120 to 130 times a minute for several minutes, is hard to miss. Once everyone was listening he would call the lions!

Walking at Phinda is also an opportunity to get the adrenalin pumping. One of the Mkuze rangers has been treed by black rhino more often than he cares to remember. Mark Tennant says that you don't feel a thing when you are going up a thorn tree. It's only when you have to climb down that you notice the thorns, the shredded clothing and the blood! Rangers at Phinda have to pass a special test before they qualify to track black rhino. They have to be knowledgeable and they have to be expert marksmen. Not only do they have to hit a 10-centimetre target repeatedly at sixty metres. They have to stand their ground facing a ton of living flesh capable of covering the distance in about five seconds. It's not something one would like to do every day!

On one of Carl Walker's visits to Mkuze, he and his party had a pair of black rhino and three white rhino in sight when two shots rang out and a badly injured rhino flashed past them as they took cover. They were not the only party tracking the rhino; there were poachers! Carl immediately radioed to Mkuze's anti-poaching team for help but the poachers did not wait around when they realised they had company.

Black rhino may be less than half the size of their cousins (they shared the same ancestor some three or four million years ago) but they more than make up the difference with their aggression. White rhino are the gentle grazers of the grasslands. Black rhino are the tough bullies of the forests. When tracking black rhino it is essential to have the rhino in

Right: Mkuze Game Reserve has a particularly lovely fig and fever tree forest. A Pel's fishing owl has made its nest in one of these giant trees, *Ficus sycomorus*, which grows on river banks where its gnarled roots are effective in preventing erosion during summer storms. In October, when the figs ripen, the green pigeons, narina trogon and many other colourful birds, make Mkuze a favourite area for walking.

Left: Three of Phinda's experienced rangers: Vanessa Strauss, Dumi Mpanza and Carl Walker. They are all keen naturalists and each has a particular interest: Vanessa enjoys the challenge of walking up to game, Carl's love is lions and leopards, which he has made a study of at Phinda, while Dumi is fascinated with the medicinal uses of plants.

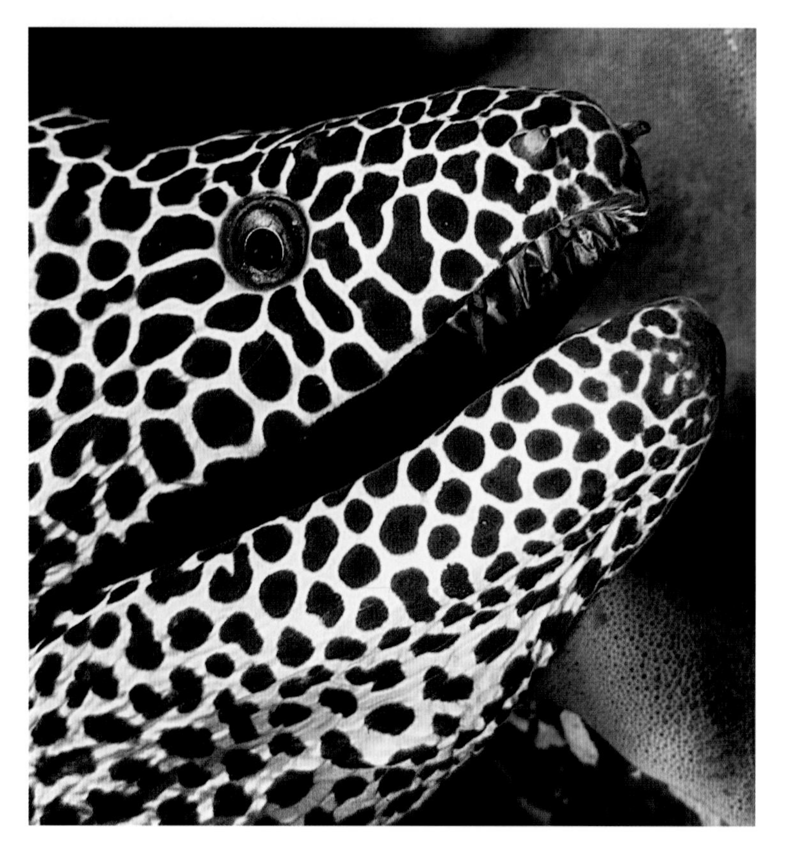

The Maputaland coast closely rivals the Great Barrier Reef of Australia in aquatic species diversity. Some of the fish photographed within the Maputaland Marine Reserve by scuba diver Peter Pinnock are: right, Coachman, *Heniochus acuminatus;* and left: from top left, semi-circle angel fish, *Pomacanthus semicirculatus;* coral rockcod, *Cephalopholis miniatus*; crescent-tail bigeye, *Priacanthus hamrur;* and honeycomb moray eel, *Gymnothorax favagineus*.

Hugh Marshall, ranger training consultant for the CCAfrica group, was talking to a guest at the Mountain Lodge pool when two snakes fell out of the sycamore rock fig tree and into a pond just below the pool. A vine snake *(Thelotornis capensis)*, which feeds principally on frogs, lizards, snakes and other cold-blooded species, had attacked a Natal green snake *(Philothamnus natalensis)*, locking it in its jaws. But the survival instinct of the green snake was powerful. Facing death, it reacted instinctively, twisting and pulling the vine snake down until the attacker's head was underwater. It was an extraordinary manoeuvre and it worked. The vine snake had to let go or drown and the green snake escaped, but not before the vine snake's fangs had punctured its skin and the deadly venom was at work.

The large number of snakes in Maputaland have a plentiful supply of food; birds that forage on the ground, birds' eggs, rodents, lizards, toads and frogs in particular abound. Forty-two different frog species have been identified on Phinda's 15 000 hectares. In comparison, the whole of Europe has only thirty-two. There are delicate little leaf frogs, frogs that change their colour, giant bullfrogs that will attack snakes, frogs that jump, leap, climb and swim. Frogs alone can be the subject of a lifetime study. Above, a painted reed frog, and below, a foam nest frog. The latter have taken up residence at Rock Lodge where they sit under the lamps waiting for insects.

one eye and your escape route mapped out with the other. If there is not a nearby tree, then you have to be prepared to stand your ground. Another safety rule is to keep as quiet as a mouse. Rhino do not have good eyesight but they have acute hearing, and even a whisper will have a rhino spinning around with remarkable agility. Some people thrive on the excitement. Despite the fact that two armed rangers accompany every party, many people prefer to watch the black rhino from a hide or from the security of a Land Rover.

Whether one swims and snorkels, watches the sea birds, or participates in a scuba safari, one will be enchanted with the Maputaland coast. Ideally, all these adventures start with a short flight by fixed-winged aircraft. The coastline is a place of magic. Imagine kilometre after kilometre of golden beach with the only evidence of man's presence the footprints one leaves behind to be washed away by the incoming tide. Imagine the thrill of a kaleidoscope of colourful fish, each rocky pool opening a new world of beauty. Or a school of hundreds of dolphin swimming close inshore up the African coast.

One of the greatest thrills of all is scuba diving in the clear water of the offshore coral reef: suddenly one senses the presence of a monster close by. For a second one wonders if it is a great white shark, and then a 15-metre-long whale shark swims into view: the gentle giant of the ocean. The coast also has blue and black marlin, sailfish, tuna, barracuda, bonito and many shark species.

The beach is not only a place to watch the scurrying crabs and seabirds. Carl Walker, who has been at Phinda since its beginning, has seen jackal, red duiker and kudu on the beach. The rangers have watched giant kingfishers diving into the sea off Black Rock and they've heard reports of leopards frolicking in the surf. They have also had their share of problems; in the early days Mark Tennant missed the low tide and was unable to return the 25 kilometres along the beach. Eventually he managed to get off the beach but lost his way trying to get around Lake Sibayi. The party finally made it back to Mountain Lodge at midnight.

On another occasion one of Phinda's guests nearly drowned. Although he was a good swimmer, he could make no headway against the strong undercurrent which carried him further and further out to sea. A number of people swam out beyond the surf zone to keep him company and to explain that there was no need to fight against the current. Experienced surfers watch the height of the surf from which they can see where the current is moving out and where it turns and heads inshore. They were able to tread water until they caught the incoming current and were carried back to the beach.

Maputaland also has a large population of snakes. Of South Africa's 130 snake species, only 14 have been known to cause human death: quite enough to make people fear these reptiles, although so many, like the Natal green snake, are not poisonous to humans. Fortunately the rangers at Phinda can identify snakes and advise visitors which are safe and which

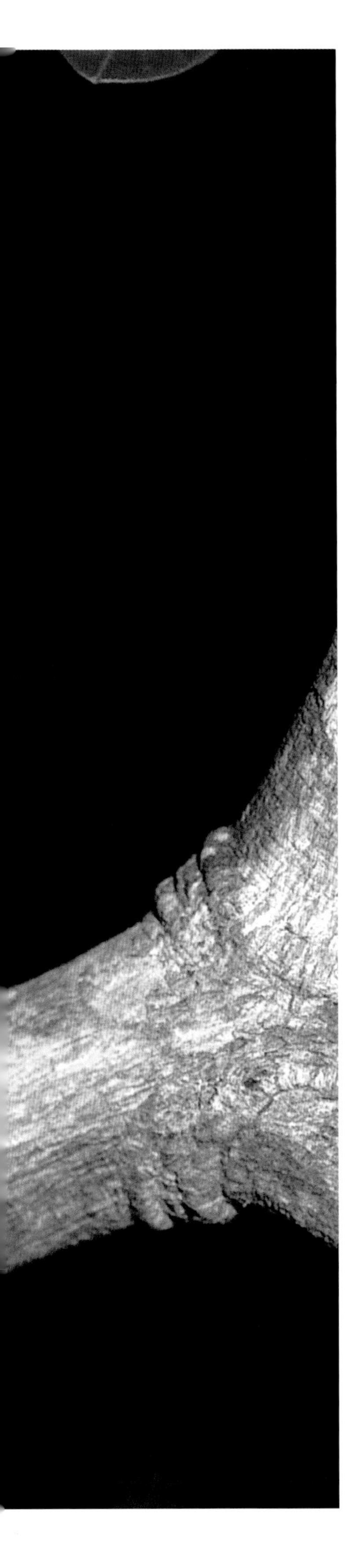

As the sun sets and the persistent buzz of thousands of cicadas slowly dies down, the sounds of the night begin. A nightjar may sing its plaintive song, owls may hoot from the trees and dikkops give their musical call. And then there are the serval, porcupines, scrub hares and pangolins, and many other birds and animals which take advantage of the dark. A common feature of nocturnal species are their big eyes such as those of the bushbaby (left).

are dangerous. Snakes are not aggressive, but they react quickly to any invasion of their territory. Some of the most poisonous, like the vine snake, are back fanged and would find it difficult, if not impossible, to penetrate a human arm or leg. But don't reach up to pick a leaf off a tree without a careful look first. Or when looking at birds' nests, remember that snakes take a keen interest in the contents. Fraser Gear, one of Phinda's rangers, watched a pair of orangebreasted bushshrikes drive a boomslang away from their nest in an *Acacia nilotica*. Like the vine snake, the boomslang is also deadly poisonous and back fanged.

* * *

When the day ends, there is still one more excitement. Phinda turns a bush dinner into an adventure. Eric Buthelezi points out that sometimes they have no choice but to delay dinner; on one occasion lions arrived just ahead of the guests. But when things go according to plan, hundreds of flickering lanterns guide you into a secluded grove deep in the forest or to giant umbrella trees, *Acacia tortillis*, where a fairy land of lights and a big log fire await. Amongst the trees you may discover a wood owl, with its big round eyes, peering down in surprise. Or a bush baby will disappear rapidly into the canopy of a tree. And then at Mountain Lodge, Sam Nguni will announce what culinary delights are in store for you. It's a magical way to bring down the curtain on an exciting day in Africa.

It is hard to believe that there was a time when black rhinoceros roamed the slopes of Table Mountain, when twenty-five white rhinoceros could be seen on one hillside in the Limpopo Valley, and when vast herds of buffalo and elephants came down to the Pongolo River to drink. Today 7.6 per cent of KwaZulu Natal is under state-controlled conservation – that is, only 704 000 hectares, while only just over five per cent of the whole of South Africa is formally protected.

Madikwe and Pilanesberg Game Reserves are amongst a growing number of public-sector developments in the past few decades. There have also been many private-sector initiatives such as the Tswalu Desert Reserve and Phinda. These projects represent the future of conservation through private-sector, community and public-sector partnerships.

Right now the Spatial Development Initiative, set up by Nelson Mandela, is unblocking the barriers to private-sector involvement in Maputaland: it has set targets for improving security, building roads, rolling back malaria and establishing training facilities. It is also rewriting the eighty-eight pieces of legislation that cripple private-sector initiatives in proclaimed conservation areas. Not least, the Lubombo SDI has established a framework for a transfrontier park linking the reserves of Mozambique and Swaziland with those of northern Maputaland.

While the SDI has concentrated on infrastructure, the Peace Parks Foundation has worked on transfrontier park development: the Kalahari Transfrontier Park has already opened the old migratory routes between South Africa and Botswana followed by antelope in their search for food. Many other schemes are in the pipeline, including extending the Kruger National Park into Mozambique and Zimbabwe and the transfrontier park straddling the Maputaland, Mozambique and Swaziland borders. Further south, the Greater St Lucia Wetland Park is on course to receive World Heritage Site status.

The development of these great parks is a formidable task. They will need leaders with vision who are prepared to speak for the earth. They will need private-sector capital and skills. And they will need the goodwill of the people. But ultimately it will be the visitors to these places of wild beauty who will be instrumental in turning the wilderness away from the spiral of destruction into which it is being swept.

The wetlands and waterways of Maputaland with their fish eagles and teeming birdlife are one of the natural wonders of the world. Could a thousand buffalo once again graze on the Mkuze wetlands as they did long ago?

A BOOK ABOUT PHINDA would be incomplete without a look at the future of Maputaland. Ultimately, Phinda will not survive as an island in a sea of destruction. It might be the last to go, but eventually its fate must be linked to that of its neighbours. On this basis alone, Phinda recognises that it must play a role in ensuring that this little corner of South Africa is not forgotten during the political and social changes that are likely to affect South Africa in the early decades of the 21st century.

A journalist once suggested that Phinda's immediate neighbour to the east, St Lucia, might well be called 'the Lake of Storms' because of all the controversies that raged over the right to mine its eastern shores. Maputaland itself might well be called 'a Land of Storms'. Two hundred years ago men from Europe tried to impose their will on the land and ever since they have left a trail of destruction in their wake. Is it too late to repair the damage? More importantly, is it possible to halt further destruction? Will the Thonga people ever again be able to live peacefully together without borders dividing them? Will the Zulu people be reconnected to the land and will they be able to rediscover the wisdom and knowledge that is so rapidly being lost? Will the elephants once again migrate from Maputaland north into Mozambique? Or will they too be stopped at border posts? We don't know. We can only hope that someone will listen to the earth.

Maputaland needs leaders who are prepared to enable the process of change: people who recognise that while life on this planet is transient, the earth is not. And no matter what the risk, and whatever it takes, they should lead the restoration process, because it is the perfection of nature's wealth that can best serve the people of Maputaland. Steps must be taken to review all forms of non-sustainable land use. Already the nutrient-poor land is overstocked with cattle. Agricultural monocultures have reached the sunset of their existence and most other forms of agriculture have failed. The Maputaland plain was once like a giant sponge filled with water. Now it is drying out. Forestry companies are already struggling with the frequent fires that tear through their plantations. Do they recognise that those fires are symptomatic of a falling water table? And that ultimately their plantations are doomed?

Phinda has led by example in showing that sustainable land use can transform a region. One only has to look at what has been achieved in ten years: wildlife has been reintroduced and is thriving, ecosystems have been reinstated, four to five hundred people are employed and for the first time have realistic ambitions for their future, and international travellers are enjoying a unique African theatre.

One of the major impediments to development is land tenure. The Spatial Development Initiative, formed to mobilise private-sector investment to generate long-term economic growth, reports that one-third of all people in Maputaland have been subjected to forced removal at least

Nkosi Simon Gumede, the Makasa community leader, has already advised Phinda that he would like to see the farm, Lulubush, returned to wildlife. The people have seen for themselves how much can be gained from working in partnership with nature. Like the great North American philosopher, Chief Seattle, he knows that man cannot own the sparkle of the water or the dew on the grass. Ultimately, man owns neither the earth, nor the wind and the stars.

There is no place for fences between wildlife and wildlife. To gain the maximum advantage for the people and the animals, fences need to be dropped, physically and figuratively, between state and private enterprise. Each could help the other in turning southern Africa into one of the great ecological playgrounds of the world.

once in their lifetimes. Although a land restitution process was set up after the first democratic elections in 1994, it is a long and slow process with many overlapping and conflicting claims. It may take years before these claims are finally resolved.

The farm Lulubush on Phinda's eastern boundary is a microcosm of what is happening in many parts of KwaZulu Natal. The five farms that make up the 2300-hectare property were acquired by the Van Rensburg family in 1948, at the time when the newly formed Nationalist government was parcelling out 'vacant' land to its supporters. That year also marked the end of the tsetse fly saga and just about the end of all wildlife in the region except what little was left in the reserves. For over forty years the farm was used for hunting and for cattle, until in 1992 it was leased to Phinda. When the lease expired five years later, no new agreement could be reached and the farm was put up for sale. However, attempts to sell the property were overtaken by a land claim by the neighbouring community, the outcome of which is still uncertain.

There are many stories like this in Maputaland. In almost every case, changing 'ownership' without recognising the limitations of this nutrient-poor land will compound the tragedy for the people, the wildlife and the land. The measure for the future should not be ownership. It should be care. For thousands of years communal ownership of land ensured that care. If Maputaland's objective of an economy based on ecotourism is to be achieved, everyone must work towards an integrated land-use system.

We are at the start of a quiet revolution. Computers and the Internet are changing industry, business, education and our domestic lives, faster and more dramatically than most of us ever imagined. Business has become global and governments everywhere have discovered that they have to loosen control over their economies. Privatisation has also shifted control, and a change from public-sector management of camps and lodges on land under conservation to private-sector involvement is in the pipeline.

In many respects the South Africa of today is a Pandora's box full of surprises. Our government has not had time to become hidebound in its policies, and there are many signs that ministers have open minds and may be less resistant to change than long-established governments. The ANC government does not have an easy ride in redirecting an out-of-control society. As one member of the Ministry of Tourism said: "It was a damned sight easier to be a terrorist than it is to run a f....ing country!" But even with many other priorities, the government has recognised that agriculture and forestry cannot continue to drain the catchment areas of water without considering the damage to ecosystems downstream.

Under President Thabo Mbeki's government, the SDI has made the Lebombo region, which includes Maputaland, one of its top priorities. In September 1999 the first draft of a World Heritage Site bill was put before parliament. This legislation will consolidate sixteen different conservation areas between St Lucia and Kosi and establish a single management

Once the eastern seaboard of southern Africa was a wilderness paradise: the wildebeest and zebra moved from north to south following behind summer storms in their search for grazing. And always close by were predators: the lions, which watched and waited.

Next page: Conservation is a long-term business involving all species on earth. Its success cannot be measured solely against bottom-line profits. As the British Airways "Tourism for Tomorrow" awards have recognised, it needs to be measured against sustainability, creativity and the participation of and benefits for rural people. The bateleur, the emblem of CCAfrica, has become a symbol of hope in many parts of Africa.

authority. It is the forerunner to recognition of the Greater St Lucia Wetland Park as a World Heritage Site.

Andrew Zaloumis, project manager for the Lubombo SDI, reports directly to the cabinet on SDI matters. He believes they have two years in which to unblock barriers to development and create a stable investment environment. "The building of the road through to Mozambique was a major step forward," he says. "We plan to roll back malaria within three years and set up training facilities for many of the people of Maputaland. We also need to change the conservation policy of the past that has not allowed private-sector development in the reserves. And we need to change it fast. In the past it has taken up to six years for the private sector to get over all the legislative hurdles in the way of tourism development. Right now we have twenty-two blocked projects. We have also identified fifteen lead sites between St Lucia and Kosi. These will be put up for bidding by the private sector, without which our blueprint for development of the region will fail." In a single step Andrew Zaloumis and the SDI have removed the frustration, which often led to anger and apathy in the past, and replaced it with excitement and enthusiasm.

A private-sector, public-sector fund has been set up with which to finance the international marketing of South Africa's tourism industry. An initial expenditure of R180 million a year is planned and a joint marketing partnership, with four representatives from the public sector and four private-sector consultants, is getting down to work. CCAfrica's marketing director, Paul Bannister, is one of the members of this partnership. They have ambitious plans which would far outstrip the initial budget, but it is a dynamic start to marketing South Africa in the new millennium.

Commercial beds outside the proclaimed reserves in Maputaland have increased in recent years from none to over 600, yet the state assets remain underutilised. Mkuze is magic. It has so many fundamental advantages. It covers 35 000 hectares. It is beautiful, with the Ubombo Mountain range at its back and the Mkuze River at its feet. The five-kilometre-long Nsumo pan is described as a "king-sized birdbath", while its fig and fever forests and population of black rhinoceros are world-renowned.

For nearly a hundred years, despite tremendous opposition, conservationists in KwaZulu Natal did a remarkable job holding on to Mkuze and their other reserves. Today, the goal posts have moved. It is not enough to survive. It is vital that the reserves become both ecologically and financially sustainable. To make Mkuze ecologically sustainable means that the offtake of water in the Mkuze River's catchment area needs to be controlled. A financially stable future will be achieved only if the needs of the people on the periphery of the reserve are recognised and if Mkuze caters for the requirements of both South African and international visitors. The latter will want quality accommodation and to see the Big Five. There is so much potential at Mkuze, but it needs to be unlocked.

Even if Mkuze raised the funds to build a fence, bring in lions and build five-star lodges, that would not ensure success. Steve Fitzgerald is

Like the lesser masked weavers (above) which build small, neatly woven nests in the trees overhanging the Mzinene River at Phinda (right) only to find that the nests do not attract a mate, ecotourism developers have discovered that much more is required than bricks and mortar. The natural courtesy of the Zulu people, the quality of service, the proximity of the birds and animals, and the wilderness and beach adventures, all add to the Phinda experience.

realistic about operating Phinda-style lodges. "It is easy to plan and build a lodge in the wilderness," he says. "Funding can be found. But at the end of the day the key to success is filling beds. We have designed our lodges to match international standards: air-conditioning, ultra comfort, five-star cuisine and great personal service. If we don't have visitors from overseas, we are not going to make ends meet. So a major part of our business is international marketing."

The other side of the coin is hospitality and training. The former is deeply engraved in the African culture and is the most vital of the intangibles of successful ecotourism. The country has a new slogan: "South Africa – Africa's warmest welcome." As Steve Fitzgerald says, "We have so much that is right. Beauty. Excitement. And a natural courtesy amongst our rural people. But ultimately it is the quality of service that brings visitors back. We work hard on every aspect of training our staff. Yvonne Short recently took a party of our chefs on a five-star trip to Cape Town to attend a conference of chefs from all over the world. They came back full of enthusiasm and with a much better appreciation of the needs of their guests. Only Sam Nguni was disappointed. He was so taken with a brilliant chef from San Francisco that he offered 50 head of cattle as lobola for her. He was dismayed that she declined the offer!"

Ecotourism also needs an army of rangers who are not only knowledgeable about the wildlife and all living species, but who are prepared to go out day after day, with smiles on their faces and have the ability to make every day in the wilderness so special that it will be remembered forever. Staff need to be happy to create an atmosphere that overrides the disappointments and discomforts of the African bush: the lion cubs that fail to appear, the heat, the rainstorms and the insects. The happy atmosphere at Phinda is one of its greatest assets. It starts with Tony Adams and the lodge managers: Jason King at Mountain Lodge, Gavin Hulett at Forest Lodge, Ansel Biesenbach at Rock Lodge and Craig McDonald at Vlei Lodge. And it permeates all the way through to the warm greetings of Jane Gridley, Lucky Ngubane and Penny Main and the welcoming face of Elias Ntombeni at the main gate.

Recently Steve Fitzgerald, Tony Adams and Les Carlisle have had discussions with the KwaZulu Natal Conservation Service on a new development that would link together the public sector, the rural communities and private enterprise. Each has something special to offer. The communities own beautiful wetlands. Mkuze Game Reserve, with its fig and fever forests and population of black rhinos, lies to the west. Phinda, with its growing populations of predators, lies to the east. A combined project would tap all their abilities: the skills and knowledge of the KwaZulu Natal Conservation Service, the centuries of wisdom acquired by the rural community, and Phinda's experience in raising finance and operating and marketing top quality ecotourism lodges in Africa. Andrew Venter, who proposed the project, is one of a new generation of people involved in conservation. For the past three years he has worked as a

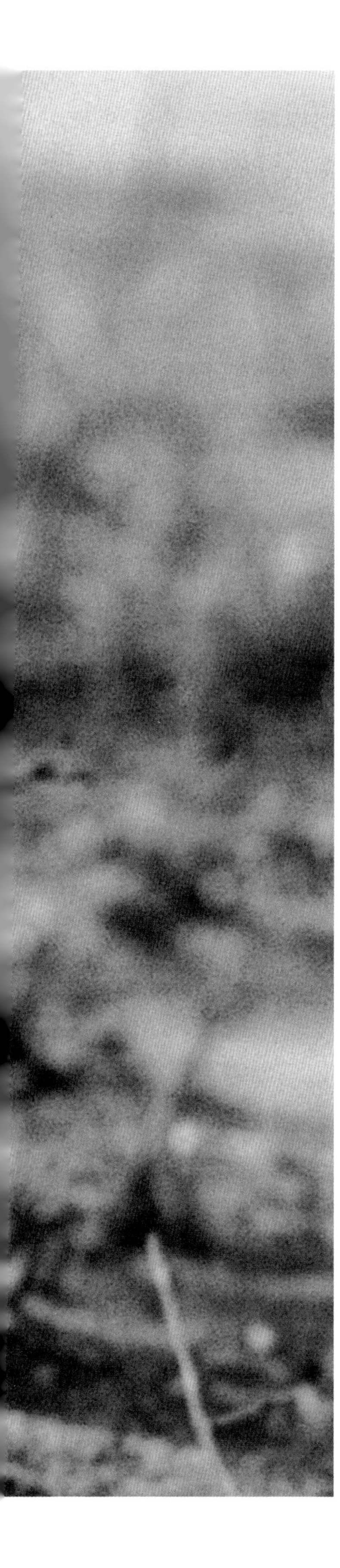

The consolidation of the Reserva d'Elefantas d'Maputa in Mozambique with the Ndumu Game Reserve and Tembe Elephant Park will create a territory big enough for elephants to roam as they did two centuries ago. There will also be space enough for all the big game animals - lions, leopards, rhino and buffalo.

consultant at Mkuze, facilitating community involvement in ecotourism development. He believes that this is an ideal opportunity to rebuild the trust that has been lost after more than 200 years of colonial and apartheid dominance, and to relink the communities to the land. It would be the start of a new era in conservation development.

The Lubombo cross-border initiative was launched in May 1998 and was wholeheartedly endorsed by President Joaquim Chissano of Mozambique, King Mswati III of Swaziland and President Nelson Mandela. A year later, in June 1999, a general protocol on the LSDI was signed by President Thabo Mbeki and the other two leaders. The Peace Parks Foundation, which is playing a leading role in conservation development in southern Africa, has interested the United Nations in investigating the Lebombo transfrontier park project, which could contribute so much to restoring the stability in the region. It would be a fitting monument to Nelson Mandela, a man who has stood, no matter what the cost, for peace and democracy in Africa. What could be better for Maputaland than a two-pronged conservation initiative: in the north the creation of a reserve, perhaps the Mandela Machel Park, and in the south, the Greater St Lucia Wetland Park?

What is to be the outcome? A return to the constrained thinking of the past, or a move towards a future of advancing the green frontiers, of partnerships and of using the wealth of the natural world to serve the people? The SDI has so much potential, but much will depend on the people at the helm. They need to cater for all sections of the market: both high- and low-density tourism, ensuring that the vast number of South Africans are able to enjoy their rich heritage. At the same time, they must also take care that the most unique of all Africa's assets, the spirit of the land, is not destroyed. Across the border in Botswana, the government has established an infrastructure for tourism that works. Private-sector camps are small, environmental impact is minimal, and beds are full. It is an example worth following.

As Ian Player says: "The time for decisions is now. If we procrastinate we will all be losers." Just over one hundred years ago the concept of the Kruger National Park was put before the council of the South African Republic under President Kruger. A series of governments ruminated over the proposal for more than twenty-six years before, finally, the park was proclaimed. We cannot afford to wait that long.

The initial stages may be tough. It will need people with flair and imagination: people like Yvonne Short, who achieved the impossible, training staff to a high level of ability within a short time. Training is vital because in the next decade skills must be transferred from the few to the many, so that the great African theatre is presented to the world by African players who are equipped to be the best.

The next step will be to make it easy for tourists to move from one place to the next without hours of bureaucratic red-tape: the passport, customs and currency queues. Ultimately, to facilitate tourism, it will need

Maputaland is on course to become one of the world's great adventure destinations. This is a new beginning for the region. In time, it could make Maputaland more valuable than all the goldfields of Africa put together. The wilderness has one big advantage. If it is cherished, it will last forever.

the creation of a United States of Southern Africa. Even with the support of the presidents of all three countries, this could be a far-off dream, but it is one that could, like Phinda, become a reality.

People from all over the world want to visit the high spots of Africa: the Victoria Falls – the smoke that thunders, the Okavango – the jewel of Africa, the Serengeti – the endless plains, the Masai Mara – the spotted lands, Mpumalanga – where the sun rises, the Kalahari – the desert splendour. These are the romantic names of Africa. Will the future of the subcontinent also include the Greater St Lucia Wetland Park – Africa's water wonderland, and the Mandela Machel Park – where the earth and ocean speak?

Phinda represents far more than the return of the wildlife, the reinstatement of the ecosystems and the creation of social opportunity and justice for people. In returning the wildlife, Phinda has shown what is possible. It could be the key to a golden future.

SPONSORING SUBSCRIBERS

Alex & Bidi Mauderli
Steve Bales
Maidie Varty
Robert B. Haas
Gary & Judith Wood
Douglas & Pippa Hutchison
Sallie & Foster Bam
Pierrette Schlettwein
Kevin & Barbara Sheehan
Anthony Barton
John Varty
Otto & Hannelore Richter

COLLECTORS' EDITION

Tony & Dee Adams & family
Tony Christodoulou
Don Barrell & family
Barry & Di Beningfield
Thomas W. Hebert
Kathryn Ecenbarger
A.W. Adlkofer
Ian Michael Robinson
Mark Getty
Andrew Dougall
The Watson family
Danie, Daniel & Christiaan Olivier
Antonio & Cristina Cristofanelli
Neale Axelson
Frank & Theresa Kent
Steve & Nicky Fitzgerald
Danie Ferreira
Anna & Frank Seyfert
Gerald & Cornelia Lyons
Christopher Sporborg
Robert Engels
Craig Clucas
Dr A.C. van Bruggen
Jonathan Klein
Bronwyn May Varty
Boyd Watson Varty
Paul Green
H.A.M. Bogaers
Sir Paul Getty
Tara & Jessica Getty
Leon Fail
Jocelyne Laraki
The Chaney family
Duncan Ross & Margaret Taylor
B J Watson
Steve Hall
Graham Bonham-Carter
Ron West
Hugh & Julie Marshall
Jill Holup & Tod Meinke
Vicki & Nigel Colne
Gill & Mike Cope
Sallie & Foster Bam
Peter & Jeffe Williams
Karen Jane Sparkes
Kunj K. Trivedi
Liz & Athol Campbell
Jim & Pauline Black
Serge Sassonia
Ivan Maseroli
Christophe Hertoghe

SPECIAL SUBSCRIBERS

Els Aarts-Velings
A.W. Adlkofer
Juha-Pekka Ahtikari
Ralph Alford
Susan, Coleman, Coley, Alexa & Abigail Andrews
Grant & Sandy Ashfield
Neale & Janet Axelson
Andrea Bach
Wendy & Brian Baird
Nico Baljer
Peter A. Ball
The Bannister family
Isabel Bardinet
Lisa Beach
Lynn, Christina, Juliana & Carol-Lynn Beaumont
Chris, Natalie, Bradley & Christyn Bedser
Archie & Glynis Bell
Antonella & Fabrizio Bernasconi
Ansel Biesenbach
Grant Bodley
Marian D. Boyer
Jerry & Susan Braet
Lawrence Brown
Carol & Christopher Browne
Eric & Roma Buchanan
Caroline Burke
Anna Canilli
Les & Lynette Carlisle & family
Inez Carlisle
Paddy & Lea Carlisle
Mike & Di Carlisle & family
Sean & Kerry Carlisle & family
Laurie & Rita Chiappini
Daniela Cicirello
Joggie & Linky Cilliers
Gian & Bernice Cocci
Robert & Hazel Conacher
Jane Conyngham
Graham Cooling
Steve Cooling
Valerie Coombe
Phillip Covell
The Columbine family
Sam Cox
Alan & Helen Dalby
Mandy & Claudio Damin
Michel Daniel
Andy Davies
Llewellyn Davies
Eric Debuyser
Pete de Kock
Michael & Ingrid Dennill
Hazel & Hugh de Quervain
Gemma Knowles de Schlettwein
Steve & Heidi de Villiers
Didier De Vos
Sara Dewar
Helen Dewar
Gill Dewar
Roger Drew
Tim & Yvonne Driman
Barbara Powers Dubbs
Bruce & Andi Durow
Richard du Toit
Kathryn Ecenbarger
Zirk Engelbrecht
Robert Engels
Jim & Liza Ervin
Gavin Faulds
Nick Finneron & Jenni Jankes
Reneé Flanagan
John & Danna Flack
Joanne Forbes
Enrico Fossati
Philip & Annette Foster
The Foster family
Michael Francies
Patricia Freeman
Harold & Edna Fridjhon
June Rahn & Norman Fisher
Rodney Mattheys & Kevin Gaffney
Mary Susan & J.D. Gallien-Clinton
Jane Ellen & Stephen Gallien-Sanders
Vincent Garrigues
Jan & Anet Geertsema
Roger O. Goldman
Steve & Jenny Goodey
Alec & Catherine Grant
Carolyn De H. Greenwood
Jim & Ellen Greenwood
Bob & Marlene Griffin
Kate Groch
Wayne Hanssen
Deborah Beck Harlan

Sal & Nick Harris
Jaclyn Hartman
Pat Harvey
Stephen & Linda Heard
Rolf Henkler
Simone Henselmans
The Hidden family
Johan & Mickey Hoekstra
Dave & Mary Hopkins
Nigel & Leslee Hosking
Martin Samuel Hughes
Staffan Huss
Libby Huysemeyer
Rob & Judy James
Leon & Marc Janks
Selwyn & Fiorina Jansen
A.R. Jones
Peter Stuart Jones
Kenneth & Birgitta Karlsson & family
Lennart & Linnea Karlsson
H. Keiper
Sarah Kent
John Kent
Mary Kent
Michael Kent
Nóra Kent
Goh Eck Kheng
Paul & Laurel Kinsley
Billy Kirsten
Didier Kling
Ralph & Lorna Kirsten & family
Joel Klotnick
Sheena Knox
Stefan Kuerzel
Michel J Ledin
Raymond & Jill Lenrick & family
Natalie Lewis
Hugo Nestor Linares
Christopher Lisanti
Gary Lötter
Allen Jones & Jennifer Lötter
M. Mercedes Lytle
Robert F MacLeod
Mike & Mary Mayer
Kathryn McCarten
Glenn & Anne McCreath
Anthea McGregor
Tom, Janet, Sara, Thomas & Kathryn McKinley
Lenny & Christine Mendonca
Patricia A Merritt
Dr Ivan Mey
Kevin & Tracey Mills
Ross W Milroy
Gail & Belinda Mingard
Geoff & Emmanuele Monezer
Dr Michael Mossmann
Stefanie Hevicke-Mossmann
Elmarié & Bessie Muhl
The Mullen family
Johan Muller
Meredith & Michael Murphy
Ruth & Rainer Neumann
Diana Niels
Bill & Dale Northcote
Kerry Ochse
Rolf & Karin Olofsson
Sarah Ord
Rudi Oudmayer
Georgette Parry
Jeff & Bev Parsley
Andrew Paterson
Lynn & Don Payne
Mike, Pat, Richard & Daniel Perry
Wolfgang & Sylvie Peter
Harsh Piramal
Richard Prager
Kevin & Kathy Pretorius
Joaquín Puig
Phil & Tally Purcell
Andrew Purnell
Selina Rainey
Starr Rambusch
Isobel Raymond
Charles Rilett
David Rimlinger
Justine Rolland
Dave & Kaye Ronayne
Byron & Val Ross
Maria C. Rovas
Rural Investment Fund
Roger & Jeandré Savy
Lawrence & Brigitte Schiller
Pierrette Schlettwein
Melanie A Schwab
Çois & Dee Schutte
Barry & Di Scott
Jessica & Emma Seger
Anique Sesink-Clee
Marthy Sesink-Clee
Melanie Shain
Roland Ivan Shaw
Daniel Siaens
Dawn Simas, 'Wild About Cats.'
Gilly Simpson
Finn Skjellaug
Mig Smyth
Ray & Judy Sowman
Lea & Francis Stamm
Keith, Charlotte, Katherine, Philippa & Clarissa Stannard
Robert Sternfels
Helen L. Stewart
Tony Stubbs
James Stewart
Johan & Elsabé Swart
David & Anne Thompson
Lyndon Thomas
Gregory & Julia Timmers
Kaushali & Prateek Trivedi
Jagdish Trivedi
Nalin Trivedi
Alan & Sally Tucker
Alec & Julia Turner
Brenda Urry
Martin Urry
Marc Valvekens
Catherine & Frans van Aart
Michael Van Eenoo-De Waele
Danie van den Heever
Peter & Maureen van den Heever
Willem & Esta Viviers
John & Cindy Wainwright
Michael Houser & Stephen Wargo
Maureen 'Gogs' Watson
Leigh Watson
Eve & Ruedi Weber
Andy Welling
John & Judy Williamson
Claus Winkler
Liesel Wright
Sue Wyllie
Nicole Young
Sally Young
Ed & Anka Zeeman

Bibliography

Baldwin, William Charles. African Hunting and Adventure from Natal to the Zambezi. Richard Bentley & Son, London. 1894.
Ballard, Charles. The House of Shaka. Emoyeni Books, Durban. 1988.
Branch, Bill. Snakes and Other Reptiles of Southern Africa. Struik. Cape Town. 1996.
Bryant, Arthur T. Olden Times in Zululand and Natal. Struik. Cape Town 1965.
Butchart, Duncan. Ecological Journal, Vol 1.
Bruton, M N, Smith, M. & Taylor, R H. A brief history of human involvement in Maputaland.
Fiske, Symond. Ploughing a Furrow. Pietermaritzburg. 1982.
Hutchings, Anne. Zulu Medicinal Plants. University of Natal Press, Pietermaritzburg. 1996.
Junod, Henri A. The Life of a South African Tribe. University Books Inc. New Hyde Park. New York. 1962.
Leslie, David. Life among the Zulus and AmaTongas. Macmillan. 1875.
London Illustrated News. 1879.
Ludlow, Captain W R. Zululand and Cetewayo. Simpkin, Marshall & Company, London. 1882.
Mandela, Nelson. Long Walk to Freedom. A biography. Macdonald Purnell. S.A. 1994.
Maclean, Gordon Lindsay. Roberts' Birds of Southern Africa. John Voelcker Bird Book Fund. 1993.
Mountain, Alan. Paradise under Pressure. Southern Book Publishers. Johannesburg.
Player, Ian. Men Rivers and Canoes. Simondium, Cape Town. 1964.
Player, Ian. Zululand Wilderness. Shadow and Soul. David Philip Publishers. Cape Town. 1997.
Pooley, Elsa. A Field Guide to Wild Flowers of KwaZulu Natal. Natal Flora Publications Trust. 1998.
Pooley, E S. Some notes on the utilization of natural resources by the tribal people of Maputaland.
Pooley, Elsa. Trees of Natal, Zululand & Transkei. Natal Flora Pub. Trust. 1994
Pringle, John. The Conservationists and the Killers. TV Bulpin & Books of Africa. 1982.
Rattray, David. Lectures on Isandlwana and Rorke's Drift.
Reader, John. Africa. A biography of the continent. Hamish Hamilton, London 1997.
Reader's Digest Atlas of Southern Africa. Cape Town
Russell, Robert. Natal. The Land. 1897.
Sinclair, I, Hockey, P & Tarboton, W. Sasol Birds of Southern Africa, Struik. 1998.
Skinner, J D & Smithers, R H N. The Mammals of the Southern African Subregion. University of Pretoria. 1990.
Skaife, S H. African Insect Life. Revised by John Ledger. Struik, Cape Town. 1994.
Struthers, Robert Briggs. Hunting Journal. 1852 – 1856. In the Zulu and Tsonga Regions.
Stuart, Chris & Tilde. Mammals of Southern Africa. Struik. 1996.
Tinley, Ken L. The maintenance of wilderness diversity in Africa. Voices in the Wilderness. 1st World Wilderness Congress. 1979.
Tinley, Ken L. The Ecology of Tongaland. Published by the Natal Branch of the Wildlife Society, Durban. 1976.
Tobias, Phillip. Ad Hominidae. Optima 1994.
Torres, J L R. The Amathonga people of Maputaland with special reference to the inhabitants of the Pongolo floodplain area.
Van der Elst, Rudy. The common Sea Fishers of South Africa. Struik, Cape Town. 1981.
Walker, Joan. Wild Flowers of KwaZulu Natal. WR Walker Family Trust. 1996.
Wilson, Monica & Thompson, Leonard. The Oxford History of South Africa. Vol I and II. Oxford at the Clarendon Press. 1971

Unpublished manuscript:
Curry, O A. Reminiscences.

PhD Theses:
Goodman, Peter Styan: Soil, vegetation and large herbivore relations in Mkuze Game Reserve.
Hunter, Luke: The Relocation of Lions and Cheetah to Phinda Game Reserve.

Illustrations

The illustrations with the drop capitals at the start of each chapter and the paintings at the end of each chapter are by Johan Hoekstra, the designer of the book.

Chapter one: Artillery passing through the bush, the death of the Prince Imperial and the burning of Cetshwayo's house: Illustrated London News. Piet Retief: by courtesy of Caroline Tinley. The impala painting on page 32 and the map on page 34, Johannesburg Reference Library.

The maps on pages 75 and 136 have been prepared by Judith Campbell.

Photography

Richard du Toit was commissioned to take the photographs for this book. He uses Canon EOS 1n camera bodies and the following Canon L-lenses: 17 – 35mm f2.8, 70 – 200mm f2.8, and 500mm f4.5. All photographs were taken on 50 and 100 ASA Fujichrome film.

The other photographers whose pictures are included in the book, are as follows:

Roger and Pat de la Harpe: Pages, 34, 35, 36, 37, 38, 76, 91, 126/127, 130 (2), 131, 133 (2), 138, 139 (K. Oxley), 140 (2), 141, 142(2), 184.
Lex Hes: Dust jacket back (leopard), pages, 6, 39, 86, 81, 90, 124, 158/159, 175, 189 (painted reed frog).
Peter Pinnock: Pages, 94 (2), 172, 186 (4), 187.
Geoff Nichols: Page 70.
Martin von Fintel: Pages 119 (3).
Andrew Lewis: Pages 13, 16, 18, 20 (2), 132 (2).
Mark Tennant: Pages,137, 184 (Carl Walker).
JBP Library: Endpaper (elephant), pages, 39, 134 (hoopoe), 135 (redheaded weaver and blue waxbill), 161 (sausage tree flowers).
Molly Buchanan: Pages 137, 188, 203.
Gallo Images: Pages: 42, 58, 114, 136, 142 (pot)), 175 (suni), 180 (pygmy kingfisher), 182, 183.
Photo Access: Pages 64, 68/69, 93.

Photographs in the introduction

All pictures in the introductory section were photographed by Richard du Toit.

Chapter introductions

The double-page photographs at the start of each chapter are by Richard du Toit except where stated otherwise:

Prologue: African Jacana on water lilies
Chapter 1: The battle of Isandlwana by C E Fripp. Courtesy of the National Army Museum, London
Chapter 2: Tawny eagle and glossy starling
Chapter 3: Pinkbacked pelican: Photo Access
Chapter 4: Lioness profile
Chapter 5: Scarletchested sunbird
Chapter 6: Zulu girl: Pat de la Harpe
Chapter 7: A tree agama or lizard
Chapter 8: Rufusbellied heron
Chapter 9: Cheetah portrait

THE CROWN

THE BREACH

THE CAPITOLIUM

THE CORE

C1

C2

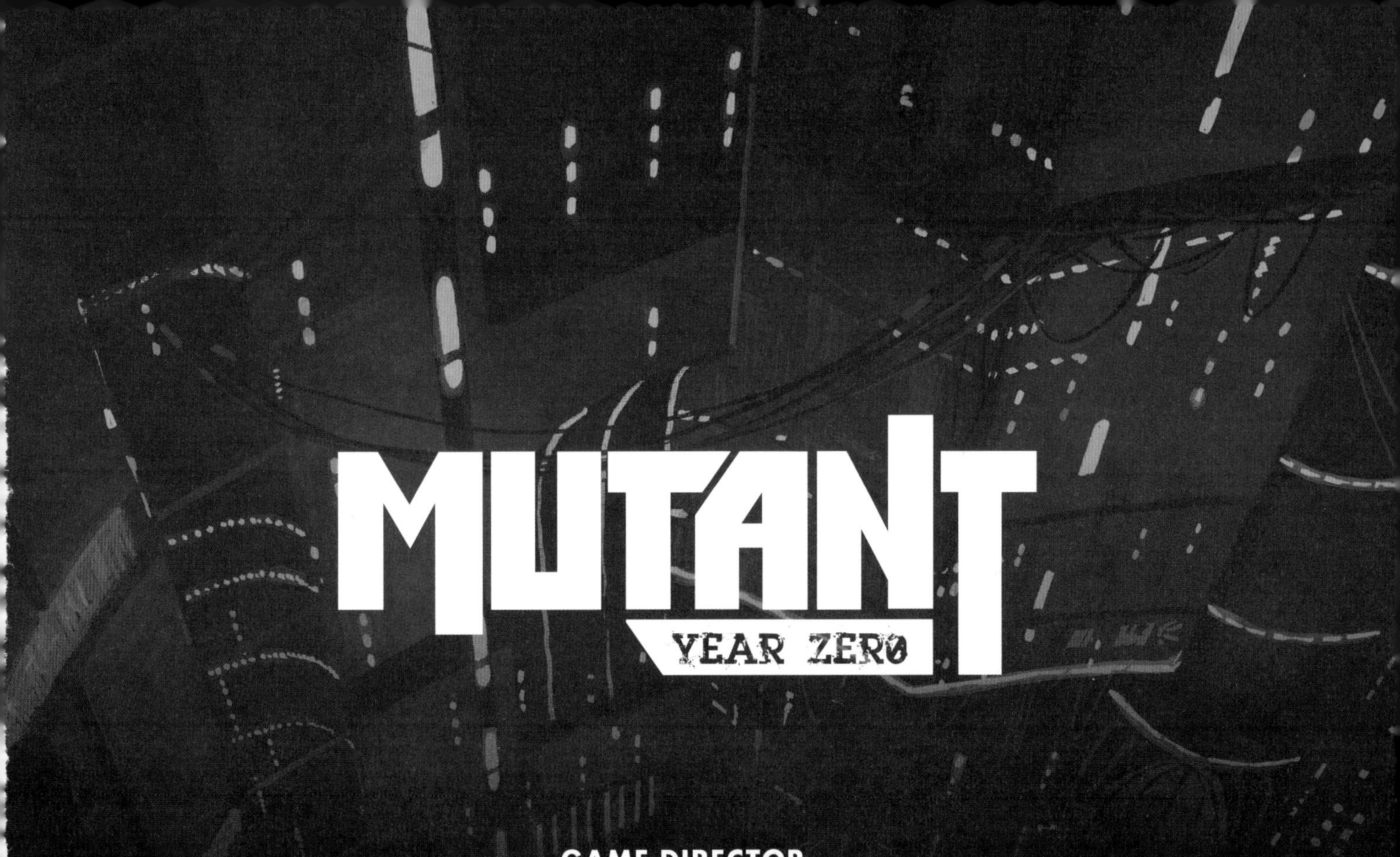

MUTANT

YEAR ZERØ

GAME DIRECTOR & LEAD DESIGNER
Tomas Härenstam

WRITERS
Tomas Härenstam, Thomas Johansson

GRAPHIC DESIGN
Christian Granath

LAYOUT & PREPRESS
Dan Algstrand

TRANSLATION
Edgardo Montes Rosa

COVER ILLUSTRATION
Simon Stålenhag

INTERIOR ILLUSTRATIONS
Reine Rosenberg

PROOFREADING
Brandon Bowling

PRINT
Livonia Print, Riga 2019

ISBN
978-91-88805-21-8

PLAYER'S SECTION

GAMEMASTER'S SECTION

11

12

HEIRS OF DOOM

When humanity falls, when nations and authorities collapse, only the most basic human bond remains – family.

While the world burns after the Red Plague, four powerful families, financial and industrial dynasties, form an alliance to survive the end of the world. The four great Houses – Warburg, Fortescue, Morningstar, and Kilgore – name their covenant Elysium, after the meadows of eternal Spring of Greek mythology.

While other Titan Powers flee into the cold darkness of space or to the bottom of the sea, Elysium's leaders decide to dig into the bedrock. There, in the depths of depths, the Houses are to weather the long atomic winter.

The first enclave is named Elysium I, home to 10,000 souls. It is no mere shelter. The leaders of the families see the enclave as the Ark of humanity, the seed of a new civilization. They find inspiration in history, especially the era of the late 19th century – it's belief in a brighter future, its traditionalist worldview, its architecture, and its aesthetics. The wars and disasters of the 20th and 21st centuries are never to be repeated.

While the rest of the world comes to the realization that humanity has been handed a death sentence, the Houses of Elysium have already left the surface behind, to secure their legacy in the safety of the depths.

Not all of the inhabitants in the enclaves belong to the great Houses – armies of workers and service personnel are handpicked from the families' countless companies and subsidiaries to support the rich and powerful.

The first decades in the enclaves go according to plan. Elysium researchers work intensively on plans to re-populate the surface, using genetic engineering, robotics and other advanced technology. But the safety in the depths is not to last. Mistrust between the Titan Powers grows, and when they eventually launch their weapons of mass destruction against each other, the effects are devastating. Most of the Elysium enclaves are utterly destroyed. The few that survive are damaged and isolated, lonely outposts in a sea of quiet destruction.

A century after the proud founding of Elysium I, contact with the last of its sister enclaves is lost. Elysium IV goes silent after an orbital attack. The residents of Elysium I realize that they are now alone, perhaps the last people on Earth.

Decades pass. Resources dwindle, despair grows. Despite its splendor, Elysium I is nothing more than mankind's golden cage, a gilded prison. Within the enclave's dim halls, fear and suspicion grow unchecked. In the shadows, people ready themselves for conflict. Enclave workers who have toiled loyally year after year, grateful for being spared from disaster, begin to organize themselves and question their masters.

After a violent confrontation between the Houses of Morningstar and Warburg that costs one hundred lives – mostly workers – the heads of the Houses decide that something needs to be done. They create the Council, a joint assembly to preside over all families.

The House leaders also enact a new law calling for total transparency of everything that occurs within Elysium I, as a way to keep each other in check. To this end, a law enforcement agency is created – a force of so-called judicators with the power to investigate crime and use force against anything that threatens law and order in the enclave. Under the new law, every unit of judicators must include at least one representative of each House.

You are one of these judicators. Alongside agents from the other Houses, it is your duty to maintain order within the enclave, investigate violations of the law, and impose the appropriate sentences. But never forget that your strongest loyalty is always towards your family. The enclave is in decline, and you fight to ensure that your House gains power and influence over the dwindling resources that remain.

You are the true heirs of doom. When humanity sets foot on the surface again, it will be your House that leads the way into the new dawn. Your lineage. Your family.

MUTANT: ELYSIUM

Welcome to *Mutant: Elysium*. This book is an expansion on the game world created in *Mutant: Year Zero*, *Mutant: Genlab Alpha* and *Mutant: Mechatron*, but also works as a complete game on its own.

PLAYER CHARACTERS

All players except for one play as judicators, problem solvers that respond and investigate when law and order are threatened in the enclave. You also belong to a House, which you serve in secret.

Your judicator is called a player character, PC for short.

You decide what your PC thinks and feels, what he does and says – but not what happens to him. It is your job as a player to breathe life into your PC. Imagine you are him. Think – how would you react if you were in his shoes? What would you do? Your PC, and those of the other players, are always the protagonists of the story. This game is about you. Your decisions, your lives.

THE GAMEMASTER

One person in your group takes the role of Gamemaster, or GM. Her job is to create Elysium I. The GM portrays all other residents in the enclave. She controls your friends and your enemies.

The GM has many tools to aid her in accomplishing this. To learn what they are, read more below and in the *Gamemaster Section*. The game is a back and forth conversation between players and

the GM, until a situation arises where the outcome is uncertain. Then it's time to get the dice – read more in Chapter 3.

The GM is not the players' enemy – her job is to challenge the PCs to create the most exciting story possible. It is not the GM's job to decide what's happening in the game – and certainly not how your story will end. The game will determine that. That's what you are playing to find out.

THE ENCLAVE ELYSIUM I

This book contains a unique game setting and a complete campaign for you to play, called *Guardians of the Fall.*

Mutant: Elysium does not begin in the Zone like *Mutant: Year Zero*, but in the enclave known as Elysium I. It is a huge underground facility, created to save mankind from extinction. The enclave is governed by the four great Houses: Warburg, Fortescue, Morningstar, and Kilgore. You can read more about these in the next chapter. Elysium I is described in more detail in Chapter 7, as well as in the *Gamemaster Section*, where the campaign *Guardians of the Fall* is found – only for the GM's eyes.

Your actions in the course of the *Guardians of the Fall* campaign can have major consequences – they can even determine the final destiny of humanity in the world after the fall.

TOWARDS YEAR ZERO: HUMANS IN THE ZONE

When the campaign is over, the people of Elysium I can spread in the devastated world as described in *Mutant: Year Zero*. The game then continues in the Zone, where people meet both human mutants, mutant animals, and robots (see *Mutant: Genlab Alpha* and *Mutant: Mechatron*).

You can then choose to play as humans from the enclave, characters from the Zone, or create a new group with a mix of different types. How humans can live in the Zone and create new settlements is explained in Chapter 12 of the *Gamemaster Section*.

RULES

This book contains the complete rules for playing a non-mutant human in the world of *Mutant*. The core game engine is the same as in *Mutant: Year Zero* and the two systems are completely compatible, but there are differences that highlight how humans differ from mutants.

If you wish, you can skip the campaign in Elysium I, and use this module to introduce enclave humans as a playable class in *Mutant: Year Zero*. You'd be missing out on an exciting experience, but if you already have an ongoing campaign in the Zone and want to continue without interruption, go right ahead.

WHAT DO YOU DO?

The *Guardians of the Fall* campaign sets the framework for your game in Elysium I. However, the campaign has an open-ended structure that gives the players a great deal of flexibility in what can be done. And there is a lot to do.

STAGE INCIDENTS

As a player in *Mutant: Elysium* you don't only control your character. On special occasions, called strategic turns, you represent the leader of your House. The Houses are tangled in intrigues trying to outmaneuver each other and engineer what in game is called Incidents – operations that increase the power and influence of one House at the expense of the others.

INVESTIGATE INCIDENTS

A central part of the game consists of sending your PC, a judicator, to investigate Incidents in Elysium. Each Incident is a short scenario tied to a certain location in the enclave, and can be resolved in a variety of ways. Most (but not all) Incidents are staged by the opposing Houses. When you investigate an Incident involving your own House you will be torn between your duty as a judicator and your loyalty to your House.

MAINTAIN LAW AND ORDER

There is dissent in the lower levels of Elysium I. The workers of the enclave have begun to express their dissatisfaction over their heavy workload and deteriorating living conditions, and some are turning to crime and violence, seeing no other way out. So far, the respect and fear of the Houses is too great for an open revolt, but that will not be the case forever. As a judicator, it is your difficult role to quench all attempts at rebellion in their infancy.

STAND FOR YOUR HOUSE

Being a judicator is your daily work, but your deepest loyalties are to your family. When the House calls you answer, even if it would mean that you neglect your duty as a judicator. Without your House, you would be nothing. The House is your blood, your life. This is what has been repeated to you since you were a child.

SAVE THE ENCLAVE FROM RUIN

Elysium I is racing towards an unavoidable collapse. The power struggle between the Houses is sometimes so intense that you risk losing sight of what is best for the enclave. Yet sometimes you will have to place the enclave's future ahead of the interests of your family. This is when your character is truly tested. Your actions can determine the place of mankind in the world after the fall.

TOOLS OF THE GAME

In *Mutant: Elysium* your creativity and improvisational ability are the most important assets. But there are a number of tools available to help you create your story.

CHARACTER SHEET

Your characters may be judicators, but they are also individuals with unique qualities, relationships, and dreams. You record everything about your character on a character sheet. One is provided at the back of this book. They are also available for download at the Free League website.

Enclave and Incident Sheets: In addition to the character sheets, there are special sheets used in the strategic game – read more about this in the *Gamemaster Section.*

DICE

There is a unique dice set for this game, available for purchase separately. The set contains 12 custom dice, in three different colors. The yellow ones are called Base Dice, the green ones Skill Dice and the black ones Gear Dice. You roll the dice when you use your skills to perform a difficult and dramatic action in the game – for the specifics of how to do that, see Chapter 3.

The dice are exactly the same as those used in *Mutant: Year Zero* and used in almost exactly the same way. The symbol ☢ usually means something good happens, while the symbols ✹ and ☣ usually means something goes wrong.

D6 AND D66

The Players and GM sometimes roll what's called a D6 or a D66. D6 means you ignore the symbols ☢, ☣, and ✹, and just read the number on the die. 2D6 means you roll two D6s and add the results together, for 3D6 you roll three dice and add, etc. Another type of roll is the D66, which means you roll two D6s of different colors – such as a Base Die and a Gear Die. Consider the first die the tens and the second die the ones. That gives you a result between 11 and 66. You can even roll a D666 – roll three dice and consider the first die the hundreds, the second die the tens and the third die the ones. That gives you a result between 111 and 666.

THE ELYSIUM CARD DECK

There is also a custom card deck for *Mutant: Elysium*, sold separately, that includes four different kinds of cards.

Incident Cards: These cards are used when you, as a player, plan Incidents as a representative of your House during a strategic turn. Read more in Chapter 10 of the *Gamemaster Section*.

Contact Cards: Describes contacts you have collected during your years in Elysium. Read more in Chapter 5.

Artifact Cards: Describes high-tech items you can find during the game. These cards are compatible with the artifacts of *Year Zero, Genlab Alpha* and *Mechatron*.

NPC Cards: Describes the dramatis personae or most important non-player characters in the *Guardians of the Fall* campaign. Read more in the *Gamemaster Section*.

THE MAP OF ELYSIUM

On the inside covers of this book you will find a full-color map of Elysium I. It shows the enclave's overall layout and levels, with highlights showing how its different sections look. A large full-color version of the map is available for purchase separately.

Unlike the Zone of *Mutant: Year Zero*, most of the enclave is well known to your PCs. All sections within the map of the enclave are described in more detail in Chapter 7. The map has a specific in-game mechanic that will come into play during strategic turns, as explained in the *Gamemaster Section*.

THE PLAYER GROUP

Unlike the previous three parts of the Mutant roleplaying game, in Elysium the PCs form a formal unit – they are judicators. This straightforward dynamic makes it easy to give the PCs common goals and tasks to solve. It is also easy to introduce new PCs into the group as needed.

However, in *Mutant: Elysium*, there is a built-in conflict between your commitment to duty and your loyalty to your House. This conflict is a central part of the game, but it must be handled with some caution. The GM must be responsive and intervene if conflicts between PCs escalate into conflicts between players. The best solution is to simply take an hour out of the game and talk directly about the matter, player to player.

In addition to the above conflict, each player character is also a person with his own driving force, relationships, and dreams. This third aspect of your PC's existence can have an effect on the conflict between duty as a judicator and duty to your House in unexpected and exciting ways.

A NOTE ON GENDER

The ruling Houses of Elysium rarely make a difference between the sexes. Men and women can become judicators on equal terms. In *Mutant: Elysium*, you can play male or female characters without gaining any special benefits or hindrances. You don't need to be confined by binary notions of sex and gender at all, and your sexual orientation is yours to decide. For the sake of convenience, we refer to unnamed characters as "he," while the GM is referred to as "she."

ROLEPLAYING? WHAT'S THAT?

If this is your first role-playing game, congratulations – welcome to a fun and creative hobby! Roleplay combines storytelling and games in a way that allows you to create your own story with your friends, with the game's rules as a frame.

Sound complicated? Please visit our forum at *frialigan.se/forum* – there you can ask any questions you wish and receive answers from both our designers and other Mutant players. Welcome!

PLAYING WITHOUT CARDS

All the information on the cards is also available in this book. If you prefer playing without the cards, you can simply keep track of the artifacts, contacts and more on your character sheet.

A TYPICAL GAMING SESSION

1. Get your character sheets, dice, and cards.
2. Play a strategic turn and decide which Incident to investigate (see Chapter 10).
3. Play your characters. Investigate the chosen Incident, balancing your duty as a judicator with your loyalty to your House.
4. Finish the game session with an evaluation.
   a. The patrol leader designates a PC in the group to Judicator of the Day (see page 23).
   b. All players vote on which PC they think was the "double agent" during the Incident (see page 23).
   c. Players and the GM decide together which actions deserve to be rewarded with Experience Points (page 25).
   d. Players may then use the XP to increase their skills or learn new talents.
   e. Players can change their PC's relationships and dreams, if they wish.
   f. The players vote for appointing a new patrol leader (see page 23).

ABBREVIATIONS

PC = Player Character
XP = Experience Points
GM = Gamemaster
NPC = Non-Player Character

YOUR HEIR

In *Mutant: Elysium* you play a judicator sent to represent your House while maintaining law and order in Elysium I.

Your judicator is your player character (PC). He is your avatar, your eyes and ears in the enclave. But your PC depends on you, the player, to make wise choices for him. Take your PC seriously and play him as if he were a real person. It will be a more rewarding and fun experience if you do so. On the other hand, do not overprotect your character against danger. The goal of the game is to create an exciting story – if you are going to be successful in this endeavor you must take risks.

Throughout the game, your PC will change and evolve. His skills can be improved upon with experience points, but you will also discover how his personality changes and is shaped in ways that cannot be quantified in numbers. This is when your PC really takes on a life of his own.

Character Sheet: To create your PC you need a character sheet. You can copy one from the back of this book, download it from the Free League website, or buy a pack of ready-made character sheets.

Small and Large Groups: A typical patrol of judicators has four members – one from each great House. However, patrols are sometimes larger or smaller in number. Read more about it below.

TO CREATE A CHARACTER

Character creation is explained in detail in this chapter. The summary below will give you an overview of the process involved. Grab a character sheet, a pencil, and follow these steps:

1. Choose your House.
2. Choose your profession.
3. Choose your name.
4. Choose your appearance.
5. Choose your age.
6. Distribute your attribute points.
7. Distribute your skill points.
8. Choose your talent.
9. Calculate your starting Reputation score.
10. Describe your relationship with the other PCs as well as NPCs.
11. Establish your character's big dream.
12. Choose your gear.
13. Describe your home.
14. Choose the designation of your patrol.
15. Start the strategic turn and appoint the patrol leader.

HOUSE

The first thing you must choose for your character is his House. The four great Houses that rule Elysium I are briefly described below, and in more detail in Chapter 7.

According to enclave law, every patrol must balance representation from all four Houses as much as possible. If the number of PCs is four or less, then they must all belong to different Houses. You and the other players need to decide who the representative for each House will be or choose randomly if an agreement cannot be reached.

Your House also determines which attribute that you have a special predisposition for. This is explained in more detail in Chapter 3.

WARBURG

To be a Warburg is to build and create. You make sure that food is always on every table, that materials are available when repairs need to be carried out, that new goods are manufactured, and that the energy the enclave needs is produced. Without House Warburg, Elysium will stand still.

- **House Color:** Blue
- **Predisposition:** Strength

FORTESCUE

House Fortescue is Elysium's first and last line of defense against any enemy. Loyalty, pride, and justice are words you live by. Everyone knows that you always follow orders and are ready to make the difficult decisions sometimes needed to combat threats to the enclave.

- **House Color:** Grey
- **Predisposition:** Agility

MORNINGSTAR

For a Morningstar, life is a blend of enjoyment and leisure, refinement and creativity. You provide Elysium with the pleasures, culture, history, and art at your disposal. Celebrations and entertainment, decadence and tradition – all are mixed in the whirl of impressions that is your House.

- **House Color:** Green
- **Predisposition:** Empathy

KILGORE

To belong to House Kilgore is to be an explorer, a researcher or scientist seeking answers or even new questions. It was a Kilgore who created the first xenogenetic creatures and took the decisive steps to combine man with machine. There is power in knowledge, of course. And with every new discovery you make, the greater your House's influence grows.

- **House Color:** Red
- **Predisposition:** Wits

PROFESSION

A judicator's job is to maintain law and order, but this can be achieved in different ways. Judicators have different backgrounds and specialist skills. In *Mutant: Elysium* you can choose from six different professions, as described at the end of this chapter. It is recommended, but not mandatory, that all PCs have different professions. The professions correspond to Roles in *Mutant: Year Zero* and *Genlab Alpha*.

PROFESSIONS IN THE ZONE

If the citizens of the enclave reach the Zone, they will bring their knowledge and culture with them. The six professions described in *Mutant: Elysium* will then be available for the mutants in the Zone. Likewise, enclave dwellers can learn a lot from encounters with the mutants. The eight roles described in *Mutant: Year Zero* will also be available to non-mutated people. The GM can read more about the effects of humans' arrival to the Zone in Chapter 12.

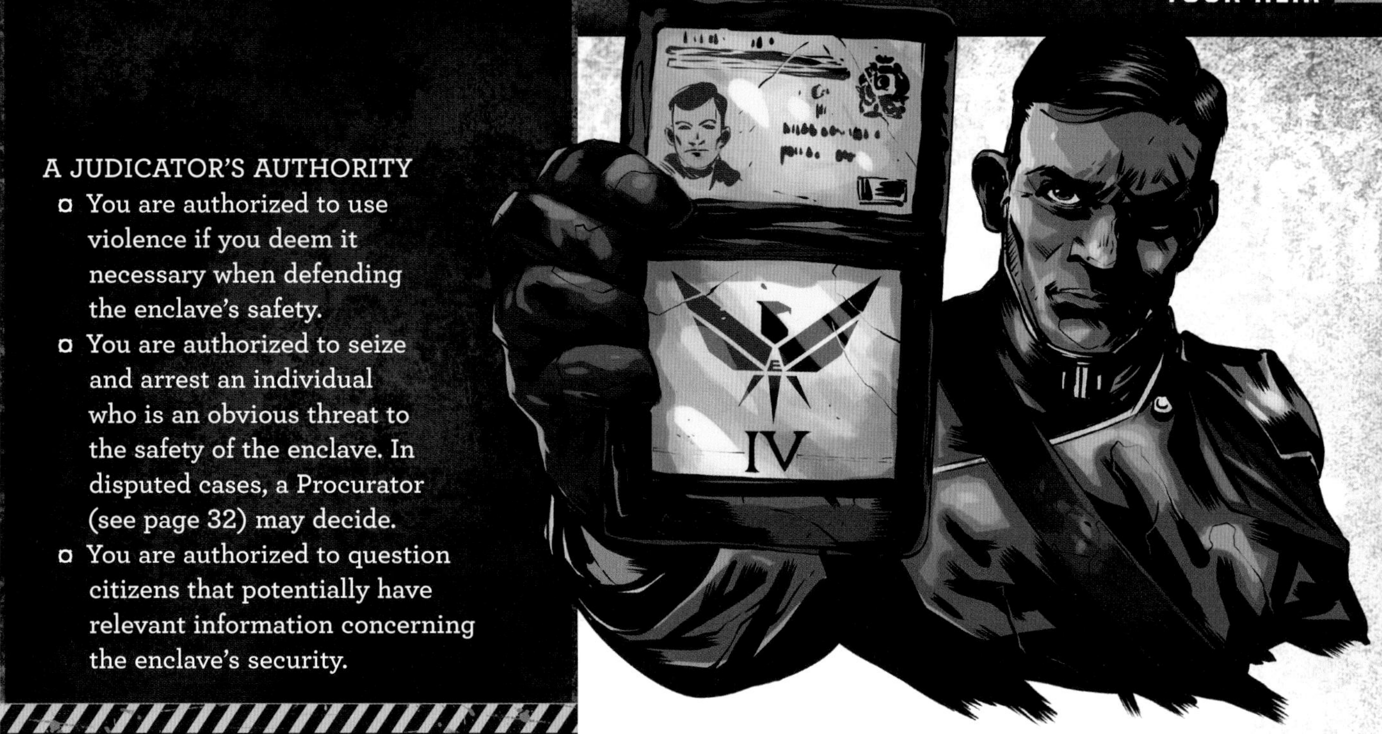

A JUDICATOR'S AUTHORITY

- You are authorized to use violence if you deem it necessary when defending the enclave's safety.
- You are authorized to seize and arrest an individual who is an obvious threat to the safety of the enclave. In disputed cases, a Procurator (see page 32) may decide.
- You are authorized to question citizens that potentially have relevant information concerning the enclave's security.

Specialist Skills: Just as in *Year Zero* and *Genlab Alpha,* every profession has a specialist skill beyond the twelve general skills that everyone can learn. Read more about skills in Chapter 3.

EXAMPLE

The player Sylvia will create her first character. After discussions with the other players, she decides to play an investigator from House Kilgore.

NAME

Each profession suggests three male names and three female names that are typical of the profession. Choose one of these names, or if you prefer, use any name you like.

EXAMPLE

Sylvia gives her investigator the name Pandora Kilgore.

APPEARANCE

On the character sheet you can record what your character's face, body, and uniform look like. The description of your profession contains suggestions – you can choose one or more words from each category. You are also free to describe your PC as you prefer. The suggestions listed under each profession have no in-game impact on the rules.

Uniform: As a judicator, you have to wear a uniform. Tradition requires that the uniform display the color of your House. That being said, you are free to modify your uniform to better suit your profession.

AGE

Patrols of judicators often have members of different ages to give the group a wide range of experience. In game terms, age is divided into three levels: young, middle aged, and old. You may choose the starting age of your character. Record your choice on your character sheet.

Your choice of age level affects your starting attributes, skills, reputation, and your contacts. Read more about these below.

AGE	YEARS
Young	18–31
Middle Aged	31–50
Old	50+

02

ATTRIBUTES

Just like in *Mutant: Year Zero*, you have four attributes that show your basic physical and mental capacity. They are measured on a scale from 1 to 5, the higher the better. Your attributes are used partly when you roll dice to perform actions in the game, and partly to determine how much trauma you can withstand before breaking. Read more about this in Chapter 6.

Starting Scores: When you create your character, you distribute a number of points amongst the four attributes. The specific amount of points you can spend is determined by your age – see the table. You must use no less than 2 and no more than 4 points on each of the attributes. However, you can spend 5 points on the attribute listed as "key attribute" for your profession.

A JUDICATORS' DUTIES

- Follow orders from commanding officers. This applies only to other judicators. For example, you have no obligation to obey officers of the Deep Watch (see page 106) – unless you have been ordered to do so by your own commander.
- Protect the enclave's order and safety. It is up to you to interpret what this means, as long as it does not go against direct orders from higher ranking officers.
- Protect fellow patrol members. You have the right and obligation to protect other members of your patrol, as long as it does not threaten the security of the enclave.
- Be mindful of the interests of the dynasties. This is not a formal duty, but since all judicators belong to a House, trying to achieve and maintain balance is an implicit duty that must be constantly juggled with your formal duties.

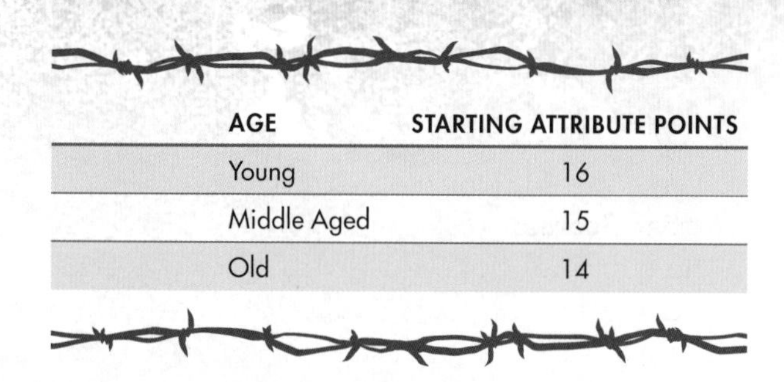

AGE	STARTING ATTRIBUTE POINTS
Young	16
Middle Aged	15
Old	14

STRENGTH

Raw physical power and endurance. Determines how much damage you can withstand. Is recovered with food.

AGILITY

Body control, fitness, and fine motor skills. Determines how much fatigue you can withstand. Is recovered with water.

WITS

Intelligence, alertness, and sharpness of mind. Determines how much confusion you can withstand. Is recovered with sleep.

EMPATHY

Your personal radiance, charisma, and ability to manipulate others. Determines how much doubt you can withstand. Is recovered through sympathy from other people.

Having decided that Pandora is middle-aged, Sylvia has 15 points to spend on attributes. She gives Pandora Strength 3, Agility 4, Wits 5 and Empathy 3.

SKILLS

Your skills are specialized knowledge, education, and experience gained during your life as a judicator. There are twelve basic skills that anyone can use. You also have a thirteenth, specialist skill unique to your chosen profession. Skills can range from a rating of 0 to 5.

You can use a general skill even if you have a rating of 0. Specialist skills however, require at least a rating of 1 in order to be used.

The twelve basic skills are listed on the character sheet, and all skills are described in detail in the next chapter.

Starting Scores: When creating your character, you get to distribute a number of points across your skills. The exact number you have to distribute is determined by your age, see the skill table. The maximum starting rating for a skill is 3, and you must have at least a rating 1 on your specialist skill. Aside from these two limitations you can allocate your points freely.

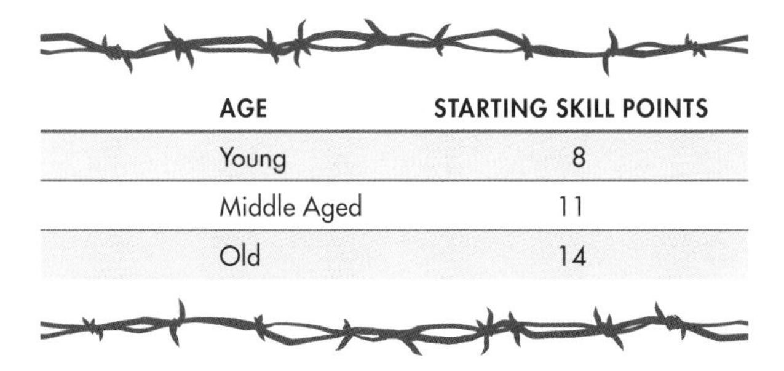

AGE	STARTING SKILL POINTS
Young	8
Middle Aged	11
Old	14

EXAMPLE

Sylvia distributes her 11 skill points, giving Pandora level 3 in Investigate, level 2 in Fight, Sneak, and Shoot, and finally level 1 in Scout and Comprehend.

TALENTS

Mutant: Elysium has a whole new and different set of talents. Talents describe small tricks and abilities. Talents can provide an advantage in some specific situations or let you use skills in difsferent ways.

Once the denizens of the enclave arrive in the Zone, they can also learn the talents described in *Mutant: Year Zero,* just as the mutants will gain access to the talents contained in Chapter 4.

You can choose one talent during character creation. Your profession determines which talents are available to you. You can learn more talents during play.

BIOMECHATRONICS

The researchers in Elysium I have, over the years, developed the knowledge and skill to graft mechanical implants into the human body. These implants can make a human being stronger and more resilient. Unfortunately, biomechatronics have been shown to have severe side effects on both body and mind, typically referred to as machine fever. Members of the Houses rarely use such implants. They are used primarily by the judicators, in order to carry out their dangerous, often violent, work.

Biomechatronics have gradually become a symbol of status within the enclave. In recent years, some younger members of the Houses have begun to acquire small and discreet biomechatronic implants, which are seen as avant garde within younger circles, but often scoffed at by older nobles.

You can choose a discreet implant during character creation, but you must choose the talent Biomechatronic. Read more about biomechatronics and how they work in Chapter 9.

Sylvia chooses the talent Intuition for Pandora.

CONTACTS

You are a judicator, but you are also a member of a powerful dynasty. As a human in *Mutant: Elysium,* your most important asset is the influence wielded by your contacts that can help you in large and small ways.

At character creation you get one or more contacts. These are explained in more detail in Chapter 5. You cannot have the same contacts as another player – you must agree who gets which contacts or let chance decide. How many contacts you get during character creation depends on your starting age:

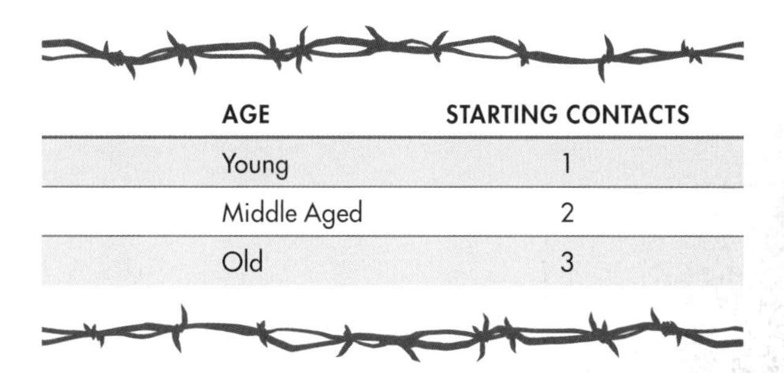

AGE	STARTING CONTACTS
Young	1
Middle Aged	2
Old	3

New Contacts: You can gain new contacts during gameplay. Learn more about how this works on page 60.

CUSTOM CARDS

In the custom card deck for *Mutant: Elysium,* there is a card for each contact included in the game. The card briefly describes what the contact can do for you. Take your contact cards and place them next to your character sheet during play.

PSIONICS

Through genetic engineering, Elysium's scientists can trigger paranormal mental abilities in humans. Termed psionic mutations, research of these abilities is extremely restricted, for in many cases subjects turned their newfound abilities against the researchers or used them for their own gain. All psionics must be registered and are monitored regularly. There are a handful of psionics among the judicators, who are treated with great suspicion by their peers.

If you have access to *Mutant: Year Zero,* you can choose to play a psionic. You will not get any contacts at all and your Reputation (below) will be lowered. In return, you get a random mental mutation.

REPUTATION

Elysium I is a strict hierarchical society. The Houses control the workers, and within these two groups there are different levels of power, prestige, and access.

Formally, enclave residents are divided into security classes (see the next page) but equally important is your informal position and reputation. This is measured by a value called Reputation. Your starting value is determined by your age and modified by your profession, see table below. Your reputation can change during the game (page 25).

Your Reputation affects social interactions – a higher value makes it easier to impose your will (Chapter 6).

STARTING REPUTATION

Age	Reputation
Young	3
Middle Aged	4
Old	5

STARTING REPUTATION

Profession	Modifier
Investigator	±0
Officer	+2
Procurator	+1
Scholar	+1
Soldier	±0
Technician	±0
Psionic	–2

SECURITY CLASS

All residents of Elysium I are divided into security classes which determine the parts of the enclave they have access to. Security classes are identified with Roman numerals, from I to VII. All residents are assigned an ID card indicating their security class. The ID card is also used for electronic payments. As a judicator you belong to security class IV. Read more about security classes on page 103.

RELATIONSHIPS AND DREAMS

As a judicator you have a duty to both your House and your profession, but you are also a person with relationships and dreams of your own.

Your relationships and dreams affect how you are awarded Experience Points (page 25). Your choices are also important for the GM, who can use these to create exciting situations in the game (see Chapter 8).

RELATIONSHIPS TO PCS

When your characters enter the game, they already have a relationship with the other characters – they belong to the same patrol.

When creating your PC, you should describe your relationship to each of the other characters you know, with a brief opinion on your character sheet. Under your profession there are suggestions you can choose from or modify. Alternately, you can simply come up with your own.

RELATIONSHIPS TO NPCs

The next step is selecting two NPCs with which you have a special relation. You should choose an

NPC you hate and another you want to protect. Just as before, your profession provides the options – it is recommended you choose from these NPCs, as they play a role during the *Guardians of the Fall* campaign (see Chapter 10).

FAMILY

The people in the enclave are not infertile like the Ark mutants in *Year Zero*. Children are born and raised in Elysium I – but live under the strict regulation of authority. The sons and daughters of the Houses are drilled from birth, conditioning them to hold a specific set of values. The upbringing of the workers is simple and harsh – they are to be prepared for a long life of hardship in the depths.

The number of children that can be born in Elysium I is limited. The consortium applies strict population control in order to prevent overload that may thin the resources of the enclave. A license to have children is not easy to come by, so not everyone gets the chance. Those seeking such a license will do their utmost for the good of the enclave – in order to prove themselves worthy.

YOUR BIG DREAM

Finally, you have to choose what your big dream is, what you desire above all else. As with the relationships, the profession has pre-made options for you to choose from.

CHANGES TO RELATIONSHIPS AND DREAMS

What takes place during the game will affect your character. Your relationships with other characters, NPCs, and your big dream can change. At the end of each game session, after the XP has been distributed (page 25), you can change your entries. You may not change during the game session.

GEAR

Your House provides you with what you need to survive, but trade and the right to ownership are the pillars of Elysium's four great Houses. This right is also something that separates nobles from the masses. In practice, there is not much space in the enclave to accumulate large amounts of

gear, therefore the possessions you have become that much more important.

You must list all the possessions you carry with you on your character sheet. Write one item per row. If it's not there, you do not have it.

Starting Gear: Your profession determines the starting gear you can choose during character creation.

ENCUMBRANCE

You can easily carry a number of regular items equal to double your Strength score. Use the base rating, not the temporary value if your character is injured (page 76).

HEAVY AND LIGHT ITEMS

An item designated as heavy counts as two regular items and takes two rows on the character sheet instead of one. In the same way, there are items designated as light – they count as half a regular item and you can then enter two light items on the same row on your sheet.

Food and Water: Up to four rations of food and/or water count as one regular item.

TINY ITEMS

Any gear smaller than light items is referred to as tiny. They are so small that they do not count against your encumbrance limit. Your ID card as well as cash credits, are all tiny items. The rule of thumb is this: if the property can be hidden in a closed fist, it is a tiny item. Tiny items must still be listed on the character sheet even if they do not encumber you.

FOOD AND WATER

Food and water are easy to come by for those belonging to a powerful House. That being said, judicators can surely still starve or die from thirst. As a judicator, you do not usually need to worry about food or water for as long as you are in the enclave, but if for some reason you find yourself without these resources you may be in danger of getting trauma. Two rations of both food and water are included in your starting equipment.

E-PACKS

Energy weapons and other devices that require electricity are charged with E-packs. These are separate artefacts and are described in Chapter 9. Read more about the reloading of weapons in Chapter 6. E-packs are treated as tiny items.

OVER-ENCUMBERED

You can temporarily carry more than your maximum limit (double your Strength rating in gear rows). The drawback is that you must make a Force skill check in order to move a significant distance. The same rule applies if you are dragging heavy objects. Failing the skill check means you must either release what you are dragging, stay where you are, or suffer 1 point of damage to carry on a little longer.

YOUR HOME

As a scion of a noble dynasty and a judicator you are entitled to a simple dwelling either in the high-quarter of the town or further down the enclave if you prefer. The accommodation is a small apartment, usually with only one room. Describe your residence with a few short words on the character sheet. For inspiration, please read Chapter 7.

DEVELOPING YOUR PATROL

There are a total of 24 judicator patrols in Elysium I. These are divided into two shifts: Alpha and Beta. Each patrol has a designation consisting of the shift name and a number from 1 to 12, for example Alpha-3 or Beta-11. Some patrols add a nickname to their moniker, while others have nicknames bestowed upon them. Some examples are the Lions, the Monarchs, or the Wolves.

Choose a designation for your patrol and include a nickname if you like.

JUDICATOR RANKS

There are around one hundred judicators in Elysium I, divided into 24 patrols, assigned to two shifts with 12 patrols each (read more on page 107). Judicators are divided into the following ranks:

RANK	DESCRIPTION
Aspirant	A new recruit. Will usually become a Commissar after one year's service.
Commissar	These form the bulk of the judicators. Characters are usually Commissars.
Chief Inspector	Commander of a Shift.
Superintendent	Commander of all the Judicators.

PATROL LEADER

Every judicator patrol has a patrol leader that can act as the group's spokesperson. The patrol leader does not actually have the power to impose orders on his fellow patrol members, as this would disturb the delicate balance between the Houses – even within a single patrol. That being said, as a patrol leader you have the right to settle disputes between other members of the patrol. The position also has a number of other in-game features:

Report: The patrol leader's most important task is to report to the judicators' headquarters. This happens immediately after each completed Incident. An

Incident is an event within the enclave which you are sent to handle as an emissary of the law. The GM can read more about Incidents in Chapter 10.

As a patrol leader, you do not need to come up with a fully comprehensive report. All you need to do is specify one of the PCs you want to highlight as being particularly active or competent. This PC is named "Judicator of the Day" and gets an additional Experience Point (XP) at the end of the session (see below). You must justify your choice with something that the PC did during the Incident.

Experience: As a patrol leader, you also automatically receive an extra XP at the end of the game session.

Strategic Game: The patrol leader has a tie-breaking vote in case there is a tie when determining which Incident the PCs are to be sent to handle. Read more in Chapter 10.

VOTING FOR PATROL LEADER

Patrol leaders are appointed by the players themselves through a secret vote. Have the vote at the beginning of the first session. Do so again after each session once you have completed an Incident, after the Experience Points have been distributed. A current patrol leader may be re-elected. Follow these steps:

1. Select a number between 1 and 6 and place a die showing this number in front of you. You may not take the same number as anyone else.
2. Then, secretly write down the number of the person you are voting for. You may not vote for yourself. You may not disclose who you are voting for or tell anyone who to vote for.
3. Reveal your votes at the same time. You are not allowed to change your vote after the votes have been revealed.
4. Not all votes are equal - instead, your vote is worth as much as your House's total number of Control Points in the sectors of the enclave. Control is explained in Chapter 10.
5. In case of a tie, the dispute is settled by the patrol leader.

MORE THAN FOUR PLAYERS?

A typical judicator patrol consists of four individuals, one from each great House. But there are patrols with more members, who have more than one representative from the same House. If you have five or more players in the group you are one of these patrols.

Characters from the same House may take turns being its official representative and can, for example, alternate amongst themselves each session. Only the character officially representing the House can participate in a vote for – and be nominated to – patrol leader. The same applies for the vote on the double agent (below) and on strategic rounds (see Chapter 10) – these are all limited to the player whose character currently speaks for his House during the session being played.

FEWER THAN FOUR PLAYERS?

There are also patrols with only two or three members. And even cases, although very rare, where a judicator works alone. The game therefore works even if you have fewer than four players in the group.

With three players, voting for the patrol leader and double agent (below) takes place in the usual way with the players available – without the GM's participation. However, if the group consists of only one or two players, there is no vote for patrol leader or double agent.

DOUBLE AGENT

During the *Guardians of the Fall* campaign, described in detail in Chapter 10, you and the other players will be sent to solve various Incidents occurring in Elysium I.

These Incidents do not happen by chance. They are, with few exceptions, triggered by the Houses themselves in their struggle to either expand their influence or sabotage their rivals' attempts at the same. The planning of Incidents is carried out by you and the other players, as representatives of your Houses, during the strategic turns.

This means that you will occasionally be sent to solve an Incident that you, plotting on behalf of your House, are responsible for staging in the first place. This also puts a burden on your character, because it is in your character's interest that the patrol's mission fails.

PLAYING THE DOUBLE AGENT

Each time your characters are sent to an Incident, one of you will be the secret "double agent." As a double agent you need to be very subtle - if it becomes obvious that you are trying to sabotage the patrol's efforts you will be reprimanded for failing your duty as a judicator. The more this happens, the harsher the punishment will be.

As a double agent your efforts should be focused on causing the mission to fail, but in a manner that does not reveal you as the culprit. Most of the time, it's worse for your House to be exposed as the cause of an Incident than for the Incident to be stopped, so don't take unnecessary risks.

REVEALING THE DOUBLE AGENT

It is not just the patrol leader who provides a report to the commanders of the judicators after the Incident has ended. All members of the patrol must comment on the behavior of the other judicators in the patrol. The purpose of this is to reveal and punish any and all who put their family's interests before those of the enclave.

In game mechanics this is managed by a secret vote after each session where an Incident has been completed, and before the Experience Points have been awarded. This is done in the same way as voting for the patrol leader (above), with the difference that every player has one vote each (House Control means nothing for this vote).

When presenting your vote, you must provide evidence to support your claim - state anything suspicious that the accused PC did during play. If you cannot provide anything, your vote is annulled. The GM has the last word.

You all cast a vote of course, even if you are the double agent - with luck and skill, you will be able to successfully deflect all suspicions onto someone else.

Note that only a maximum of four players (one per House) can cast a vote. See the sidebar entitled "More than four players?"

Results: If a single PC is accused of being the double agent by *all* other players, the PC is found guilty. It does not matter whether this PC was actually the double agent or not. If no PC is unanimously voted as the double agent by all other PCs in the patrol, then no one is revealed as a double agent - the guilty character gets away with it.

When a double agent is "revealed" (whether guilty or not), all PCs who voted for him get an additional XP each at the end of the session.

Penalty: A revealed judicator will be punished for misconduct, see below.

MISCONDUCT

Judicators who have been revealed as double agents or who otherwise failed to fulfill their duties are punished for misconduct. However, they usually keep their position the first and second time they are revealed, as suitable people to fill the ranks are scarce and the balance between the Houses is very sensitive.

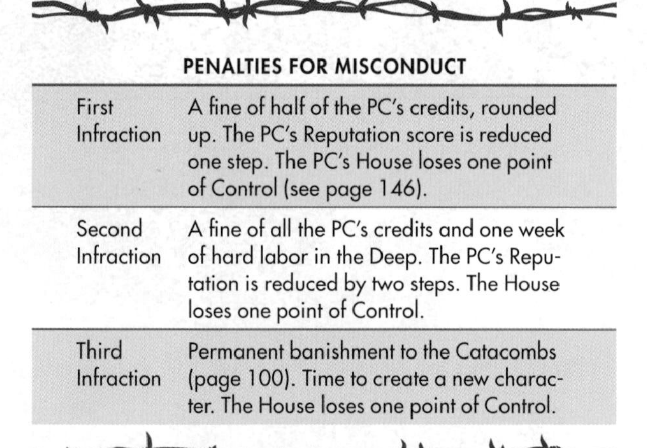

PENALTIES FOR MISCONDUCT

First Infraction	A fine of half of the PC's credits, rounded up. The PC's Reputation score is reduced one step. The PC's House loses one point of Control (see page 146).
Second Infraction	A fine of all the PC's credits and one week of hard labor in the Deep. The PC's Reputation is reduced by two steps. The House loses one point of Control.
Third Infraction	Permanent banishment to the Catacombs (page 100). Time to create a new character. The House loses one point of Control.

Punishment for the House: A judicator being punished for misconduct brings shame upon the whole House, thus the loss of a point of Control. Control comes into play during the strategic game (read more in Chapter 10).

CONFLICTS IN THE GROUP
There is a risk that the system for voting for the double agent can lead to resentment within the patrol, or worse, between the players themselves. Roleplaying is usually about collaborating. If this mechanism is a poor fit for your group, feel free to discard it. The game and the campaign will work fine without it.

DEVELOPING YOUR CHARACTER

Life as a judicator consists of many challenges and you can be sure that surviving these challenges will change your characters. They may even learn a thing or two along the way. You can develop your character in several ways during the game.

EXPERIENCE

The lessons you learn during the game are measured in experience points (XP). You will get your XP after the end of the session. Have a debriefing and let the entire group discuss the session's events. For each of these questions you can answer yes to, you will win 1 XP:

- Did you attend the game session? (You get an XP just for being present.)
- Have you sacrificed or risked anything for the NPC you want to keep safe?
- Have you sacrificed or risked anything to confront the NPC you hate?
- Have you sacrificed or risked anything to reach your big dream?
- Are you the patrol leader?
- Were you selected as the "Judicator of the Day" by the patrol leader?
- Were you the double agent during an Incident without being discovered, and the patrol failed to resolve the Incident? You get 2 XP for this.
- Did you reveal through votes a double agent in the group?

The GM has the last word about how much XP each PC will be awarded, but let all players participate in the discussion.

RAISE A SKILL OR GAIN A NEW TALENT

Once you have accumulated 5 XP you can improve your character. You can either increase a skill by one level or gain a new talent. Once you've decided, delete the XP used and start collecting experience again. When you have accumulated another 5 XP you will be able to make a new improvement.

CHANGING REPUTATION

Your Reputation in Elysium I will fluctuate depending on your actions during games. This happens during the debrief after XP is awarded.
For each of these questions you can answer yes to, your Reputation score increases by one step:

- Did you successfully resolve an Incident during the game session?
- Were you appointed patrol leader during the game session?
- Were you chosen as the Judicator of the Day during the game session?

For each of these questions you can answer yes to, your Reputation is decreased one step:

- Did your patrol fail to resolve an Incident during the game session?
- Were you revealed to be a double agent, or were you caught committing a crime or breaking protocol during the game session?

The GM may also raise or lower the Reputation of a character as a result of exceptional actions during play, provided such actions were made public knowledge.

NEW RELATIONSHIPS AND DREAMS

After each game session you can change which NPC you want to protect, your rival, or change your dream.

NEW CONTACTS

You can gain new contacts during gameplay, and you can also lose contacts if you abuse, mistreat or cross them somehow. Read more in Chapter 5.

ELYSIUM

MUTANT YEAR ZERO

ATTRIBUTES

Attribute	Value	Trauma	
Strength	3	Damage	○○○○○
Agility	4	Fatigue	○○○○○
Wits	5	Confusion	○○○○○
Empathy	3	Doubt	○○○○○

CONDITIONS

Starving	○	Dehydrated	○
Sleepless	○	Hypothermic	○

Critical Injuries:

SKILLS

Endure (Strength)	
Force (Strength)	
Fight (Strength)	2
Sneak (Agility)	2
Move (Agility)	
Shoot (Agility)	2
Scout (Wits)	1
Comprehend (Wits)	1
Know the Zone (Wits)	
Sense Emotion (Empathy)	
Manipulate (Empathy)	
Heal (Empathy)	
INVESTIGATE	3

ROT POINTS

○○○○○○○○○○

EXPERIENCE POINTS

○○○○○○○○○○

Name: PANDORA | Age: 36

Profession: INVESTIGATOR | House: KILGORE | Reputation: 4

APPEARANCE

Face: HOLLOW CHEEKS, PALE

Body: SKINNY

Clothing: WORN, ILL-FITTING, COAT

TALENTS

INTUITION

GEAR

1. E-PACK
2. 2 EMERGENCY RATIONS OF FOOD
3. 2 EMERGENCY RATIONS OF WATER
4. CLASS IV ID CARD
5. COMM RADIO
6.
7.
8.
9.
10.

Credits: 3

CONTACTS

PARAMOUR

SNITCH

INFLUENCE POINTS

⊗○○○○○○○○○

ARMOR

Armor	Rating

WEAPONS

Weapon	Bonus	Damage	Range	Special
GYROJET PISTOL	+3	3	SHORT	4 ROCKETS
VIBRO KNIFE	+2	2	ARM'S	LIGHT WEAPON

RELATIONSHIPS

	Patrol Leader
PC 1: SEEMS TO BE HIDING SOMETHING	⊗
PC 2: IS USEFUL AND WILLING TO HELP, BUT MAY BE A BIT SLOW	○
PC 3: SHOOTS FIRST AND ASKS QUESTIONS LATER, BUT I TRUST HE HAS MY BACK	○
PC 4:	○

I Hate: THE GRAY EMINENCE CREON. HE SABOTAGED MY MURDER INVESTIGATION.

I Need to Protect: MY LITTLE SISTER THEODORA WHO TEACHES AT THE ACADEMY.

My Big Dream: TO BE ABLE TO TRUST ANOTHER PERSON.

ELYSIUM

MUTANT YEAR ZERO

PEOPLE I'VE MET	Role	Notes
Eminence Creon	Temple leader	He sabotaged my murder investigation
Theodora Kilgore	Scholar	My little sister. Teaches at the Academy.

THE PATROL

Designation: Alpha 4

Patrol Leader: Douglas Fortescue

Other: Alpha 4 is nicknamed "The Wolves"

MY DEN

Description: Shabby, smoked-in apartment in Hindenburg.

Gear Stashed:

Other: Pandora is always behind with the rent and avoids her landlord.

TINY ITEMS

NOTES

02

INVESTIGATOR

They say that Elysium I is the paragon of society. The type the world will be modeled after once humanity returns to the surface. But you know better. In the enclave's underbelly, behind the polished facade of the Houses and in the depths of the tunnels bloom dark dealings, corruption, and violence. It is your job to reveal the criminals for what they are, and bring the truth to light. You are an Investigator.

Key Attribute: Wits
Specialist Skill: Investigate

Name: Your last name is the same as the name of your House. You can come up with your own first name or choose one of the following: Aiken, Conrad, Walter, Avon, Nara, Pandora

APPEARANCE

- **Face:** High cheekbones, combed hair, stubble beard.
- **Body:** Skinny, gangly, muscular.
- **Uniform:** Worn, ill-fitting, long coat.

TALENTS

Choose one, you can learn more later. Talents are explained in Chapter 4.

- **Intuition**
- **Many Faces**
- **Well Connected**

RELATIONSHIPS TO OTHER PCS

Choose from one of the options below or come up with one on your own:

... seems to be hiding something.
... is useful and willing to help, but may be a bit slow.
... shoots first and asks questions later, but you trust that he has your back.

RELATIONSHIPS TO NPCS

Choose from one of the options below:

You hate:

- The Gray Eminence Creon, Temple leader. Sabotaged your murder investigation by silencing all the witnesses. The Council does not understand the extent of the Temple's influence.
- The Scrap King. Gang leader in the Catacombs, responsible for the loss of more lives than anyone else in the enclave. One day you will put him where he belongs.
- Valentino Morningstar, host of the Voice of Dawn. You were childhood friends but have followed different paths in life. He symbolizes everything that is wrong and corrupt with Elysium I.

You want to protect:

- Ephraim Dunkle. A scarred and belligerent reconstructed worker who hates the social order. Despite the difference in status, you have enjoyed each other's company in the past.
- Molly Finkel. Bar owner in the Core. You have drowned your sins at Molly's bar counter many a dark evening over the years.
- Theodora. Your little sister and a skilled teacher at the Academy. You have tried to protect her from all evil and so far, have succeeded quite well.

YOUR BIG DREAM

Choose from the options below or come up with one on your own:

- To get the heads of the Houses to pay for the crimes they have committed.
- To become part of a new community where you can finally be yourself.
- To be able to trust another person.

GEAR

Choose one of the following weapons during character creation: Gauss pistol, gyrojet pistol (with D6 rockets). You also get a vibro knife, an E-pack, two emergency rations of both food and water, a class IV ID card and a comm radio.

Credits: D6

OFFICER

Leading others is not just your right – it is your duty. Your destiny is to lead humanity into a new dawn, and you will be at the forefront when it is time to return to the surface world. Until then, you will lead the way for the other judicators in your patrol. They follow your word as if it were the law – for the most part. You are an Officer.

Key Attribute: Empathy
Specialist Skill: Command

Name: Your last name is the same as the name of your House. You can come up with your own first name or choose one of the following: Cameron, Douglas, Rayburn, Audrey, Blythe, Farrah.

APPEARANCE

- **Face:** Hawk nose, high cheekbones, well-trimmed mustache.
- **Body:** Slender, straight-backed, short.
- **Uniform:** Well-groomed, decorated, worn out.

TALENTS

Choose one, you can learn more later. Talents are explained in Chapter 4.

- **Commander**
- **Feared Enemy**
- **Icy Voice**

RELATIONSHIPS TO OTHER PCS

Choose from the options below or come up with one on your own:

... is always eager for action. What are his true intentions?
... has rebellious tendencies. Someone should put him in his place.
... is your right hand. If he were not from another House, you would not hesitate to put your life in his hands.
... seems to be hiding something. Best to keep an eye on him.

RELATIONSHIPS TO NPCS

Choose from the options below or come up with one on your own:

You hate:

- Antonius Block, labor activist and your brother. Once, he was an Officer like yourself, but was sentenced to hard labor after killing another officer during a riot in the Deep.
- Creon, Gray Eminence. The bearded hierophant of the Temple and his annoying novices are always putting their noses where they don't belong.
- Toddy Somerset, socialite. Party, dinner, or theater – whatever social event you attend, he is always there to steal the spotlight from you.

You want to protect:

- Casimir Montague, colonel of the Deep Watch. A competent officer you met when you were both in the school for cadets. You have always admired him.
- Valeria Warburg, actress. You were close friends or even lovers a few years ago, and she is still in love with you.
- Melina. Old childhood friend, now a brilliant Scholar at the Academy. (Which House Melina belongs to is decided by the GM during play).

YOUR BIG DREAM

Choose from the options below or come up with one on your own:

- To finally retire, if only you could trust your successors.
- To start a revolution and take your place among the enclave's leadership.
- To lead the people out of the enclave to repopulate the surface world.

GEAR

Choose one of these weapons during character creation: Gauss pistol, gyrojet pistol. You also get one E-pack or D6 gyrojet rockets. Additionally, you get two emergency rations of both food and water, a class IV ID card, and a comm radio.

Credits: 2D6

PROCURATOR

Elysium is a society founded on laws and rights. Certainly, the laws are written by and for the great dynasties. Even so, without rules and regulations to keep these powerful Houses in check, the enclave would surely collapse. You understand the law inside and out, you know where the loopholes and contradictions exist, and you can turn every paragraph to your advantage. You are a Procurator.

Key Attribute: Wits
Specialist Skill: Prosecute

Name: Your last name is the same as the name of your House. You can come up with your own first name or choose one of the following: Aston, Aldrich, Stanley, Beverly, Godiva, Hazel.

APPEARANCE

- **Face:** Sharp eyes, well-combed hair, big mustache.
- **Body:** Upright, overweight, graceful.
- **Uniform:** Polished shoes, short cloak, trouser stripes

TALENTS

Choose one, you can learn more later. Talents are explained in Chapter 4.

- **Defender**
- **Pettifogger**
- **Public Servant**

RELATIONSHIPS TO OTHER PCS

... has no respect for law and order.
... has admirable principles, but what are his true intentions?
... exercises his right to kill with perhaps an excessive zeal.

RELATIONSHIPS TO NPCS

Choose from the options below or come up with one on your own:

You hate:

- The Gray Eminence Creon, Temple leader. Respected by all except for you – he won a court case over you a few years ago.
- Antonius Block, labor activist. A former heir and Officer accused of murdering another commander. You got him convicted, but he avoided being exiled to the Catacombs and was sentenced to hard labor in the Deep instead.
- Ephraim Dunkle, Informant. You condemned him for stealing in the Bazaar. He claimed he was innocent and swore revenge.

You want to protect:

- Rupert Acton, security officer. He lied in order to support you in an important legal case.
- Florian, judicator. Your son or younger brother. Has spent his whole life trying to prove himself to you and make you proud.
- Toddy Somerset, socialite. He has some dirt on you and you are prepared to do anything to keep what he knows a secret.

YOUR BIG DREAM

Choose from the options below or come up with one on your own:

- To build a new society on the surface world, one based on the rule of law.
- To reform the laws of Elysium, which you know to be corrupt.
- To break the law for a change.

GEAR

As a field Procurator, you get a stun gun with an E-pack. You also carry your beautifully bound lawbook and two emergency rations of both food and water. Additionally, you have a class IV ID card and a comm radio.

Credits: 2D6.

SCHOLAR

As always, knowledge has been the torch that showed humanity the way through darkness and chaos. It is your holy mission to make sure that this torch never goes out. Elysium's inhabitants may be the last people of the world, and so you carry the most precious of burdens, the seeds of a new civilization. You are a Scholar.

Key Attribute: Wits
Specialist Skill: Enlighten

Name: Your last name is the same as the name of your House. You can come up with your own first name or choose one of the following: Alvin, Erskine, Milton, Alcott, Edith, Isolda.

APPEARANCE

- **Face:** Pale, vacant stare, glasses.
- **Body:** Slender, short, hunched.
- **Uniform:** Smooth and buttoned, long coat, short coat.

TALENTS

Choose one, you can learn more later. Talents are explained in Chapter 4.

- **Bearer of Knowledge**
- **Crucial Insight**
- **Judge of Character**

RELATIONSHIPS TO OTHER PCS

Choose from one of the options below or come up with one on your own:

... is your apprentice and you wish to teach him everything you know.
... is ill-mannered and should be disciplined.
... has knowledge you thought was unimportant that proved to be otherwise.

RELATIONSHIPS TO NPCS

Choose from the options below or come up with one on your own:

You hate:

- Sonya Carp, labor leader. She's an agitator who questioned your assessment after a mine explosion. It was not your fault that the tunnel collapsed.
- Theodora, a fellow Scholar and your former colleague. An imbecile, totally undeserving of her career at the Academy. It should have been you. If Theodora is another PC's sister, she belongs to the same House as this PC.
- Valentino Morningstar, the host of Voice of the Dawn, spreading rumors and lies to increase his own fame and influence.

You want to protect:

- Melina. Brilliant Scholar of the Academy and your former teacher. You've always looked up to her. (The GM will determine which House Melina belongs to during gameplay).
- Creon, Gray Eminence of the Temple. He possesses a knowledge and wisdom that is unappreciated by the Council.
- Oswald Bentick. A Scholar at the Academy and an old classmate of yours. Long ago, you once had a romance.

YOUR BIG DREAM

Choose from the options below or come up with one on your own:

- Record the history of the enclave and safeguard it for future generations.
- Learn about the surface world and maybe even experience it. You suspect that the Council is not saying everything they know on the subject.
- Find out the truth about the Temple and its eminence. You are sure they are hiding something.

GEAR

Choose one of these weapons during character creation: Gauss pistol, stun gun. You also get an E-pack, two emergency rations of both food and water, a class IV ID card, and a comm radio.

Credits: 2D6

SOLDIER

Elysium has enemies – both inside and outside its walls. You are the sword that cuts down any threat to the enclave's survival. When so much is at stake, there is no room for doubt or hesitation. The only things that matter to you are your orders and your mission. They are all need when you fight. You are a Soldier.

Key Attribute: Agility
Specialist Skill: Press On

Name: Your last name is the same as the name of your House. You can come up with your own first name or choose one of the following: Brock, Cade, Nash, Afton, Holly, Kyla

APPEARANCE

- **Face:** Scarred, sharp features, blank stare.
- **Body:** Muscular, wiry, maimed.
- **Uniform:** Armored, worn, unkempt.

TALENTS

Choose one, you can learn more later. Talents are explained in Chapter 4:

- **Beefy**
- **Biomechatronic**
- **True Grit**

RELATIONSHIPS TO OTHER PCS

Choose from one of the options below or come up with one on your own:

... can't be trusted. Do not turn your back on him.
... is a true fighter. You like him, even though you belong to different Houses.
... is an inflated snob who thinks he is better than you.
... is a true leader, worth fighting and dying for.

RELATIONS TO NPCS

Choose from the options below or come up with one on your own:

You Hate:

- Casimir Montague, colonel of the Deep Watch. Your former commander, who never missed a chance to torment the soldiers. A real bastard.
- The Scrap King, gang leader. Leads the Cravats gang, based in the Catacombs. Several of your squad mates were killed during a raid against them a couple of years ago.
- Valentino Morningstar. Host of Voice of the Dawn and the most famous celebrity in the enclave. He interviewed you once and made you say something you regret to this day.

You want to protect:

- Antonius Block, labor activist. Was once your commanding officer but was sentenced to hard labor in the depths after killing another officer who opened fire against protesters.
- Rupert Acton, security officer. A former lover and still good friend who can be trusted with anything.
- Valeria Warburg, childhood friend. You've kept in touch over the years despite her becoming a famous actor.

YOUR BIG DREAM

Choose from the options below or come up with one on your own:

- To one day lead your own squad and get the respect you deserve.
- To stop fighting and find a place where you really feel safe.
- To give your life fighting to defend the enclave.

GEAR

Choose two of the following weapons during character creation: Gauss rifle, gyrojet carbine, explosive grenade, stun baton. You also get two E-packs, one set of combat armor, two emergency rations of both food and water, a class IV ID card and a comm radio.

Credits: D6

TECHNICIAN

When Elysium I was built, it was an unprecedented monument, a modern wonder, proof that necessity can drive humanity to perform miracles. That was then. Now, several centuries later, the enclave is a crumbling underground maze. It is your duty to repair whatever breaks down or needs improving. You know the tunnels, shafts, and cables of the enclave like the back of your hand. You are a Technician.

Key Attribute: Wits
Specialist Skill: Tinker

Name: Your last name is the same as the name of your House. You can come up with your own first name or choose one of the following: Bromley, Chilton, Hilton, Alvina, Ethel, Locke.

APPEARANCE

- **Face:** Glasses, double chin, receding hairline.
- **Body:** Short, wide, gangly.
- **Uniform:** Stained, extra pockets, reinforced knee pads.

TALENTS

Choose one, you can learn more later. Talents are explained in Chapter 4.

- **Biomechatronic**
- **Field Surgeon**
- **Grease Monkey**

RELATIONSHIPS TO OTHER PCS

Choose from one of the options below or come up with one on your own:

... has no respect for his equipment. He'll have himself to blame if his weapon malfunctions when he needs it the most.
... has your back so you can work undisturbed.
... is good to have around because he does as you say.

RELATIONSHIPS TO NPCS

Choose from the options below or come up with one on your own:

You hate:

- "Nutty Nadya," psychopath and gang leader in the Deep. Her gang, the Sooty Hand, killed your best friend and colleague, Althea.
- Reginald, overseer in the mines. Your father. He always favored your brother over you when you were growing up, and you cannot stand the sight of him.
- Toddy Somerset, socialite. A diva who does not respect you or other judicators, even though he does not belong to any of the ruling Houses.

You want to protect:

- Sonya Carp, labor leader in the Deep. She is a threat to the Houses' authority, but you support her and her struggle.
- Cassandra. Your sister, who was named Ashley before she changed it. She left her prestigious position at the Academy to become a novice in the Temple.
- Beldon, mining technician. Your younger brother. You wish for him to be more self-sufficient but cannot help but take care of him.
- Molly Finkel. Bar owner in the Core. A source of stability in your life.

YOUR BIG DREAM

Choose from the options below or come up with one on your own:

- To build something new from scratch instead of just maintaining and tweaking old machines.
- Building a brand-new settlement for the people of Elysium I.
- To create a machine intelligence with its own consciousness.

GEAR

Choose one of the following weapons during character creation: Gyrojet pistol, stun gun, stun baton. You also get an E-pack or D6 gyrojet rockets, two emergency rations of both food and water, a class IV ID card and a comm radio.

Credits: D6

SKILLS

Role playing is a conversation. The GM sets the scene, you describe what you do, the GM describes how the NPCs react – then you respond, and so on, back and forth. The story develops one step at a time. But sooner or later you will come to a decisive position, the point without return, a conflict that the cannot be solved through conversation. This is when you get the dice out and use your skills.

ROLLING THE DICE

There are twelve basic skills in *Mutant: Elysium*. These can be used by any human. Additionally, each profession adds a unique thirteenth skill. Every skill is connected to one of the four basic attributes: Strength, Agility, Wits, and Empathy.

☢ MEANS SUCCESS

After you describe what your character wants to do, grab a number of Skill Dice (green) equal to your skill level, and a number of Base Dice (yellow) equal to the current rating of the connected attribute. If you are using an applicable tool you also get a number of Gear Dice (black), see page 44 for more information. Then roll all the dice together.

In order for your action to succeed you must roll at least one ☢ symbol – otherwise the action fails. If you roll more than one ☢ you can perform stunts (see page 46).

THE TWELVE SKILLS

- Endurance (Strength)
- Force (Strength)
- Fight (Strength)
- Sneak (Agility)
- Move (Agility)
- Shoot (Agility)
- Scout (Wits)
- Comprehend (Wits)
- Know the Zone (Wits)
- Sense Emotion (Empathy)
- Manipulate (Empathy)
- Heal (Empathy)

The ☣ symbol: On the Base Dice the 1 is replaced with the ☣ symbol. It does not come into play unless you push your roll. Read more about pushing rolls on the next page).

ROLLING WITHOUT SKILL LEVELS

You can always roll for a skill even if your current level is 0 – just roll the Base Dice for the corresponding Attribute plus any Gear Dice. The only exemptions to this rule are the specialist skills – in order to use these, you need at least a skill level of 1.

03

EXAMPLE

The judicator Pandora Kilgore is sitting in an interrogation room with Nutty Nadia, the gang leader of the Sooty Hand. She tries to determine if Nadia is lying to her and rolls for Sense Emotion. Sylvia describes how Pandora locks eyes with the gang leader, shoves her, and tries to read the reactions. She rolls three yellow Base Dice (Empathy 3) and 1 green Skill Die (Sense Emotion 1).

THE ART OF FAILURE

If you roll no ☢, something goes wrong. You are now at the GM's mercy, and she decides what happens. The only thing she can't say is "nothing happens." Failure should always have consequences. The final decision is up to the GM. It could be that you suffer trauma, lose something valuable, need to make a detour, or face a new threat or obstacle of some kind. But if you desperately need to succeed there is one final lifeline available - you can push your roll (more below).

Conflicts: In conflicts (Chapter 6), a failed attack doesn't need to have further consequences. It is usually enough for your attack to miss the opponent - it is now his turn to act. However, the GM may introduce further complications such as the missed shot hitting someone other than the intended target.

PUSHING YOUR ROLL

If you are in a desperate situation you can push your roll. This means that you can take all dice that did not land on a ☢, ☣, or 💥, and roll them again. You get a second chance at rolling more ☢. You can never push dice that landed on ☣ or 💥 - they remain as they are on the table.

ONLY ROLL WHEN NEEDED

It's hard to succeed with actions in *Mutant: Elysium*. If you do not have good gadgets or friends that help you, chances are you are going to fail. Don't roll unnecessarily. Save the dice for truly dramatic situations.

DESCRIBE YOUR ACTION

In *Mutant: Elysium*, you are all creating a story together. Rolling for a skill is a dramatic highlight – first describe what you want to achieve, so that everyone knows what is at stake. Then you roll the dice. Interpret the result and tell everyone what is happening. Describe what you are doing, what you say or how you think. How your opponent reacts. If you push your roll, describe how. Do it yourself, do not wait for the GM – only if you go beyond the results you achieved will the GM step in.

You cannot pick and choose which dice to reroll - when you push your roll you must reroll all remaining dice that show neither ☢ nor ☣.

For the most part you will only push failed rolls. However, you can still push a roll that successfully got ☢ during the first roll in order to score additional successes and unlock stunts. But pushing a roll is not without risk - read more about risks below.

How a pushed roll plays out in the story depends on the skill being used. It could be a great physical exertion, a moment of total mental focus, or an emotional strain.

Gear Dice: When you push a roll, you must also push any Gear Dice (below).

Only Once: You can only push a roll once. If you don't succeed on the second attempt your luck has run out - all that is left to do is to take the hit and suffer the consequences.

☣ HURTS YOU

When you push yourself there is always a risk of injury or fatigue. For every ☣ you roll, you suffer one point of trauma to the attribute rolled. Read more about trauma and its various forms in Chapter 6.

PREDISPOSITIONS

The four ruling Houses of Elysium are great dynasties comprised of individuals from many different backgrounds. The Houses each have a specific and fundamental purpose, one that requires members to be particularly suited to performing certain tasks.

In game terms, this is reflected by the fact that each House is bound to one of the four attributes – see table below. When you push a roll for the attribute associated with your House, you can re-roll all the dice you want – even those that show ☣ from the original roll. This means that you run less risk of trauma, and have a greater chance of success, when pushing a roll for the attribute associated with your House.

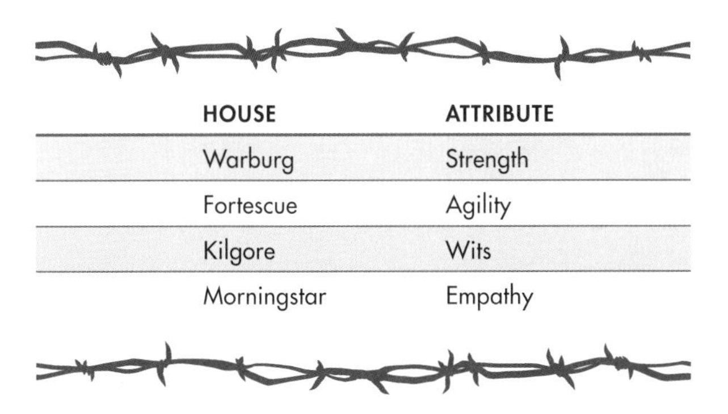

HOUSE	ATTRIBUTE
Warburg	Strength
Fortescue	Agility
Kilgore	Wits
Morningstar	Empathy

EXAMPLE

Sylvia did not roll any ☢ when she used Sense Emotion against Nutty Nadia, but she did roll one ☣. Sylvia is considering whether to push the roll. Because she belongs to House Kilgore and their main attribute is Wits, she must avoid rolling any more ☣ – she will take at least 1 point of trauma to Empathy if she pushes the roll. She nevertheless chooses to do that and re-rolls two Base Dice and one Skill Die. Now she gets one ☢! Sylvia and the GM together describe how Pandora refuses to give up and continues to push Nadia, even though the gang leader tries to throw the judicator off balance by talking about her dead partner. Finally, Pandora realizes that Nadia is lying, but as a consequence of pushing the roll, she also gains 1 point of doubt (trauma to Empathy).

ONLY ONE SHOT

As a rule, you usually only have one shot at a particular action. Once you have rolled the dice and perhaps pushed the roll you cannot roll again for the same action. You must try something else, wait until the circumstances have changed in a tangible way, or let another PC give it a try.

During conflicts (Chapter 6) the GM should be more forgiving. You can attack the same enemy over and over until you bring it down – it is enough to simply describe the different methods you employ.

CHANCE OF SUCCESS

When you are rolling a lot of dice it can be hard to judge your chances of success. The table below shows the chances of success in percentages when rolling from 1 to 10 dice. The third column shows the chances of success if you push the roll.

NUMBER OF DICE	CHANCE OF SUCCESS	PUSHED ROLL
1	17%	29%
2	31%	50%
3	42%	64%
4	52%	74%
5	60%	81%
6	67%	87%
7	72%	90%
8	77%	93%
9	81%	95%
10	84%	96%

NPCS AND SKILLS

NPCs use skills in the same way as the PCs. The GM rolls dice for them and they can push their rolls just like the PCs. But the GM only needs to roll for actions that directly affect a PC – for example, if an NPC attacks or tries to Heal a PC. When an NPC performs an action that does not directly affect a PC, the GM can simply decide what happens, without rolling dice.

GEAR BONUS

With the right gear you can increase your chances of success. For example, it might be a weapon in combat or a sensor when investigating a crime scene.

A useful item gives you Gear Dice (the black dice in the *Mutant: Year Zero* dice set). How many Gear Dice you get depends on the gear, as shown on the weapons table on page 74 or on the Artifact Cards. You roll the Gear Dice along with the Basic Dice and Skill Dice, counting successes in the same way: ☢ mean success.

You can normally use only one piece of gear for any given action.

GEAR BREAKS

When you use a piece of gear and push your roll (above) you run the risk of damaging or even breaking it. When you push, you must reroll all dice that do not show ✸ or ☢. For each die that shows ✸ after you have pushed the roll, the item's Gear Bonus is reduced by one. The gear simply will not work as well anymore.

If the Gear Bonus reaches zero, the gear will no longer work at all. A Technician can repair gear. It takes a couple of hours of work and a successful Tinker roll. If the roll is successful, the gadget is restored. If the Technician fails, the Gear Bonus is permanently decreased to the current level. If the Gear Bonus is lowered to zero, the gear is permanently rendered useless.

EXAMPLE

Pandora is down in the Deep and comes into conflict with striking workers. One of them attacks her using a bottle. He has a Strength of 4 and a Fight skill level of 2, and the bottle gives him a Gear Bonus of +1. He then rolls four Basic Dice, two Skill Dice and a Gear Die.

COMMON GEAR

Here are some examples of gadgets you can use:

- **Rope:** Grants a +2 Gear Bonus to Move rolls when climbing.
- **Weapon:** Grants a +1 Gear Bonus to Fight rolls.

Artifacts often grant Gear Bonuses. See Chapter 9 or Artifact Cards.

MODIFICATIONS

Sometimes certain factors can help you succeed at an action. These may grant extra dice to your roll. At other times, factors will hinder your efforts. In those cases, you may be forced to roll fewer dice than the situation would normally call for. These are called modifications.

A modification of +1 means you may roll an extra Skill Die, +2 that you can roll two additional Skill Dice, and so on. A modification of –1 means you roll one less Skill Die than usual, –2 means two fewer, and so on.

Modifications only affect Skill Dice - never Base Dice or Gear Dice.

You can have multiple modifications affecting you at once - combine them all to calculate the total. For instance, a modification of +2 and a –1 will be combined into a +1.

Negative Dice: If, after modification, you end up with exactly zero Skill Dice, you only roll your Base Dice and any Gear Dice you are entitled to. If your Skill Dice pool goes below zero, you must roll a die for each point that the pool drops below zero. These are called negative dice. Any ☢ on a negative die negates a ☢ rolled on the Base Dice or Gear Dice. If you push the roll, you have to re-roll the negative dice too (except those that show ☢).

You can get modifications in two ways: through the difficulty of the action itself or through help from others.

DIFFICULTY

The GM, most of the time, won't fuss over the difficulty of an action. You roll the dice during challenging situations - plain and simple. But there are times when the GM might want to highlight that external

factors either help or hinder the PCs during an action. The GM can use the table below for guidance:

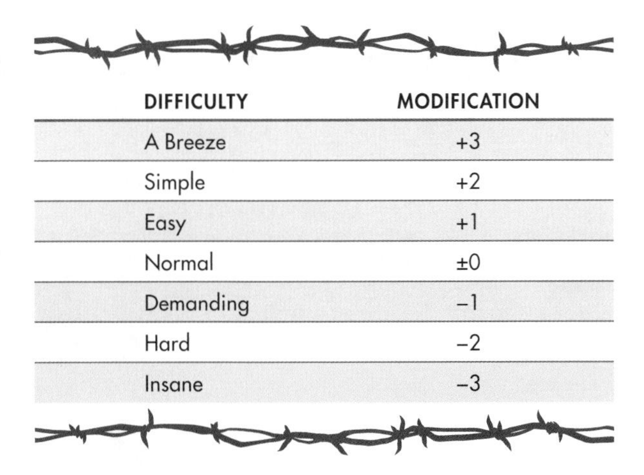

DIFFICULTY	MODIFICATION
A Breeze	+3
Simple	+2
Easy	+1
Normal	±0
Demanding	−1
Hard	−2
Insane	−3

There are also cases when modifications are imposed by the rules, like when you aim carefully with a gun (Chapter 6), shoot at long range, or if you are in a bad bargaining position when trying to Manipulate someone. Some talents can also grant a positive modification.

HELP FROM OTHERS

Other PCs or NPCs around you can help you succeed. An attempt to help must be declared before the dice are rolled. It must also make sense within the context of the story – those helping have to be physically present and be able to support your action in a direct and tangible way. The GM has the final say.

For each person helping you, you receive a +1 modification. No more than three people can help for any given roll, making the maximum possible modification through help to be a +3.

Anyone who is helping you with a roll during a conflict (see Chapter 6) loses their own action for that turn. However, you can help another PC while simultaneously making a maneuver (page 68).

NPCs can help each other in the same way as the PCs. Having the NPCs act in groups instead of individually is often an easy way to handle a large number of NPCs during conflicts.

EXAMPLE

Three more workers join the conflict. Instead of making a separate roll for each of them, the GM rolls for only one of the workers, who gets a bonus of +3 (+1 from each of the three additional opponents lending a hand).

SIMULTANEOUS ACTIONS

You and the other PCs cannot help each other when you are acting simultaneously, that is, performing the same action side by side – you would have to all roll individually. If you wish to help someone you must sacrifice your own action in order to do so.

If your roll is very successful some skills allow you to still help a friend, who in turn would not have to roll for himself. You can help them in this way even after they have rolled and failed themselves.

OPPOSED ROLLS

Sometimes rolling ☢ is not enough to succeed at a skill roll. In certain cases, you will need to overcome your opponent in an opposed roll. In order to win an opposed roll, you must score more ☢ than your opponent. Every ☢ rolled by your opponent negates a ☢ of your own. Only the person initiating the roll can push the roll.

You and your opponent can roll for the same skill or different skills, depending on the situation. Opposed rolls are used when you attempt to Manipulate or Sneak, and when someone uses these skills against you. The GM can also use opposed rolls when she feels it is appropriate, for example a Force vs Force roll to resolve an arm-wrestle.

Conflict: During a conflict (Chapter 6) an opposed roll only counts as an action for you (the initiator of the roll), not for your opponent (the defender).

EXAMPLE

Pandora tries to persuade Casimir Montague, colonel of the Deep Watch, to grant her passage into a restricted sector. She rolls for Manipulate while Montague rolls Sense Emotion to see through the Manipulation attempt. They each roll a ☢. Pandora chooses to push her roll. She gets one more ☢ but also one ☣. Montague eventually yields, but Pandora takes 1 point of doubt (trauma to Empathy).

BASIC SKILLS

This section describes the twelve basic skills that PCs and NPCs can use regardless of their profession. Some skills also describe the special stunts you can perform when rolling more than one ☢.

ENDURE (STRENGTH)

Life for a patrician is rarely one of manual work or toil, after all that's what the workers are for. Nonetheless, your physical endurance will sometimes be tested.

Failure: You just can't take it anymore. You must rest, if only for a while.

Success: You manage to push on, ignoring the pain just a little longer.

Stunt: For each ☢ you roll in addition to the first, you can help a friend (PC or NPC) in the same trouble you are facing. He succeeds without having to roll the dice. You can choose this stunt even if you only rolled a single ☢ – you will then help your friend succeed at your own expense.

FORCE (STRENGTH)

Physical roughness is usually the workers' bread and butter, but the job of a judicator is full of unexpected surprises. You use Force for all tests of physical strength.

Failure: It's just too heavy. You need to find another way. And what if the noise you made attracted unwanted attention?

Success: With a groan, you push through and get whatever it was out of your way.

Stunt: For each additional ☢ rolled beyond the first, you can choose one of the following effects:

- You push or throw the object with great force. An enemy within Arm's Length range will receive an amount of damage equal to the amount of extra ☢.

- If it is reasonable within the scene, you find a hidden passage or a hidden object. The GM determines exactly what it is.

FIGHT (STRENGTH)

Regardless of the specialization, all judicators receive some training in close combat to protect themselves and their colleagues. Roll for Fight when you attack someone in close combat.

Failure: You stumble and miss. Now it's your opponent's turn...

Success: You hit and inflict weapon damage (page 76) on your opponent.

Stunt: For each additional ☢ rolled, you can choose one of the following effects:

- You inflict one additional point of damage. You can select this effect multiple times.
- You subdue or tire your enemy. He suffers one point of fatigue (page 76).
- You increase your initiative score by 2 (page 67), starting next turn.
- You knock or pull a weapon or other object from your opponent's grasp. You choose which. During a conflict, picking up a dropped object counts as a maneuver (page 68).
- Your opponent falls to the ground or is pushed back, for example through a doorway or down a shaft.
- You hold the opponent in a grapple. He needs to successfully Fight you to break free and can't perform any other action (or maneuver) until he has done so – or until you are Broken or let him go.

Weapon: When you fight you can use weapons. See page 75.

Defend: When someone Fights you, you can try to defend yourself. When you defend, you also roll for Fight, with a specific set of stunts available. Read more on page 72.

SNEAK (AGILITY)

Often enough, it's wiser to avoid conflict and instead Sneak by your enemies. Use this skill when you try to move without being noticed or when you attempt a sneak attack (see page 69). Roll an opposed roll using your Sneak score against a Scout roll for your enemy.

Failure: Your enemy sees you or hears you, and the element of surprise is lost.

Success: You move like a shadow, noticed by no one.

Stunt: When setting up a sneak attack, you get a +1 modification to your first attack for every extra ☢ rolled after the first.

MOVE (AGILITY)

A competent judicator knows it's better to flee than to die needlessly. Roll Move to get out of a conflict or another dangerous situation.

Failure: You are pinned down, backed into a corner with no way out. Get ready for a fight.

Success: You get out of the sticky situation and live to fight another day.

Stunt: For every ☢ you roll, you can help a friend (PC or NPC) in the same spot of trouble as you. He makes it out and doesn't have to roll himself. You can even choose this stunt when you only roll one ☢ – that means you help your friend while sacrificing yourself.

Acrobatics: Also use the Move skill when balancing, jumping or climbing. Failure in these cases can be fatal!

SHOOT (AGILITY)

As a judicator you are issued your service weapon – usually a gauss pistol, but specialists can also use more powerful weapons. Roll for Shoot when you fire the weapon against an opponent.

Failure: The shot misses your target. Maybe it hits something else? And the sound of gunfire could attract unwelcome attention...

Success: You hit and inflict weapon damage (see page 76) on your target.

Stunts: For every extra ☢ you roll, choose one of these stunts:

- You inflict one more point of damage. You can choose this stunt multiple times, if you roll several extra ☢.
- You pin down your enemy. He suffers one point of fatigue (see page 76).
- You increase your initiative score by 2 (see page 67), starting next turn.
- Your target drops a weapon or another hand-held object. You choose which.
- Your opponent falls to the ground or is pushed back, for example through a doorway or down a shaft.

E-Pack: Most firearms in the enclave must be loaded with an E-pack in order to work. If your E-pack is depleted, the weapon must be reloaded, which counts as a maneuver in a conflict. Read more in Chapter 6.

SCOUT (AGILITY)

Careful observation is the key to success as a judicator, and you must always be mindful of your surroundings. You use your Scout to detect someone

DO NOT ROLL TO SPOT HIDDEN THINGS

Don't roll Scout when searching for hidden objects close to you, such as secret doors or hidden clues. If you describe searching in the right place, the GM should simply let you find whatever is there. No dice roll is needed.

who is sneaking (opposed roll, see above). You can also use this skill when you see something or someone at a distance and want to know more about them.

Failure: You can't really make out what it is, or you mistake it for something else (the GM feeds you false information).

Success: You can make out what it is, and whether it looks like a threat to you or not. The exact information you get is up to the GM.

Stunts: For every extra ☢ you roll, you get to know the answer to one of these questions:

- Is it coming for me?
- Are there more of them close by?
- How do I get in/past/away?

COMPREHEND (WITS)

Technical knowledge and scientific education are what distinguishes the heirs of the Houses from the servants. For Scholars, this skill is particularly important. Whenever your understanding of something is put to the test, you make a Comprehend roll.

Failure: The object of your study makes no sense to you at all, or you are mistaken (in this case, the GM can feed you false information about the object):

Success: You understand the nature or function of the object. If it's an artifact, you can use it, provided it's in working order.

Stunts: For every ☢ rolled beyond the first, you can teach someone else how to use the artifact.

KNOW THE ZONE (WITS)

Areas outside of the enclave are forbidden even to judicators – expeditions to the outside world are extremely rare. Even Elysium's experts have limited knowledge on the matter, but they try to piece together the puzzle with what little has been uncovered. Roll for Know the Zone when you want to know something about a creature or phenomenon out in the Zone.

Failure: You have no, or the wrong, idea. The GM can feed you false, or a mix of true and false, information (in this way, you will know that you have failed your roll, but not what information to trust.)

Success: You know what it is, and its basic traits or effects.

Stunts: For every extra ☢ you roll, you get the answer to one of these questions about the creature or phenomenon:

- How can it hurt me?
- How can I hurt it?

SENSE EMOTION (EMPATHY)

Being able to read other people and see through lies and bluffs is a pivotal ability for a judicator. Roll Sense Emotion when someone tries to Manipulate you (opposed roll). Read more below. You can also use the ability to assess an NPC's mood. You must be close and have a few minutes for observation.

Failure: You fail to read, or misread, the NPC. The GM can feed you false, or a mix of true and false, information.

Success: The GM must reveal the NPC's current, most powerful emotion – hate, fear, contempt, love, etc.

Stunts: For every extra ☢ you roll, you get the answer to one of these yes/no questions about the NPC:

- Is he telling the truth?
- Does he want to hurt me?
- Does he want something from me?

MANIPULATE (EMPATHY)

As a judicator, you have the right to use violence in the line of duty, but you can often achieve your goal through persuasion, threats or cold reasoning. There are many ways to get another person to see things your way. Make an opposed roll (page 46) using your Manipulate against the opponent's Sense Emotion. Your chances of success are affected by your bargaining position (see page 70) and the Reputation score of you and your opponent.

Failure: He won't listen, and he won't do what you want. He might start to dislike you, or even attack you if provoked.

Success: He reluctantly does what you want but requires something in return. The GM decides what this is, but it must be something you can reasonably do. It is up to you whether to accept the deal or not.

Stunts: Rolling extra ☢ means you sow fear and doubt in your opponent's heart. He suffers one point of doubt (see page 76) for every additional ☢ you roll after the first one. If he is broken by doubt, he does what you want without demanding a favor in return.

> **NO MIND CONTROL**
> Manipulating someone does not give you mind control. In order to persuade an opponent, you must be reasonable, otherwise the GM has the right to deny the attempt.

SHOOT

Being Manipulated: NPCs and other PCs can Manipulate you. If their roll succeeds, you must offer them a deal of some sort. It's then up to the GM (or the other player) to accept or decline it.

HEAL (EMPATHY)

Caring for a fallen colleague is a matter of course for a judicator, even when you belong to different Houses. The skill can be used in two ways:

Mend the Broken: A person who has suffered enough trauma to reduce any of the four attributes to zero is broken and can't carry on. If you successfully Heal a broken person, he gets back to his feet and immediately recovers a number of attribute points equal to the number of ☢ you rolled. No resources are needed for this recovery. A failed roll has no further effect.

Save a Life: The most important use of the Heal skill is to give first aid and stabilize critical injuries – which might save your patient's life. A failed roll in this situation could kill him, however, so be careful. Read more about this on page 79.

SPECIALIST SKILLS

In addition to the twelve general skills available to all PCs and NPCs, each profession has a unique specialist skill.

THE INVESTIGATOR'S SKILL: INVESTIGATE (WITS)

You see what others usually miss. Your job is to notice small details and make sense of them. Roll to Investigate when you want to study a room or similar location. Each attempt takes a few minutes.

Failure: You can't find any significant clues. What are you missing?

Success: You may ask the GM one of the following questions:

- Is there anything hidden here, and if so, where?
- Are there any details here that are out of place, something that's out of the ordinary?

Investigate can also be used for studying a dead body. In this case, each ☢ gives you the answer to one of these questions:

- What was the cause of death?
- How long has the person/creature been dead?

The GM must answer truthfully, but she does not need to provide exhaustive answers or answer follow-up questions. The GM can provide ambiguous answers.

Stunt: For each additional ☢ rolled, you can ask the GM an additional question.

THE OFFICER'S SKILL: COMMAND (EMPATHY)

As an Officer, it's your duty to lead. Your subordinates need to trust that your orders are the right ones. Roll for Command when you order someone else to Endure, Force, Fight, Sneak, Move, or Shoot. The order must be simple enough to perform with one dice roll. During a conflict, giving an order counts as an action (however, see the Quick Command talent).

Failure: Your underlings take no heed of your words. What is the world coming too?

Success: You give a +2 bonus on the person's roll to complete the action. If you Command the same person again before the first order is completed, the bonus of the first order is lost.

Stunt: For each ☢ you roll beyond to the first, the person you Command receives an additional +1 bonus on the roll to fulfill the order.

THE PROCURATOR'S SKILL: PROSECUTE (WITS)

Elysium is an orderly society built upon laws and regulations. You are a master at bending these in your favor and using any legal loophole to maximum effect. Roll for Prosecute instead of Manipulate when you need to get your way by citing a specific clause in the law that would support your actions. The exact phrasing is up to you. The effect is the same as with Manipulate, but instead of an opposed roll you make just a straight roll (see the sidebar for legal restrictions).

Reputation: Just as when you Manipulate, your chances of succeeding with the Prosecute skill are affected by the Reputation score of you and your opponent. In Elysium I, the law is not equal for all. However, your bargaining position (see page 70) will have no effect on the roll.

Conflict: When used in a conflict, using the Prosecute skill counts as an action.

Law Duel: If you use this skill against another Procurator, make an opposed roll against your opponent.

Please note that this skill can only be used against individuals living under the same set of laws as you, such as Elysium I or a community that has developed the Rule of Law project (see Chapter 12).

IN THE NAME OF THE LAW
You cannot use the Prosecute skill to make someone do something that is blatantly illegal. For example, you can't make someone kill an innocent person in cold blood. The legal interpretation that you invoke must be within reason. The GM has the last word.

THE SCHOLAR'S SKILL: ENLIGHTEN (WITS)

You know everything. That's what others say about you anyway. Of course, that's not true, but, unquestionably, over the years you've accumulated huge amounts of what others rarely call "useless knowledge." Roll for Enlighten when the road ahead is unclear and you or your colleagues need a pointer towards what the next step could be.

In order to keep the result of your roll secret, the GM rolls for your skill behind the GM screen if she has one. This is, therefore, an exception to the basic rule in *Mutant: Year Zero* – that all rolls are open. You must also decide whether to push the roll without knowing whether you succeeded or not, or how many ☢ you rolled – the GM only announces how many points of confusion you get if you decide to push the roll.

Failure: You think you know something, but in fact the conclusion you've drawn is false and leads the group in the wrong direction.

Success: You have some odd piece of knowledge that may actually be helpful. Exactly what is up to the GM, who gives you a little bit of information that can nudge you in the right direction. The GM may provide incomplete or ambiguous information.

Stunt: Unlike other skills, rolling additional ☢ provides no bonus because this would immediately reveal whether the roll was a success.

THE SOLDIER'S SKILL: PRESS ON (AGILITY)

As a Soldier you fulfill your orders, no matter the pain. Roll to Press On when broken by damage (see page 77).

Failure: The damage is too much to bear. You stay down. You can push the roll, but if you fail you cannot try again.

Success: You immediately recover as many points of damage as the number of ☢ rolled. The skill has no effect on critical injuries.

Comment: The Press On skill can be combined with the Never Surrender talent (see *Mutant: Year Zero*). You can then roll for both Press On and Never Surrender if you have been broken.

THE TECHNICIAN'S SKILL: TINKER (WITS)

You are a master at operating and exploiting technical systems and structures. You can roll for Tinker to achieve a variety of outcomes. Examples:

- Open a locked door
- Shut off an alarm.
- Control a surveillance camera
- Find a hidden passage
- Destroy an item
- Weaken a structure such as a wall or building

The GM can give you a modification on the roll if what you are trying to achieve is particularly difficult. In order to be able to Tinker with an object or technical system, you must first understand it.

Failure: The effects of your attempt are completely different from what you hoped – the GM determines the details.

Success: You achieve the desired result.

Stunt: For each additional ☢ you roll, you gain an unexpected side effect. You may suggest what it is, but the GM has the last word. The bonus effect must be less significant than the original objective.

Optimize: You can also use Tinker to optimize an item for a particular purpose. It takes a few hours of work. For each ☢ you roll, the item grants the user a +1 bonus for a specific task, which you must describe when you make the roll. The bonus applies only to a single roll. If your roll fails, the gear is rendered unusable, its Gear Bonus reduced to zero.

04

TALENTS

As a judicator in a patrol you are constantly cooperating with others, while simultaneously seeking your own niche, something you and no one else can do. One way of doing this is through *talents*. Talents can change how you use skills or allow you to do things that would otherwise be impossible.

STARTING TALENTS

You start with one talent. Your profession determines which three talents you can choose from during character creation.

NEW TALENTS

You can learn new talents by spending XP (see page 25). When you have earned 5 XP you can trade them in for a new talent. You can then choose to learn one of the talents unique to your profession or one of the general talents available to all professions.

YEAR ZERO AND GENLAB ALPHA

Mutant: Year Zero and *Mutant: Genlab Alpha* include more talents. If you have access to these books you can use all the general talents included therein – your PC in Elysium can learn general talents from *Year Zero* or *Genlab Alpha* and vice versa.

THE INVESTIGATOR'S TALENTS

◘ INTUITION

You have an empathic understanding of when something is not right. You can roll for the Investigate skill using Empathy instead of Wits.

◘ MANY FACES

You are skilled at changing your appearance with the help of clothes and makeup. You can use this skill to avoid being recognized or to resemble someone else. Creating a disguise requires some hours of work. To see through your disguise, others must roll for Sense Emotion against your Manipulate roll. If you are trying resemble someone the target knows, the GM can impose a negative modification to the roll.

◘ WELL CONNECTED

You always take good care of your contacts. You get one extra Influence Point at the start of each game session, but you must state which of your contacts you have curried additional favor with and how.

THE OFFICER'S TALENTS

☐ COMMANDER

You can roll for the Command skill instead of Heal to get a broken person back on their feet (see page 50). You cannot however, use Command to heal critical injuries.

☐ FEARED ENEMY

You can use the Command skill to strike terror in your enemies. Make an opposed roll for Command against your target's Sense Emotion. The target must be able to hear and understand what you are saying. If you win the roll, the target takes one point of doubt for each ☢ you roll more than the target.

☐ LEADER FROM THE FRONT

You lead by example rather than by barking orders. You can roll for Command using Agility instead of Empathy.

THE PROCURATOR'S TALENTS

☐ DEFENDER

You can roll for Prosecute if you or another patrol member has been exposed as a double agent (see page 23). If the roll succeeds, you successfully exonerate yourself or your client, avoiding any punishment. When defending someone in your patrol you can always stipulate a form of payment for your service, whether it be currency, a favor or something else.

☐ PETTIFOGGER

You have mastered the art of manipulating other people's emotions to make them see things your way. When using the Prosecute skill, you can roll for Empathy instead of Wits.

☐ PUBLIC SERVANT

When working on the projects Tribunal, Surveillance, Free Enterprise, Autocracy, Collectivism, Suffrage, Currency, or Code of Law, you can use the Prosecute skill instead of the indicated skill. You also get +2 modification to the roll. Read more about projects in *Mutant: Year Zero*.

THE SCHOLAR'S TALENTS

☐ BEARER OF KNOWLEDGE

When you roll for a project in a Zone settlement (see Chapter 12), you can replace the Comprehend skill with Enlighten. You also get a +2 modification to the roll.

☐ CRUCIAL INSIGHT

You always find a way out of the most desperate situations. You can roll for Comprehend instead of Move when the skill is used to get out of a dangerous situation.

☐ JUDGE OF CHARACTER

You have studied human body language carefully and have learned to see signs of lies and manipulation. You can roll for Enlighten instead of Sense Emotion when resisting someone's attempt to Manipulate you.

THE SOLDIER'S TALENTS

☐ BEEFY

Your body can withstand large amounts of punishment. You can roll for Strength instead of Agility when you roll for Press On. Use your unmodified rating in Strength, not your temporary score (which is zero when you are broken).

☐ BIOMECHATRONIC

You have a biomechatronical implant – choose from the list on page 139. You can only choose this talent during character creation – during play, all professions will be able to buy biomechatronical implants.

☐ TRUE GRIT

You can roll for Press On immediately when you get broken by damage. This roll does not count as an action. If the roll succeeds, you can immediately perform one bonus action or maneuver before your collapse. If your action requires a roll, this roll is made with your full attribute score.

THE TECHNICIAN'S TALENTS

◻ BIOMECHATRONIC

You have a biomechatronical implant – choose from the list on page 139. You can only choose this talent during character creation – during play, all professions will be able to buy biomechatronical implants.

◻ FIELD SURGEON

You have knowledge of human anatomy and can use the Tinker skill instead of Heal to save the life of someone who has suffered a lethal critical injury. You cannot replace Heal in other situations (for example, getting a broken person back on their feet).

◻ GREASE MONKEY

You get a +1 modification when you roll Tinker to repair an item. This modification applies only when making repairs, not for other uses of the skill.

GENERAL TALENTS

◻ BACKSTAB

You can roll for the Sneak skill instead of Fight when performing a sneak attack (see page 69).

◻ DOUBLE WIELDER

You have mastered the art of fighting wielding a weapon in each hand. Only one-handed weapons such as pistols and knives can be used with this talent. As a single action on your turn, you can perform one attack with each weapon. If you attack the same enemy with both weapons you get a -2 modification on both attacks. If you attack separate enemies, you get -3 on both attacks and you also lose your maneuver during that turn.

◻ ELUSIVE

In combat, parrying for you counts as a maneuver instead of an action. It can be combined with Good Footwork (see *Mutant: Year Zero*) or Defensive (see *Mutant: Genlab Alpha*), but not with Stonewall (*Mutant: Genlab Alpha*).

◻ FAST HEALER

You are very resilient and recover quickly from injuries. The healing time of critical injuries (see page 79) is halved for you.

◻ FENCER

The saber is mostly used by the Honor Guard during official ceremonies, but some within the Houses have taken pride in learning to fight with this ancient weapon. With this talent, you can roll for Agility instead of Strength when you Fight with a saber.

◻ MACHINE AT HEART

You are abnormally resistant to machine fever, that is, the side effects caused by biomechatronical implants. You can ignore one ☢ rolled when reading the fever table on page 138.

◻ OVERSEER

When you work on a project in a community or an Ark (see *Mutant: Year Zero*) you can always choose to roll for Manipulate instead of whichever skill is specified by the project.

◻ RAPID FIRE

During overwatch (see page 74), you can fire two shots in quick succession as a single action. Both shots get a -2 modification. This talent can only be used with a weapon that does not need to be reloaded after each shot.

◻ REPUTABLE

You are adept at cultivating and maintaining your reputation. When deciding how your Reputation changes after a gaming session, you may refrain from answering one of the questions on the list (see page 25).

◻ ROBOT HUNTER

When using this talent while attacking a robot, you can choose which attribute of the robot you want to damage, or if you want to damage a specific module. That means you can select your result on the table on page 88 of the *Mutant: Mechatron* core book, instead of rolling a random result.

◻ ROT RESISTANT

You have a natural resistance to the Rot. It gives you an Armor Rating of 3 against Rot Points. This can be combined with the effects of protective gear.

CONTACTS

You are a dynast, a descendant and heir to the rich and powerful elites who against all odds escaped the Fall and survived in the depths. As a member of one of the Houses, you are never alone – you are part of a vast and powerful social network.

Despite your role as a judicator, your most important assets are neither biomechatronics nor gauss guns. Your most powerful resources and weapons are your contacts.

This chapter describes the 20 different in-game contacts. These contacts are also available on the playing cards included in the custom card deck for *Mutant: Elysium*. At the beginning of the game, you get a number of contacts determined by your age, see page 19. You can gain more contacts during gameplay.

You choose which contacts you want, but each is unique and may not be shared by any other player. You will have to agree on who gets which contacts, allowing chance to decide through dice rolls if there is no consensus.

NPCS AND CONTACTS

NPCs don't have contacts in terms of a game mechanics point of view. Only PCs have contacts and IP.

ACTIVATE CONTACT

You can impel a contact at any moment during gameplay by using one or more Influence Points (IP). There is no dice roll required, but you always run the risk of backlash (below).

Communication: This is an important caveat – to employ a contact, you must be able to communicate with it in some way that the GM finds reasonable. Some contacts are specifically exempt from this rule.

INFLUENCE POINTS

To use your contacts, you need Influence Points (IP). These measure the extent of your social influence.

- Prior to each gaming session you will receive a number of IP equal to your House's total number of Control points in the strategic game (see page 146).
- You can gain additional IP by cultivating your contacts (below).
- You may not save unused IP from one gaming session to the next – influence is renewed each session.
- You can never have more than 10 IP.

CULTIVATING CONTACTS

In the social game you must both give and take. Your contacts have their own interests and in order for them to help you, you sometimes need to help them.

Once per game session you can cultivate a contact. Select one of your contacts and describe a service you perform to care for the contact. You are free to come up with what you like, but it's usually something related to your profession.

You can handle this summarily with a simple dice roll, or play out in detail how to help your contact with something. It can even give the GM ideas for whole storylines in your campaign.

Cultivating a contact gives you 1–3 extra IP. See the table for details.

CULTIVATING YOUR CONTACTS

SERVICE	INFLUENCE POINTS
You perform a significant service, but without risk to yourself.	1 IP
You sacrifice something valuable to you for your contact.	2 IP
You risk your life for your contact.	3 IP

BACKLASH

Your contacts can be of great help, but the social arena is full of pitfalls. For each IP you use when you activate a contact, roll a Base Die. If you roll one or more ☣, something unexpected happens. Roll another Base Die and check the table to see what happens.

ROLL	EFFECT
☣	The contact feels offended and exploited by you. The contact refuses to help you and you lose the contact, which becomes an enemy instead and will do everything in its power to hamper your actions. The GM determines the details. If this contact was your only one, you can choose a new one for the next game session. If you want, you can roleplay in detail how you acquired this new contact.
2	The contact does as you asked, but requires in return that you first do some favor. There is some risk involved but it should be resolved quickly. The GM determines the details.
3	The contact does as you asked, but requires you to perform a difficult service at a later moment. You cannot activate this contact again until you complete this task.
4	The contact does as you asked, but wants a payment of D6 credits for its efforts.
5	The contact does as you asked, but also takes some other action to benefit itself. This should be something that can create problems for you. The GM determines the details.
☢	The contact gets really invested in the case, and convinces an additional individual to support your cause. You get a new contact – you can choose which one. If you want, you can roleplay in detail how you acquire this new contact.

CONTACT DESCRIPTIONS

Below are the 20 available contacts in the game. Each contact is a specific individual, but they are not named because your contacts often belong to the same House as the intended player and will share their same last name. Instead, the players and the GM should work together to name the contacts and then record their names on their individual character sheets.

ASSASSIN

You have a contact in the underworld that can make people disappear. Permanently. The cost in IP varies from 1 to 3 depending on who the target is. Some individuals, such as the heads of the Houses, cannot be targeted by your contact, as the security around them is too strong.

Effect: The targeted NPC dies. If you suffer a backlash and roll a ☣ on the backlash table, the assassin will try to kill you.

BLACK SHEEP

You have a sibling who has developed psionic powers. This, of course, is extremely shameful and the sibling is rarely released from the family's estate. But sometimes his/her powers can come in handy. Note that this contact can only be used if you have access to the *Mutant: Year Zero* core book. *Zone Compendium 5: Hotel Imperator* has even more information about psionic powers.

Effect: Determine randomly which psionic mutation your sibling has. In exchange for IP, the sibling will use his/her mutation to help you. The number of mutant points (MP) that can be used is equal to the number of IP you spend.

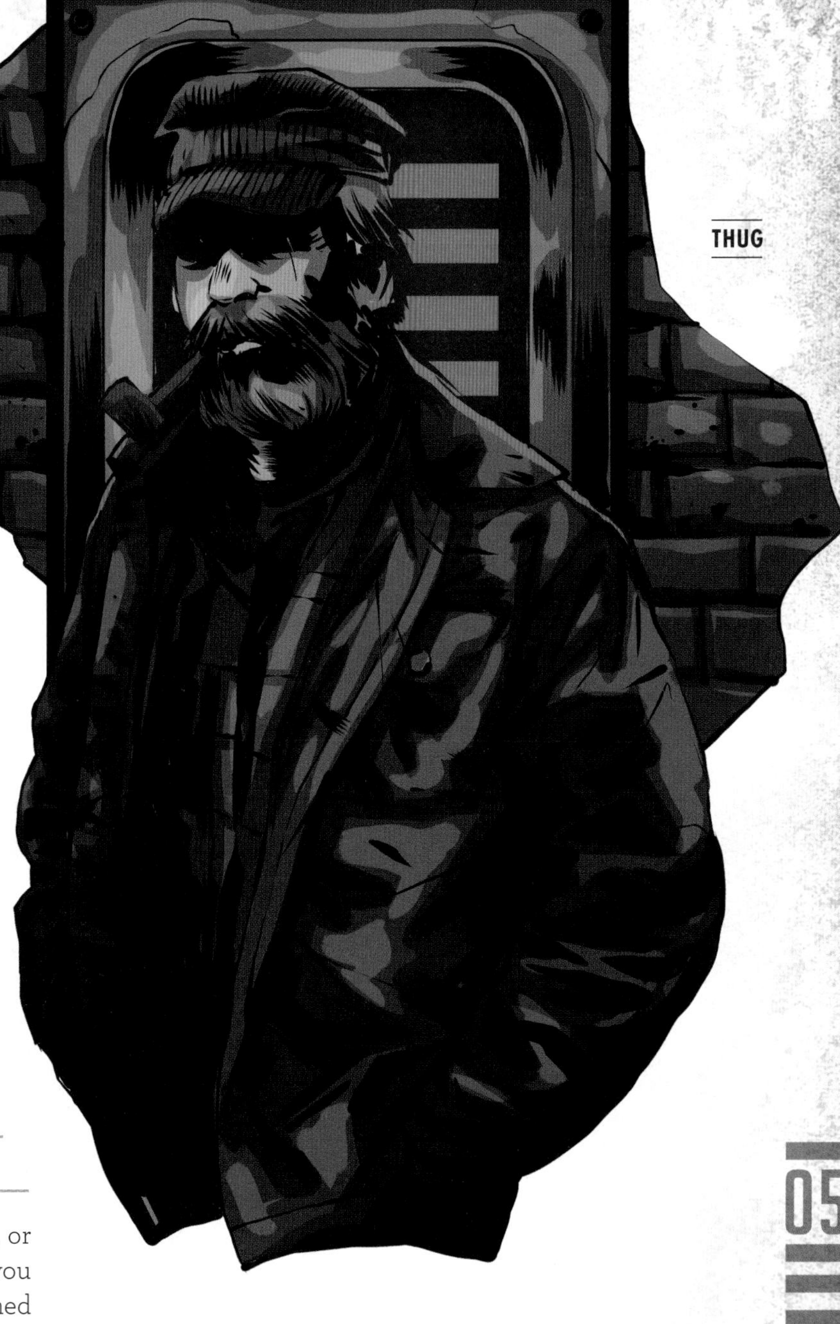

THUG

BUTLER

You have a faithful servant at your beck and call. For the most part. Sometimes the Butler utters a candid word or two, without you asking for it.

Effect: Your Butler is always available and can perform everyday tasks in your home. This does not cost any IP. However, for an expenditure of one IP, the servant can also help you out in the field with a single task. The servant has a rating of 3 in all attributes and level 3 in a skill of your choice.

CLUB OWNER

You are friends with the owner of a club, casino, or brothel within the enclave (or community if you play out in the Zone). This contact is well informed and knows almost everyone's dirty secrets.

Effect: Through this contact you can gain the upper hand on an NPC in the enclave/community. The more IP you spend, the better the dirt you dig up on the target. For every IP you spend, you get a +2 modification to Manipulate this NPC. The effect lasts until the secret becomes public knowledge – unless the target tries to silence you first.

DEADBEAT CHILD

You have an adult son or daughter who constantly disappoints you. He or she never succeeds in living up to your very reasonable expectations. To help you when needed is the least he/she can do.

Effect: When you spend one IP, your child comes immediately and helps you complete a dice roll for a general skill. The roll succeeds automatically.

DEAR UNCLE

Since you were a child, you have always been close to your uncle. All throughout your life, he has appeared in the most unexpected situations to save the day.

Effect: Your uncle comes to the rescue and saves you in the nick of time. You do not need to communicate with your uncle to activate this contact – surprisingly, he seems to always pop up just when he is needed the most. A rescue in the enclave/community costs one IP, while help outside in the Zone costs two IP. The GM can increase the cost further if whatever trouble you got into is particularly difficult. Note that your uncle will not solve your tasks for you, just save your skin for the moment.

FAITHFUL SPOUSE

You are married and have a spouse who brings you both joy and heartache. Life as a married person is not always easy. When life gets difficult, your spouse is a solid foundation that supports you.

Effect: When you spend a little time with your spouse (talking via link is not enough) you will immediately heal one point of trauma (of any kind) for each IP you spend. This has no effect on critical injuries.

FAVORITE CHILD

One of your children is your favorite, the light of your eyes, and can do no wrong.

Effect: The first time you activate this ability, you must choose which profession (or role, out in the Zone) your child has. For one IP, your child will immediately assist you on a roll using his or her special skill. The roll succeeds automatically.

FEARED FATHER

Your father is a prominent officer, rock-hard and infamous for his ruthlessness. The mere mention of his name can make anyone shudder in horror.

Effect: If you are going to Manipulate someone, you can first consult your father and ask him to apply some pressure on your behalf. The attempt then succeeds automatically without requiring a dice roll. This costs one IP. This effect can only be used on an NPCs living in the enclave or belonging to the same community as you (in the Zone).

GANGSTER

You have contacts in the underbelly of the enclave/community. You are a personal friend of a gangster boss who can provide anything for you – for a service in return.

Effect: By spending IP your criminal friends can get any item for you. A normal item available for purchase in the community costs one IP, a rare or expensive item costs two IP, and a specific and unique item costs three IP. The GM has the last word about what is possible. In exchange, the gangster requires an appropriate favor or service in return – the GM determines what this favor will entail.

GRANDFATHER'S TROVE

Your House has accumulated precious items for generations. Your old grandfather has made it his life's mission to safeguard this legacy.

Effect: Your grandfather can search for any object within the family's vaults. A normal item available for purchase in the enclave/community costs one IP, a rare or expensive item costs two IP, and a specific and unique item costs three IP. The GM has the last word about what is possible. You must return the item after you have used it – you cannot activate this contact again until you do so.

JUDGE

You have close ties with one of the four judges in the Tribunal (see page 105), which gives you the opportunity to trump up charges against specific victims.

Effect: By spending IP, you can have your contact make an accusation against a specific NPC. An accusation of a minor crime costs one IP. The cost increases to two or three IP for serious crimes. As a judicator, you have the right to impose the appropriate punishment. Out in the Zone, this contact can only be used when the Tribunal project has been completed.

LOAN SHARK

You are familiar with Elysium's underworld and have a contact that can always offer a loan when you are low on credit. But make sure you pay it back ...

Effect: Effect: For each IP you spend, you can get a loan of 2D6 credits. However, these must be repaid within D6 days. In addition, the loan shark charges an interest rate of 1 credit for every D6 borrowed. If you fail to pay back the full amount on time, you lose this contact and it becomes your enemy, as if you would have rolled a ☣ backlash on the table.

MENTOR

You have an old teacher who contributed a lot towards your personal and professional development. You often turn to your mentor for advice and support.

Effect: By talking with your mentor for a while, you get one extra XP for each IP you spend. You can use this contact when the XP is awarded at the end of the game session.

SNITCH

PARAMOUR

You have a secret romantic relationship with someone you should not. He or she is influential, has a large network of contacts, and wields extensive influence that you can use for your own pursuits – but the costs are great.

Effect: When you enable this contact, you can use any of the other available 19 contacts in the game. This is your lover's contact, not your own. However, the cost in IP is double the normal amount.

POWERFUL MOTHER

Your mother has great influence within the Council and can pull the right strings to help you in the enclave's political game.

Effect: You can enable this contact when designating who will be the patrol leader (see page 23) and when determining which incidents the patrol should be sent to investigate (see page 150). Each IP you spend gives you an extra point of Control on the vote for both.

Out in the Zone, this contact is used to implement projects (see *Mutant: Year Zero*). Each IP you spend immediately reduces the number of remaining Work Points by one. You can work on the same project yourself, but you can choose not to.

RICH AUNT

Your aunt has always been well off. She seems to have a credit stash for you whenever you are in a pinch.

Effect: For each IP you spend, you get D6 credits from your aunt. In a community in the Zone, the Currency project must be implemented before this contact can be used.

ROBOT SERVANT

You have a mechanical servant who obeys your every command but has the annoying inclination to always point out errors and flaws in your behavior.

Effect: Your robot servant is always available and can perform everyday tasks in your home. It does not cost any IP. The robot has Processor 2 and Network 2 (see *Mutant: Mechatron*), and one module (you decide which one). For one IP, the robot butler can also help you out in the field with a single task. If the robot is to use its module, you must spend additional IP – one IP for each Energy Point that the robot will use. This contact can only be used if you have access to the *Mutant: Mechatron* core book.

SNITCH

You have a friend in the underworld who has eyes on everything that happens in the enclave.

Effect: For one IP you can get information about an individual or event in the enclave/community, such as the location of a person or something they have done. If the information might put the informant at risk, the GM may raise the price to two or three IP. Note that this contact cannot be used to reveal which House is behind an Incident in the enclave.

THUG

You have contacts in the seedy underbelly of the enclave/community, something that can be very useful when a bit of extra muscle is needed.

Effect: For each IP you spend, one thug (stats as a robber, see page 127) or enforcer (out in the Zone) shows up, ready to help you during a roll or conflict. These contacts are handled as NPCs. How long it takes for help to arrive depends on the situation. The GM determines what is reasonable.

CONFLICT & TRAUMA

As resources dwindle inside Elysium I, distrust and hostility grow. As a judicator your first option should always be to seek out peaceful resolutions to conflicts. Sometimes however, you have no choice but to use force in order to maintain order. Whether it is with words or violence, a conflict arises when you clash with someone else.

TURNS & INITIATIVE

A conflict starts when you use the Fight or Shoot skills against someone – or when someone else does the same to you. Then it's time to roll initiative. Roll initiative before you make any skill rolls.

The Manipulate skill can also be used to initiate conflicts of a nonviolent kind, but these generally don't require an initiative roll – the one who initiates such a conflict simply rolls first. Then, if the conflict continues, roll initiative.

INITIATIVE ROLL

Each participant in the conflict, voluntary or not, rolls a D6. No skill is used, and you can't push the roll. The result is your initiative score.

The initiative scores determine the order in which you act. Break any ties using current Agility score. If it's still a tie, break it with any unmodified die roll.

THE TURN

When all combatants have acted, the turn is over, and a new turn starts. The order of initiative is set for the entire conflict – you only roll initiative on the first turn. Initiative scores can be modified during a conflict however, changing the turn order.

Time: In the game, a turn can represent between ten seconds and several minutes, depending on circumstances and the actions taken.

NPCs: The GM makes initiative rolls for all NPCs. For groups of NPCs with identical stats, the GM only needs to roll one initiative roll for the entire group. These NPCs act at the same point in the turn order. The order in which the NPCs within the group act is up to the GM.

INCREASING INITIATIVE

You never re-roll your initiative during a conflict, but you can boost your initiative in a number of ways:

- A surprise attack (see below) will increase it by +2. You keep this bonus throughout the combat.
- The Overdrive biomechatronical implant (page 140) lets you increase your initiative score.
- Stunts for some skills (Chapter 3) can also increase your initiative on upcoming turns.

DECREASING INITIATIVE

When it's your turn, you can, instead of acting, decrease your initiative to any lower number you like. You simply bide your time and hold your action. When it becomes your turn again, you can choose to act or wait further. If all other combatants have acted, you must then act or forfeit your chance do do anything during that turn.

A voluntarily decreased initiative score stays in effect for upcoming turns as well. You cannot go back to your previous initiative score. Some stunts for attacks can lower your enemy's initiative score. More on that below.

EXAMPLE

In an unexpected moment, the gang leader Nutty Nadia attacks the judicator Pandora. They roll for initiative. Pandora rolls a 4, Nadia a 3. Because it is a surprise attack, Nadia gets a +2 bonus to her initiative for a total score of 5. The gang leader acts first.

ACTIONS & MANEUVERS

During your turn, you can perform one action and one maneuver, or two maneuvers. An action usually means that you roll for a skill, but some actions don't require a roll. Maneuvers always succeed automatically. Some examples of a maneuver are:

- Move one range step
- Seek cover
- Get up from the ground
- Get an item from your gear
- Pick up an item from the ground
- Draw a weapon (not needed for mounted weapons)
- Aim a ranged weapon
- Reload a weapon
- Assume an overwatch position
- Use an item

HELPING

Helping another PC or NPC (see page 45) will replace your own action for that round. However, you can still perform a maneuver while helping someone else.

NPC GROUP ROLLS

NPC groups that are working together can attack as a single unit, making one adjusted roll instead of making multiple rolls. This works the same as getting help from others (see page 45). Anyone who helps gives a +1 modification to the attack. This makes the encounter easier and quicker to handle for the GM.

BIOMECHATRONIC

Biomechatronic implants usually have reinforcing or reactive effects and require no action or maneuver to activate. Any exceptions to this rule are specified under entry for the respective implant. Read more in Chapter 9.

IN A TURN YOU CAN:

- Perform an action and a maneuver

...or...

- Perform two maneuvers

RANGE & MOVEMENT

During conflicts, the distance between you and the enemy is expressed in five range categories:

- **Arm's Length:** Right next to each other, within reach
- **Near:** A few steps away
- **Short:** Up to 20–30 yards
- **Long:** Up to a few hundred meters
- **Distant:** As far as you can see

ADVANCING & RETREATING

To move towards or away from an enemy, you use maneuvers. As long as you go no further than a Short distance (20–30 yards), moving one range category requires one maneuver. To move more than a Short distance, you need two maneuvers in direct succession in the same turn to move one range category – meaning you can't perform an action in the same turn.

Some artifacts and biomechatronic implants can make you move faster than normal.

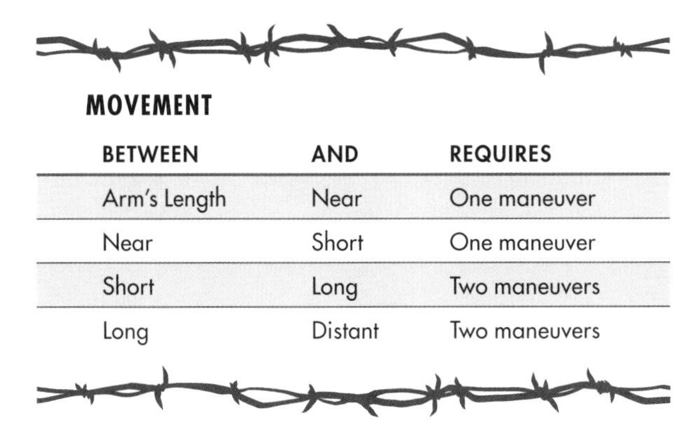

MOVEMENT

BETWEEN	AND	REQUIRES
Arm's Length	Near	One maneuver
Near	Short	One maneuver
Short	Long	Two maneuvers
Long	Distant	Two maneuvers

FLEEING A CONFLICT

When a fight is not going your way, it may be better to retreat, and perhaps return later with reinforcements. If you want to get out of a conflict, roll for the Move skill – a successful roll means you find a way out, and the conflict ends. However, if you flee you must go back the way you came – you can't use this option to get around an enemy blocking your way forward.

The GM can modify your roll depending on how hard the environment is to hide in. The distance to your closest enemy also matters – see the table below.

FLEEING A CONFLICT

DISTANCE	MODIFICATION
Arm's Length	–2
Near	–1
Short	±0
Long	+1
Distant	No roll needed

Note that you only need one successful roll to get out of harm's way and leave the conflict. Also note that you don't need to roll at all if you are at Distant range.

If your roll fails it means that you are pinned down and unable to get away for the moment – you remain at the same range. The GM can let some other misfortune happen to you as well. You can try to flee again next turn.

EXAMPLE

Nutty Nadia tries to escape from Pandora. She has no skill level in Move, but Agility 5. She is at Arm's Length (-2 modification) and thus gets only 3 Base Dice (5 - 2). She rolls them, but does not get any ☢ and is unable to escape from Pandora's reach.

OTHER TYPES OF MOVEMENT

There are, of course, other types of movement in conflict besides advancing, retreating and fleeing. For these, the GM assesses the situation and what you are trying to accomplish. To run a short distance to seek cover, for example, only requires a maneuver. If the movement is harder to complete, like lunging through a bunker gate that is about to close, you'll need a Move roll to succeed.

AMBUSHES & SNEAK ATTACKS

The key to winning a conflict is often to attack when your enemy least expects it. You can achieve this advantage in several ways.

Surprise: If you attack in a way that the GM deems likely to surprise your enemy, you get to add +2 to your initiative roll.

Sneak Attack: When you stalk someone and your attack catches them unawares, it's called a sneak attack. First, roll an opposed roll for Sneak vs Scout (page 46). You get a modification according to how close you are to your target, see the table below. To attack in close combat, you'll most often need to get within Arm's Length. If you fail, your target spots you at your starting distance – roll initiative. If you succeed, you get a free action (but not a maneuver) before you roll initiative.

If several people attempt to sneak attack together, all must make separate rolls for the sneak attack to work. If anyone fails, the attackers are spotted.

Ambush: A special kind of sneak attack is the ambush – you hide and attack your enemy when he passes. When you ambush someone roll to Sneak, but instead of the roll being modified by the distance to your target, you automatically get a +2 modification because you are lying in wait while the enemy approaches.

SNEAK ATTACK

DISTANCE	MODIFICATION
Arm's Length	–2
Near	–1
Short	±0
Long	+1
Distant	+2

SOCIAL CONFLICTS

During conflicts without physical violence, roll for the Manipulate skill (see page 50). Procurators can also roll for Prosecute. Make an opposed roll against your opponent's Sense Emotion. Both you and your opponent roll dice, but it only counts as an action for you.

Whatever you wish to obtain from the other person must be reasonable. The GM has final say as to what lies within reason, but remember, NPCs will never act entirely against their own interests, no matter how successful the roll.

BARGAINING POSITION

To be able to Manipulate someone, you need:

- A subject that can hear or otherwise understand you.
- An offer that isn't completely unreasonable.

If the GM thinks both of these conditions are met, she will determine your bargaining position and give you a modification based on it.

Each of the following factors give you a +1 modification:

- You have more people on your side.
- What you ask for doesn't cost your opponent anything.
- The opponent has suffered trauma.
- You have helped your opponent earlier.
- You plead your case very well (GM's judgement).

Each of the following factors give you a -1 modification:

- Your opponent has more people on his side.
- What you ask for is valuable, or dangerous.
- Your opponent has nothing to gain by helping you.
- You have difficulties understanding each other.
- The range between you is Short or longer.

REPUTATION

Your ability to Manipulate is also affected by your Reputation, as well as that of your opponent. If your Reputation is higher, you'll gain a +1 modification. If your Reputation is twice as high or more, you get a +2 modification. If your Reputation score is lower, you get a -1 modification. If your opponent's Reputation is twice that of yours or more, you get a -2 modification.

Note that Reputation only comes into play when you Manipulate someone living in the same community as you.

GROUPS IN SOCIAL CONFLICTS

When you want to Manipulate a group of people, it is normally the group's leader or spokesperson that you will make your skill roll against. Remember that you get a -1 modification if he has more people behind him. If you push the leader in your preferred direction, the other NPCs will generally follow. If there is no clear leader in a group of NPCs, you'll need to Manipulate them separately.

GEAR

Some gear – most often artifacts – can provide a Gear Bonus to your attempts to Manipulate.

EXAMPLE

The judicator Pandora tries to persuade Nadia to surrender. Pandora has no skill level in Manipulate, but her Empathy is 3. Nadia has level 5 in Sense Emotion and Empathy 4. No easy feat! However, Pandora gets a +2 bonus, as she has a Reputation of 4 against the gang leader's 2.

EFFECTS

When you successfully Manipulate someone this usually means that they do what you want – but only if you give them something in return. They decide what it is they want, but it must be something that you can reasonably accomplish. It is up to you whether to accept the deal or not.

Stunts: Extra ☢ on your roll mean you sow fear or doubt in your opponent's heart. He suffers one point of doubt for every additional ☢ you roll beyond the first one. If he is broken by doubt, he does what you want without demanding a favor in return.

CLOSE COMBAT

When you attack in close combat you roll for the Fight skill. Melee usually occurs at Arm's Length. You can attack from Near range with certain weapons. The opponent decides whether to give up his own action to defend himself (see below) or risk taking the hit so he can take an action during his turn.

Stance: To be able to attack an opponent in close combat, you must be standing up. If you are prone, you must first use a maneuver to get up before you can attack.

EFFECTS

When your Fight roll succeeds the enemy takes weapon damage. For each extra ☢ you roll in addition to the first you may choose one of the following bonus effects:

- You inflict one additional point of damage. You can select this effect multiple times.
- You subdue or tire your enemy. He suffers one point of fatigue (see page 76).
- You increase your initiative score by 2 (see page 67), starting next turn.
- You knock or pull a weapon or other object from your opponent's grasp. You choose which. During a conflict, picking up a dropped object counts as a maneuver (see page 68).
- Your opponent falls to the ground or is pushed back, for example through a doorway or down a shaft.
- You hold the opponent in a grapple. He needs to successfully Fight you to break free and can't perform any other action (or maneuver) until he has done so – or until you are Broken or let him go.

DEFENSE

When someone Fights you, you can try to defend yourself. When you defend, you also roll for Fight. Roll your dice at the same time as the attacker. For each ☢ you roll, choose one stunt:

- You eliminate one ☢ rolled by the attacker. If he has no ☢ left, his attack has no effect.
- You increase your initiative score by 2 (see page 67), starting next turn.
- You knock or pull a weapon or other object from your opponent's grasp.
- Your opponent falls to the ground or is pushed back, for example through a doorway or down a shaft.
- You tire your enemy, inflicting 1 point of fatigue.
- You counter-attack against your enemy and inflict weapon damage. You cannot increase this damage by using several ☢.

Note that you can choose to make a counter-attack instead of stopping your opponent's attack. That means you may hit each other simultaneously.

Limitations: There are several limitations to the defense move:

- You must declare that you are defending before the attacker rolls his dice. If he misses anyway, your defense is wasted.
- If you defend, you lose your next action – in this turn if you haven't acted yet, otherwise in the next turn. You keep your maneuver.
- You can only defend yourself against one attack per turn.
- If the attacker uses a close combat weapon of some kind but you don't, you get a -2 modification to your defense roll.

EXAMPLE

The gang leader Nutty Nadia attacks the judicator Pandora in close combat. Nutty Nadja has Strength 4 and skill level 5 in Fight, for a total of nine dice despite being unarmed. Pandora chooses to defend. She has Strength 3 and level 2 in Fight, but she is also armed with a stun baton that grants a +2 Gear Bonus. Pandora rolls seven dice in total. She's lucky enough to roll two ☢ while Nadia rolls only one. Pandora uses one ☢ to stop the gang leader's attack and the other to counterattack with the stun baton.

GRAPPLING

As a stunt when you Fight someone, you can choose to grapple him. To break loose, your opponent needs to win an opposed Fight roll against you. This roll counts as an action for your opponent but not for you. While pinned, your opponent can perform no other action requiring physical movement.

Grapple Attack: While grappling someone, the only physical action you can perform is a grapple attack. This counts as a close combat attack, with these differences:

- You can't use a weapon.
- You get a +2 modification.
- Your enemy cannot defend against the attack.

GYROJET CARBINE

RANGED COMBAT

When you attack someone at a distance you roll for the Shoot skill. You'll need a ranged weapon of some kind. The table on page 75 indicates the maximum range at which the weapon can be used.

Cover: You can't defend against ranged attacks. Instead, you can seek cover (page 77) to avoid harm.

MODIFICATION

The farther away your target is, the harder it is to hit. At Short range you get a -1 modification, and at Long range you get -2. At Arm's Length you get -3, because it's hard to aim at an enemy in close combat. This -3 modification does not apply if you fire at a defenseless or unwitting enemy.

RANGE MODIFICATION

DISTANCE	MODIFICATION
Arm's Length	–3*
Near	±0
Short	–1
Long	–2
Distant	–3†

* Does not apply for defenseless enemies.
† Requires aiming.

AIMING

Before you Shoot you can spend one maneuver to aim carefully. That gives you a +1 modification. If you also have some solid piece of cover to lean on, the modification increases to +2. You must aim and fire in the same turn – you cannot save the bonus for a later turn.

EFFECTS

When your Shoot roll succeeds, the opponent is hit and suffers weapon damage. For each extra ☢ you roll after the first you can choose one stunt:

- You inflict one more point of damage. You can choose this stunt multiple times, if you roll several extra ☢.
- You pin down your enemy. He suffers one point of fatigue.
- You increase your initiative score by 2, starting next turn.
- Your target drops a weapon or another handheld object. You choose which.
- Your opponent falls to the ground or is pushed back, for example through a doorway or down a shaft.

AMMUNITION & RELOADING

Depending on the weapon type, firearms must be loaded with either bullets, gyrojet rockets, or E-packs. The ammunition type will determine when each weapon needs to be reloaded. Reloading a weapon requires a maneuver.

Bullet Weapons: Scrap weapons and simple firearms like revolvers must be loaded with bullets. Each time you fire the weapon, one bullet is consumed.

Scrap weapons must be reloaded after each shot. Weapons that use magazines can be fired several times before they need to be reloaded. To minimize book keeping, simply assume that magazines will last the entire conflict as long as you have bullets left.

For the sake of simplicity, no distinction is made between different types of bullets. You can read more about this in *Mutant: Year Zero.*

Gyrojet Weapons are loaded with small gyrojet rockets, which are rare and expensive. Each time you fire the weapon, one rocket is consumed. Some gyrojet weapons have magazines and don't need be reloaded after each shot. The magazine is assumed to last for the whole combat, as long as you have gyrojet rockets left.

Energy Weapons are powered by electricity. Gauss weapons fall in this category – they hold hundreds of very small projectiles, but it is the energy required to fire them that is the limiting factor.

Energy weapons are charged with E-packs (artifact, see page 135). A weapon loaded with an E-pack can be fired multiple times – but if all rolled Gear Dice show ✸ (on the initial roll, not after pushing the roll), the E-pack is exhausted. If this happens the attack then has no effect, and the weapon cannot be fired again until you load it with a new E-pack.

EXAMPLE

Nutty Nadia acts first in the next round and moves a to Short range from Pandora. The judicator draws her gauss pistol (one maneuver) and shoots (one action). Pandora has skill level 2 in Shoot and

Agility 5. The gauss pistol gives a +2 Gear Bonus. The Short distance gives a -1 modification. Pandora rolls a total of eight dice (five from the attribute, two from the skill, two from the weapon, minus one for the distance).

GAUSS RIFLE

OVERWATCH

As a maneuver, you can assume an overwatch position in a specified direction, as long as you have a ranged weapon and no enemies within Arm's Length.

Effect: Overwatch means that you aim in the specified direction and are ready to shoot. Between the time you assume the overwatch position and the beginning of you next turn, you can fire your weapon against a target in the chosen direction.

You can fire whenever you want in the turn order, and your shot is resolved before all other actions - even if they are already declared. For example, if an enemy in the direction you are aiming declares that he wants to Shoot, you can Shoot first. The enemy is not allowed to change his attack after your overwatch attack.

Firing when in overwatch position counts as a regular action. Therefore, you must save your action in the turn for any overwatch attack you want to make.

If both you and an enemy assume overwatch positions against each other, and one of you chooses to fire against the other, then an opposed Shoot roll (without any Gear Bonus) will determine which attack goes first. This roll does not count as an action for either of you.

Losing Overwatch: You keep your overwatch position as long as you do nothing but shoot in the chosen direction. If you perform any other action or maneuver, the overwatch position is lost. It is also immediately lost if either of the following occurs:

- You are attacked in close combat.
- You suffer damage.

FULL-AUTO FIRE

Some weapons may fire in full-auto mode. When firing in full-auto, roll for Shoot as usual. The difference is that you can push the Shoot roll as many times as you want. As usual, you risk fatigue and damage to your weapon (see page 44).

Ammunition: For weapons loaded with bullets or gyrojet rockets, one bullet/rocket is spent each time you push the roll.

CLOSE COMBAT WEAPONS

WEAPON	BONUS	DAMAGE	RANGE	COST	COMMENT
Unarmed	–	1	Arm's Length	–	
Blunt Instrument	+1	1	Arm's Length	–	
Stun Baton	+2	1	Arm's Length	2	Inflicts D6 fatigue. Energy weapon.
Stun Whip	+1	1	Near	3	Inflicts D6 fatigue. Energy weapon.
Laser Welder	+2	2	Arm's Length	2	Light weapon. Energy weapon.
Vibro Knife	+2	2	Arm's Length	3	Light weapon. Energy weapon. Reduces armor value by 3.
Combat Saw	+2	3	Arm's Length	4	Energy weapon.
Saber	+2	2	Arm's Length	2	

Multiple Targets: When firing on full-auto, you can add targets for each roll you push. The first ☢ you roll for a new target will deal weapon damage to that target. Additional ☢ on the same target each increase the damage by one.

PCs from House Fortescue may reroll a ☣ only once, even when firing on full-auto. After the first pushed roll, even a Fortescue leaves ☣ dice on the table. Read more about predispositions on page 42.

WEAPONS

Weapons increase your effectiveness in combat and are needed for ranged combat. Below you will find lists of weapons that can be found in the enclave.

ADVANCED WEAPONS

Judicators usually use gauss weapons, which generate strong magnetic fields that hurl tiny projectiles at devastating speeds. The gauss weapons were developed by Elysium during the Enclave Wars, when their armor-piercing properties were used to great effect against the robot armies of enemy Titan Powers.

Other types of advanced weapons, such as gyrojet and ultrasonic weapons, are more rare and used mainly by the Deep Watch, the military force of the enclave.

All advanced weapons are described in more detail in the artifacts section of Chapter 9.

GAUSS PISTOL

SCRAP WEAPONS

Gang members and other criminals in the enclave often use simple scrap weapons, which are secretly manufactured and are prohibited by Elysium law.

RANGED WEAPONS

WEAPON	BONUS	DAMAGE	RANGE	COST	COMMENT
Thrown Object	–	1	Short	–	
Scrap Pistol	+1	2	Short	1	Light weapon.
Scrap Rifle	+1	2	Long	1	
Scrap Thrower	+1	2	Short	3	Full-auto.
Stun Gun	+2	2	Short	3	Light weapon. Energy weapon. Deals fatigue instead of damage.
Gauss Pistol	+2	2	Long	3	Light weapon. Requires E-pack. Ignores 3 points of armor.
Gauss Rifle	+2	2	Distant	5	Requires E-pack. Ignores 3 points of armor.
Gauss Carbine	+2	2	Long	6	Full-auto. Requires E-pack. Ignores 3 points of armor.
Gyrojet Pistol	+3	3	Short	4	Requires gyrojet rockets. Ignores range penalties. Weapon damage of 1 within Near range.
Gyrojet Carbine	+3	3	Long	6	Requires gyrojet rockets. Full-auto. Ignores range penalties. Weapon damage of 1 within Near range.
Ultrasonic Carbine	+2	2	Short	7	Deals both damage and fatigue. Armor does not offer protection against the fatigue.

WEAPON FEATURES

Below are tables describing specific weapons and their features.

Bonus: Bonus indicates how many Gear Dice you roll when using the weapon. Remember that the Gear Bonus can be degraded if you push your roll – the bonus will decrease by one for each ✹ rolled when pushing (see page 44). If the Gear Bonus reaches zero, the weapon is broken and must be repaired by a Technician.

Damage indicates how much damage the enemy will take if you succeed with your attack. For every additional ☢ rolled, you can increase the damage by one.

Range indicates the maximum range category at which the weapon can be used.

Light Weapons only take up half an inventory line on your character sheet.

Automatic Weapons: Weapons with this feature can fire on full-auto mode.

Armor Piercing: Gauss weapons are effective against armor. When rolling for armor hit by a gauss weapon, the Armor Rating is counted as three steps lower than normal.

TRAUMA

There are four types of trauma in the game. Each type will decrease one of your four attributes. You indicate trauma that you suffer by using the checkboxes on your character sheet.

Damage: Bruises, bleeding wounds and broken bones. Decreases your Strength.

Fatigue: Physical exhaustion, sweating and panting. Decreases your Agility.

Confusion: Lack of clarity, bewilderment and misjudgment. Decreases your Wits.

Doubt: Lack of confidence, distrust, disappointment and sadness. Decreases your Empathy.

SUFFERING TRAUMA

You can suffer trauma in several different ways:

- **From external attacks.** When someone successfully Fights you or Shoots at you, you suffer damage equal to the weapon damage – more if the attacker gets stunts and spends them on increasing the damage. You can suffer doubt when someone Manipulates you.
- **By getting** ☣ when you push a roll. If this happens you suffer one point of trauma for each ☣ rolled. The kind of trauma depends on the attribute you were rolling for – damage when rolling for Strength, fatigue for Agility, confusion for Wits, and doubt for Empathy.
- **From exposure to the Rot** (see page 85), from dehydration, starvation and extreme cold (page 81) and from explosions (page 82).

ARMOR & SHIELDS

The effect of armor is determined by its Armor Rating. You can only wear one piece of armor at a time. When you suffer damage, roll a number of Gear Dice equal to the Armor Rating. For each ☢ you

ARMOR & SHIELDS

TYPE	ARMOR RATING	COST	COMMENT
Scrap Armor	3	1	
Reconnaissance Armor	6	12	Also protects against Zone Rot. Provides ability to fly. Requires special fuel.
Combat Armor	9	5	Also protects against Zone Rot.
Energy Armor	12	15	Also protects against Zone Rot. Gives a Gear Bonus of +3 to Force, Fight, and Move. Requires an E-pack.
Riot Shield	6	2	

roll, the damage is reduced by one. This roll is not an action and cannot be pushed.

Unless all damage is absorbed by the armor, each you roll degrades the Armor Rating by one. Armor can be repaired by a Technician.

Armor does not protect against any trauma you inflict on yourself while pushing a roll.

Shields work just like armor. You can carry a shield and wear armor at the same time. When you are hit, first roll for the shield's Armor Rating, then the armor.

COVER

When you get into a firefight, finding adequate cover may save your life. Taking cover counts as a maneuver. Cover has an Armor Rating and works exactly like armor, but only protects against ranged attacks.

Cover can be degraded in the same way as armor. Cover can be combined with armor and/or a shield – first roll for the cover, then the shield, and finally, the armor.

Aiming: Cover can also be useful to rest your arms on when Shooting. The bonus for aiming carefully (see page 73) increases to +2 when firing from cover.

TYPICAL COVER

COVER TYPE	ARMOR RATING
Furniture	3
Wooden Door	4
Metal Door	5
Brick Wall	6
Concrete Wall	7

BROKEN

When an attribute score hits zero, you are broken. You've had enough and lack the will or ability to keep going. Exactly what it means to be broken depends on what attribute has been depleted.

Strength: You are knocked out, or in paralyzing pain. Being broken by damage is much more dangerous than by other types of trauma, because it also means you suffer a critical injury (below).

Agility: You are physically exhausted.

Wits: Your brain is overloaded and you can't think straight.

Empathy: You break down in fear, self-pity or sorrow.

EFFECT

When broken, you cannot use any skills, perform actions or activate mutations (not even reactive ones). You can, however, perform one maneuver per turn (see page 68).

BROKEN NPCS

NPCs are broken in the same way as PCs. An NPC can Heal a PC, and vice versa. However, the GM doesn't roll dice when an NPC Heals another NPC – instead, she simply dictates the outcome. The GM can also rule that a minor NPC who is broken by damage is simply killed outright.

COUP DE GRACE

When broken, you are an easy target. An enemy can attempt to perform a coup de grace and kill you outright. To do this, he only needs to make a Fight or Shoot roll. As long as he rolls at least one ☢, you are dead. Conversely, you can finish off broken enemies in the same way.

GYROJET PISTOL

CRITICAL INJURIES TABLE

D66	INJURY	LETHAL	TIME LIMIT	EFFECT DURING HEALING	HEALING TIME
11	Lost Breath	No	–	None.	–
12	Stunned	No	–	None.	–
13	Sprained Wrist	No	–	–1 to Shoot and Fight.	D6
14	Sprained Ankle	No	–	–1 to Move and Sneak.	D6
15	Concussion	No	–	–1 to Scout and Comprehend.	D6
16	Damaged Shin	No	–	–1 to Move and Sneak.	2D6
21	Broken Nose	No	–	–1 to Manipulate.	2D6
22	Broken Fingers	No	–	–1 to Shoot and Fight.	2D6
23	Broken Toes	No	–	–1 to Move and Sneak.	2D6
24	Teeth Knocked Out	No	–	–1 to Manipulate, +1 Intimidate.	2D6
25	Groin Hit	No	–	You suffer one point of damage for every roll you make to Force, Move or Fight.	2D6
26	Thigh Wound	No	–	–2 to Move and Sneak.	2D6
31	Biceps Wound	No	–	–2 to Shoot and Fight.	2D6
32	Severed Achilles Tendon	No	–	–2 to Move and Sneak.	2D6
33	Dislocated Shoulder	No	–	–3 to Force and Fight, can not use two-handed weapons.	D6
34	Broken Ribs	No	–	–2 to Move and Fight.	2D6
35	Broken Forearm	No	–	Can not use two-handed weapons.	3D6
36	Broken Leg	No	–	–2 to Move and Sneak.	3D6
41	Ear Torn Off	No	–	–1 to Scout.	3D6
42	Gouged Eye	No	–	–2 to Shoot and Scout.	3D6
43	Punctured Lung	Yes	D6 days	–2 to Endure and Move.	2D6
44	Damaged Kidney	Yes	D6 days	You suffer one point of damage for every roll you make to Force, Move or Fight.	3D6
45	Crushed Knee	Yes	D6 days	–2 to Move and Sneak.	4D6
46	Crushed Elbow	Yes	D6 days	–2 to Force and Fight, can not use two-handed weapons.	4D6
51	Crushed Foot	Yes	D6 days	–3 to Move and Sneak.	4D6
52	Bleeding Gut	Yes	D6 hours	You suffer one point of damage for every roll you make to Force, Move or Fight.	D6
53	Crushed Face	Yes	D6 hours	–2 to Manipulate.	4D6
54	Busted Intestine	Yes	D6 hours	You suffer one Rot Point per hour until Healed.	2D6
55	Damaged Spine	No	–	Paralyzed from the waist down. Effect is permanent unless Healed during healing time.	4D6
56	Neck Injury	No	–	Paralyzed from the neck down. Effect is permanent unless Healed during healing time.	4D6
61	Internal Bleeding	Yes, –1	D6 minutes	You suffer one point of damage for every roll you make to Force, Move or Fight.	2D6
62	Severed Arm Artery	Yes, –1	D6 minutes	–1 to Endure and Move.	D6
63	Severed Leg Artery	Yes, –1	D6 minutes	–1 to Endure and Move.	D6
64	Severed Jugular	Yes, –1	D6 turns	–1 to Endure and Move.	D6
65	Pierced Heart	Yes	–	Your heart beats one last time, then you die. Time to make a new PC.	–
66	Crushed Skull	Yes	–	You die instantly.	–
–	Non-Typical Damage	Yes	D6 days	You are incapacitated until you die or you are Healed.	–
–	Pushed Roll Damage	No	–	None.	–

CRITICAL INJURIES

Being broken is always bad but being broken by damage is especially dangerous – it can mean your death.

Before you are broken, damage points represent bruises and minor cuts. Painful, but quickly recovered (below). But when your Strength falls to zero, you suffer a critical injury. Roll D66 on the table to the left to determine what your critical injury is. Note it on your character sheet.

DEATH

If your critical injury is listed as lethal, someone must make a successful Heal roll to save you – otherwise you die when the time period indicated has passed. If you get back up on your own (below) before you die, you can try to Heal yourself – but with a -2 modification to the roll. Each person trying to Heal you can only roll once.

Instant Kill: Note that there are two critical injuries that kill you outright. If you roll either of these, that's it. Time to create a new judicator to join the ranks.

RECOVERY

The fastest way to recover from being broken is for someone else to successfully Heal you.

In most cases though, you don't need to be Healed to get back on your feet. As long as you're not dehydrated, starving or hypothermic (below), you recover after D6 hours even if no one Heals you. You get back one point of the relevant attribute score, and you can keep going.

Once back on your feet, you can recover the rest of your trauma with the help of resources (below).

Critical Injuries: If you are broken by damage and have suffered a critical injury (above), you might die unless someone Heals you in time. Read more below.

RESTORING ATTRIBUTE POINTS

To recover trauma and restore lost attribute points, two things are needed:

- At least four hours of rest.
- A resource that is determined by the type of trauma.

When these conditions are met, you restore lost attribute points of the relevant type. You can even recover multiple types of trauma simultaneously, as long as you have access to the resources needed:

Strength: A ration of food per point of Strength to be restored.

Agility: A ration of water per point of Agility to be restored.

Wits: At least four hours of sleep. Restores all lost Wits.

Empathy: A moment of closeness with another person. It could be a deep conversation, a trip to the theater with someone, enjoying a good dinner together, or physical contact. Restores all lost Empathy.
The resources needed for recovery are in addition to your daily needs of food, water and sleep (below).

HEALING CRITICAL INJURIES

Each critical injury has a specific effect that you suffer during the healing time indicated (measured in days).

Care: If someone rolls to Heal you during the process of healing a critical injury, the remaining healing time is reduced by half. Any roll to save your

FOOD & WATER IN THE ENCLAVE

As members of a powerful House in Elysium, your basic physical needs are taken care of. Food and water are usually available to you – so far. When you are inside the enclave, you don't need to worry about tracking rations of food and water, simply assume you have what you need. In extraordinary conditions, lack of food and water can become a factor.

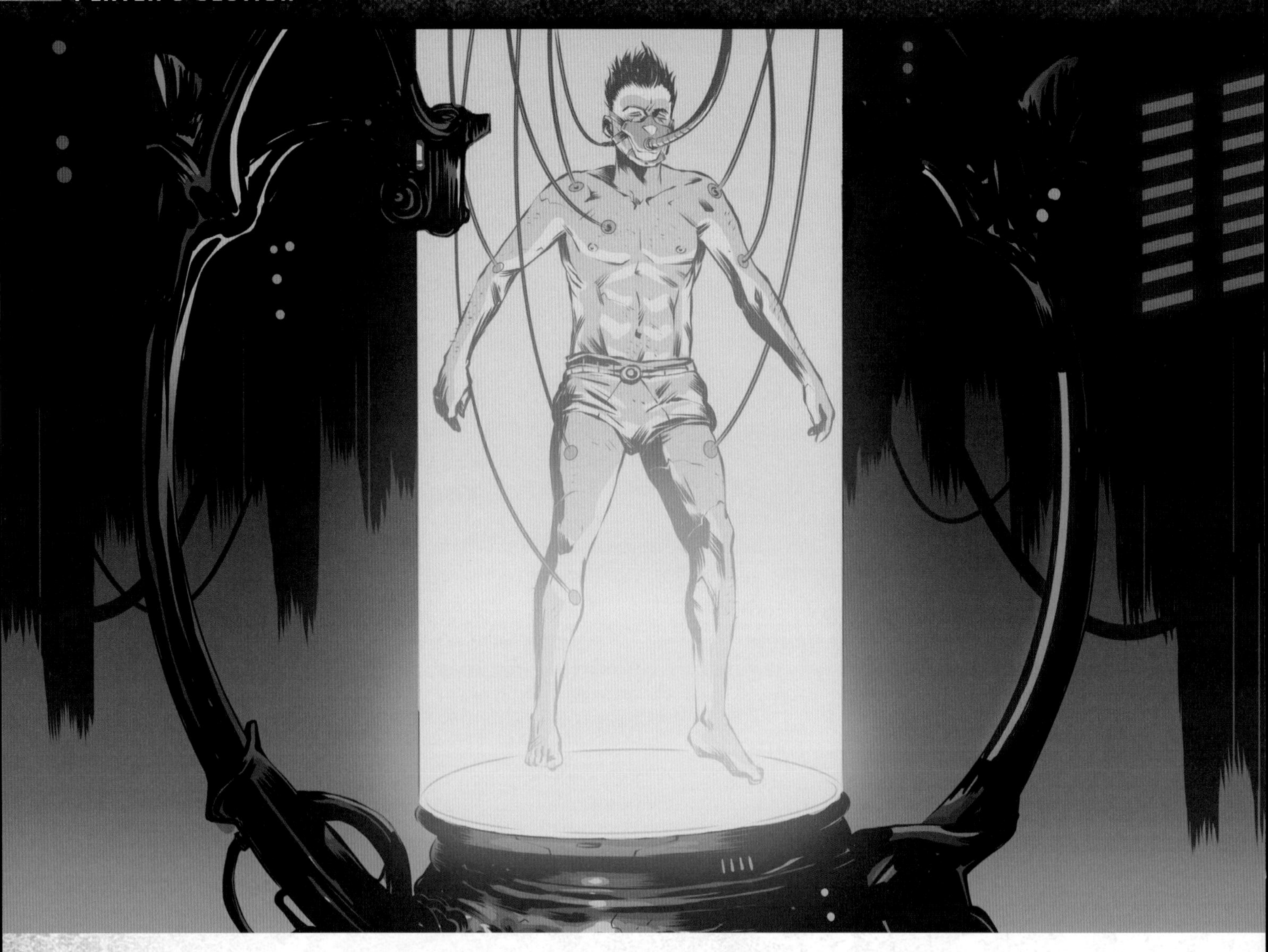

life (above) does not count toward this – a new Heal roll needs to be made to reduce the healing time.

Trauma: Note that you can restore all of your Strength (all damage points are recovered) but still suffer the effect of your critical injury.

NON-TYPICAL DAMAGE

For some types of damage – for example from noxious gas, acid, or fire – the critical damage table doesn't work very well. If you are broken by a non-typical kind of damage like this, don't roll on the table – instead, use the line at the bottom named "Non-Typical Damage."

PUSHED DAMAGE

There is one case where you don't suffer any critical injury at all when broken by damage: When you push a Strength roll so hard that you break yourself (see page 42). It's very rare, but it can happen. This means you can never kill yourself by pushing a dice roll.

CONDITIONS

In the game there are four conditions: starving, dehydrated, sleepless and hypothermic. These conditions can cause trauma and block recovery.

STARVING

Every day, you must eat at least one ration of food, on top of what is needed to recover lost Strength (above). After one day with no food, you are starving. Note this in the checkbox on your character sheet. Starving has several effects:

- You cannot recover damage (restore Strength) in any way. If broken by damage, you need to eat some food before you can get back on your feet. You can recover other types of trauma.
- You suffer one more point of damage per day without food. If broken by damage while starving you will die after another day has passed, unless you are given food.
- As soon as you have eaten one ration of food, you are no longer starving, and can recover normally. To recover all damage (above) you need to consume another ration of food.

DEHYDRATED

Every day, you must drink at least one ration of water, on top of what is needed to recover lost Agility (above). After one day with no water you are dehydrated. Note this in the checkbox on your character sheet. Being dehydrated has several effects:

- You cannot recover any type of trauma. If broken, you need to drink some water before you can get back on your feet.
- You suffer one point of damage and one point of fatigue per day without water. If broken by trauma (of any type) while dehydrated, you will die after another day has passed.
- As soon as you have imbibed one ration of water, you are no longer dehydrated, and can recover normally. To recover all fatigue, you need to consume another ration of water.

SLEEPLESS

Every day, you must get at least four hours of continuous sleep. After one day without enough sleep, you become sleepless. Note this in the checkbox on your character sheet. Being sleepless has several effects:

- You cannot recover confusion (restore Wits) in any way. If broken by confusion, you need to sleep for four hours or more before you can get back on your feet. You can recover other types of trauma.
- You suffer one more point of confusion per day without sleep. If broken by confusion while sleepless you will collapse and fall unconscious for four hours or more.
- As soon as you sleep for at least four hours, you are no longer sleepless, and can recover Wits normally. To recover all confusion, you need to sleep another four hours.

HYPOTHERMIC

You are usually protected from severe cold within the enclave, but in the outer world, the cold can be a threat as deadly as the Rot. It doesn't have to be a frozen atomic winter either – if you're poorly dressed for the weather, the cold can take your life even when wandering around in above-freezing temperatures.

When you are exposed to a cold environment, the GM can have you make Endure rolls at regular intervals. The colder it is, the more often you must roll. Around the freezing point, once per day or so is enough – in the deep atomic winter, you might need to roll every hour. Things that keep you warm, like an old blanket or a jacket, can give you Gear Dice to use.

If the roll fails, you become hypothermic. This has several consequences:

- You immediately suffer one point of damage and one point of confusion – the cold makes the blood flow more slowly to your brain.
- You may experience strange hallucinations – the details are up to the GM. It is said that someone who is freezing to death will experience a burning heat, making them tear their clothes off in the final moments before dying.
- You keep rolling to Endure at the same intervals, with the same effect if you fail a roll. If broken by damage when hypothermic, you die the next time you are called upon to roll.
- As long as you are hypothermic, you cannot recover Strength or Wits. It is only once you are warm again, even if heated by just a simple campfire, that you can sleep and eat to recover them.

DARKNESS

When you are in complete darkness, and you don't have any gear or mutations to light your path, you have no choice but to feel your way around. To make your way through the darkness, you need to make a Move roll. As a general rule, you suffer one point of damage or doubt (the darkness is frightening) if you fail the roll.

In total darkness you can attack targets at Arm's Length or Near range normally, but first need to make a Scout roll to get a good look at them. That roll does not count as an action in conflicts – you can Scout and attack in the same turn. You can't Shoot targets at Short range or further in total darkness.

FALLING

Falling on a hard surface from a height of more than two yards can cause damage. To determine how much, roll as many Base Dice as the height of the fall (in yards) minus two. Each ☢ will translate into a point of damage suffered (armor protects from this damage in the usual way).

EXPLOSIONS

The force of an explosion is measured in Blast Power. When the detonation occurs, the GM – or the player whose PC built the bomb – rolls a number of Base Dice equal to the Blast Power for each person within Near range of the blast. For every ☢ rolled, the victim suffers one point of damage. The roll cannot be pushed. Victims at Arm's Length from the detonation suffer one extra point of damage.

Effect Radius: Powerful charges, with a Blast Power of 7 or more, can harm people even at Short range. The Blast Power is then reduced by 6. If there are many people within Short range of the blast, the GM can simplify the process by rolling once and applying the result to all victims.

Shrapnel: Normal explosions have a weapon damage of 1 – the damage is simply equal to the number of ☢ rolled (except at Arm's Length, where it is one point higher). But some explosives, like grenades, can be loaded with shrapnel. In this case, the weapon damage of the blast is increased to 2 – i.e. the first ☢ rolled inflicts two points of damage, and each additional ☢ increases the damage by one.

Vehicles: Explosions can harm vehicles (below). Roll for the damage to the vehicle as if it was a person.

VEHICLES

There are several types of vehicles within Elysium I, from hoverbikes to large transports like freight trucks. See the table below. Each vehicle has a Gear Bonus that reflects how maneuverable and fast it is.

Starting a Vehicle: To jump into (or onto) a vehicle requires a maneuver. To start the engine of a motor-powered vehicle takes another maneuver to accomplish. Thus, if you get into a vehicle and start the engine you can do nothing else in the same turn.

Fuel: Elysium's hover vehicles, as well as reconnaissance armor (see page 137), are powered by high-octane jet fuel. The amount of fuel is measured in doses. Fuel consumption is measured in doses per day of active use. Hoverbikes cannot be jury-rigged to run on booze (see *Mutant: Year Zero*). Monorail trains run on electricity and don't require an internal fuel source.

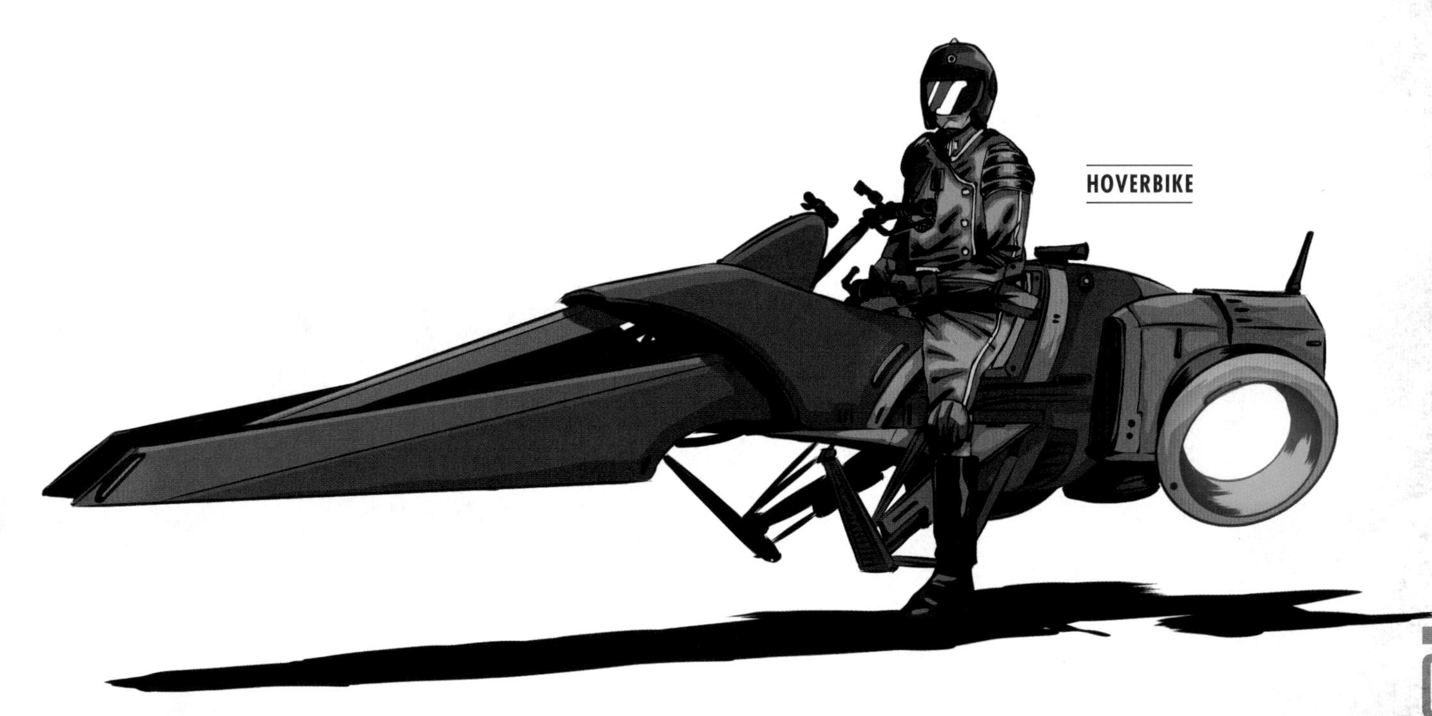

HOVERBIKE

VEHICLES

VEHICLE	BONUS	FUEL	RESILIENCE	ARMOR	OCCUPANTS	COST
Kickbike	+1	–	1	–	1	1
Hoverbike	+3	1	1	–	1	6
Patrol Hovercraft	+3	2	2	3	4	10
Attack Hovercraft*	+3	3	3	12	8	30
Troop Transport	+2	4	4	9	12	18
Hover Freighter	+2	6	5	3	3	15
Monorail Train	+1	–	15	3	50	–

* Has a gauss carbine mounted on the fore.

HOVERFREIGHTER

Passengers: Most vehicles can carry passengers. The vehicles table indicates how many people can occupy the vehicle in total, including the driver.

VEHICLES IN COMBAT

In a conflict, you can move faster in a vehicle than on foot. Every maneuver spent on movement counts as two. For example, with only one maneuver you can move directly from Short distance to Arm's Length, or from Long to Short distance.

Escaping From Danger: In a tight spot you can use your vehicle to escape. Roll to Move as usual but use the Gear Bonus of the vehicle.

Ramming Enemies: Most vehicles can be used as weapons to simply run over your enemies. The attack must occur at Arm's Length. Roll to Fight but use your Agility and your Move skill instead.

VEHICLE DAMAGE

Just like any other gear, vehicles can break down and lose Gear Bonus when you use them. When the Gear Bonus reaches zero, the vehicle won't start any more, and needs to be repaired.

Resilience: The Gear Bonus of a vehicle can also be reduced by external damage. When a vehicle has taken a number of damage points equal to its

Resilience rating, its Gear Bonus is reduced one step. When the total amount of damage inflicted on a vehicle reaches twice the Resilience rating, the Gear Bonus is reduced another step, and so on.

Armor: Some vehicles have a metal hull protecting the vehicle itself and its occupants.

Ramming a Vehicle: You can also use a vehicle to ram another vehicle – but only if your vehicle has an equal or higher Resilience rating than the target vehicle. You carry out the attack in the same way as you ram a person (above).

If you hit, first roll for the armor of the target vehicle. Any remaining damage is inflicted against every occupant in it. The target vehicle itself also suffers this damage, but multiplied by the Resilience of the attacking vehicle.

Hovercrafts are equipped with powerful turbines that keep them aloft. These vehicles can thus move freely in the air. If a hovercraft's Gear Bonus is lowered to zero it crashes, which can cause serious injury to passengers (see Falling, above).

THE ROT

Everyone knows what the Rot is, yet as a resident of Elysium I, the Rot is something you rarely have to face directly. The Rot is what killed the outside world, and once it is gone humanity will be able to rise to the surface world.

Here and there, the Rot has managed to worm its way into the enclave. This is particularly true in the Catacombs (page 100), where large parts are said to be contaminated.

The effects of the Rot are unpredictable. One victim might suffer pain and vomiting, another gets the shakes with fever and chills, and a third could suffer terrible nightmares and hallucinations.

ROT LEVEL

The worst thing about the Rot is that it permeates your body and will accumulate over time. When you are subjected to the Rot, you suffer a Rot Point. Mark it down in the checkboxes on your character sheet. Contaminated areas have a Rot Level, from 1 to 3. The Rot Level determines how often you suffer Rot Points.

1	**Weak Rot.** You suffer one Rot Point every day.
2	**Strong Rot.** You suffer one Rot Point every hour.
3	**Hotspot.** You suffer one Rot Point every minute. You will die quickly here.

ROT ATTACK

You can also accumulate Rot Points from certain events such as consuming contaminated food or coming into contact with contaminated creatures.

EFFECTS OF THE ROT

Every time you suffer a Rot Point, you must immediately roll a number of Base Dice equal to your total amount of Rot Points. For every ☣ you roll, you suffer one point of damage (trauma to Strength).

DECONTAMINATION

Once you have left the contaminated area, you remove one Rot Point every day. If you wash your body in clean water, half of your Rot Points are immediately eliminated (round up).

PERMANENT ROT POINTS

When you are contaminated by the Rot, there is a risk that it will stay in your body forever. Every time you are about to lose one Rot Point, roll one Base Die. If you roll a ☣, the Rot Point stays, and becomes permanent. Mark this on your character sheet. Permanent Rot Points stay with you for the rest of your life, no matter how hard you scrub yourself

During decontamination, only non-permanent Rot Points will disappear – permanent Rot Points are not counted for this purpose.

LIFE IN ELYSIUM

When the world fell apart, the structures of society broke down. Nations, authorities and companies one by one collapsed as panic spread across the globe. In the end, only the most basic human structure remained – the family.

While the world burned, four powerful dynasties formed an alliance, a covenant to survive the fall of humanity. Their goal was as drastic as it was simple: create huge underground cities, enclaves where, alongside their offspring, they would wait for a new tomorrow. They named their aspiring society Elysium, after the meadows of eternal spring in ancient Greek mythology. In remote lands they dug into the bedrock and constructed their new homes. Each of these enclaves was to be self-sufficient, to allow the great families to survive the long atomic winters that followed.

The rich industrialist and landowning Warburg family provided the lands and tools for the project. The media and entertainment empire of the Morningstar family celebrated amidst the chaos of the Red Plague and made life tolerable. The private armies and security forces of the Fortescue family effectively silenced critics and protected the remote construction sites from prying eyes. The Kilgore dynasty, owning a global research conglomerate with unique patents in genetics and biotechnology, became the fourth member of the covenant.

Other powerful entities drew up plans similar to those of Elysium and formed their own alliances with similar goals. These alliances became known as the Titan Powers. Elysium was the first of them. Two of these Titan Powers took the names of Mimir and Noatun, monikers plucked from Norse mythology. The former fled into the cold darkness of space while the latter sought refuge at the bottom of the ocean.

THE SEED OF HUMANITY

Each of the Titan Powers built what they thought of as an ark for humanity – a seed for a new civilization and the path to a life in the new world after the fall. Elysium was inspired by the dynasties that formed the world hundreds of years earlier. The ambitions and traditional values of Victorian times became models for Elysium to follow, along with the design and culture of the era. This was blended with a form of society in which the family, not the individual, was of foremost importance. To highlight this message, the enclaves of Elysium were modeled after an architectural style mimicking that of the late 19th century. In this way too, the founders of Elysium wanted to show their disapproval of the wars and disasters that had followed that time, that "golden age," as they believed it to be.

The first enclave was named Elysium I. Construction of more enclaves quickly followed. In order to support and serve the families veritable armies of workers and staff were needed. Tens of thousands of carefully selected people employed by the houses were given the chance to accompany them into self-imposed exile. When the rest of the people of Earth finally realized that human civilization was doomed, the gates of the enclaves had been closed and sealed, their inhabitants safely underground.

While the outside world burned, work within the enclave continued at a hectic pace. Elysium's scientists searched for a way to re-populate the world and restore the civilization laid to ruins above their heads. Over the decades that followed, they made amazing discoveries. They created technologies superior to anything the surface world had ever seen. The researchers found materials stronger than carbon fiber and diamond. The manufacture of independent and intelligent machines and advances in medicine were now realities that surface dwellers had only dreamed of. Within what became known as the disciplines of xenogenetics and biomechatronics, the researchers attained mastery over life itself.

JUDICATORS

The first generation who populated Elysium soon realized they would never experience the new tomorrow they were trying to create. They understood that it would take many decades, maybe centuries, before the Earth's surface could be colonized again. Elysium's founders were forced to accept that their destiny was to live the rest of their lives underground and that their progeny would be the ones to carry out their ultimate goal. A small number of selected, so-called Eminences were placed in cryosleep, regularly awakened for year-long shifts, with the mission to ensure that the ruling Houses did not deviate from the founding values of Elysium.

New generations grew up underground, having never seen the sky above. A deceptive calm engulfed them as silent frustrations festered within. Despite its splendor, the enclaves were inescapable prisons. Anger and distrust grew among the residents and against the other Titan Powers. Strife between the four ruling families tore at the fabric of their society. Already strong family ties grew even stronger, but at the same rate, confidence in society in general decreased.

Suspicions and uncertainty inevitably lit a spark of action. Members of the Morningstar and Fortescue dynasties clashed with bloody results. The enclave reeled in shock as hundreds died and the conflict seemed to escalate. Luckily, at that time enough people were able to regain their senses. Representatives of the four leading families met, and from this meeting the Council of Elysium was born.

The four families concluded that full insight into what was happening in the enclave was necessary and agreed to set up a force with the authority to intervene against anyone who tried to overthrow the established order. The officers of this force were called judicators, and they became the law of the enclave. In order to secure a balance between the Houses, it was decided that each unit of four officers would include one representative from each of the ruling Houses.

THE ENCLAVE WARS

The new order restored some calm, but under the surface resentment lingered. Perhaps as an outlet, envy and mistrust of the other Titan Powers increased. Nowhere was this more evident than in Elysium I. The enclave was built with outdated technology compared to its successors. Its people were said to enjoy a special status within Elysium as a symbol of the human spirit and the will to survive. But the enclave was in many ways a relic – cramped, dark, and worn by age. Plans were made to connect Elysium's many enclaves, plans that might have become reality had the Enclave Wars not broken out.

The causes that led the enclaves to declare war against each other were as narrow-minded and petty as humanity's previous attempt to annihilate itself on the surface world. Arrogant leaders promised their followers more than they could deliver, fragile egos misread the intentions of others, while some eyed what others had with jealousy or lust. Fateful words in closed chambers turned to action, this time without wiser wills prevailing.

ENCLAVE SOCIETY AND HIERARCHY

Elysium I is governed by the Council, which consists of the heads of each ruling House – Warburg, Fortescue, Morningstar and Kilgore. Each House oversees one aspect of the enclave in accordance with the specialty that they once brought with them into the alliance that became Elysium. There are other families of importance in the enclave, some even have significant influence, but nowhere close to the power or influential of the ruling Houses. All other families are connected in one way or another to one of the four main dynasties. Loyalties often shift, changing the balance of power in the enclave.

The vast majority of the enclave's population work in some way for the various leading families. A few people have been licensed to run their own businesses, but these are also part of the enclave's strict hierarchy.

Your ID card shows who you are and where you belong. Individuals can climb the social ladder, but the family you are born into will always be the most important factor when it comes to the status you enjoy. The social mobility of the lesser families is extremely limited. It is very rare for any of the lower dynasties to move up or down on the social ladder. Exceptional individuals are often held back by their families and those who violate rules and laws are disgraced and reprimanded, if they are allowed to keep their lives at all.

THE RULING HOUSES

Each of the four ruling Houses is in charge of a certain aspect of Elysium I. The Warburg family is responsible for production and energy, the Fortescue family for defense and security, the Morningstar family for culture and communication, and the Kilgore family for technology and science. Of the

approximately 10,000 inhabitants of the enclave, about 2,000 belong to one of the four main dynasties.

WARBURG

Being a Warburg means possessing a will to build and create. Your family ensures that food is available on tables, that materials are available when repairs are to be carried out, that new goods are manufactured and that the energy the enclave needs is produced. Without these things, Elysium grinds to a halt and its inhabitants would starve. On your shoulders rests the unimaginable burden and challenge that is meeting the essential needs of the enclave. Resources are already scarce while needs and requirements only grow.

Gertrud Warburg is responsible for everything produced in the enclave, from food to gadgets of all sizes. Supporting her is her cousin Bertha, who is in charge of the maintenance of the enclave, and Manfred Warburg, responsible for power plants and energy supply. Among those of the Warburg family who have significant responsibilities are Ursula, Alvina, Herbert, Ernest and Otto.

House Color: Blue

FORTESCUE

The Fortescue family is Elysium's first and last line of defense against any enemy. Loyalty, pride and justice are words to live by for a Fortescue. Everyone trusts you to make the difficult decisions that are sometimes needed to combat any form of threat to the enclave. As a Fortescue, there are always challenges to face and your vigilance

GERTRUD WARBURG

VALERIA FORTESCUE

is constant. If it's not rebellion and dissent that threaten Elysium's delicate balance, it is the incursion of threats and dangers from the devastated outside world. Even when others refuse or can't assist you in protecting the enclave, you do not hesitate to tackle the threat yourself, armed with whatever is available.

The head of the Fortescue family, who also serves as the head of the Central Data Agency (CDA) is Valeria Fortescue. Almost as influential is General Margot Fortescue, commander of the Deep Watch, the main military force of the enclave. Other important people within the family are Alexis, Damien, Killian and Nadine.

House Color: Gray

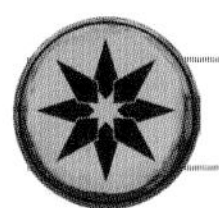

MORNINGSTAR

For a Morningstar, life is a blend of enjoyment and leisure, refinement and creativity. Within Elysium, you are the providers of pleasure, culture, history and art. Celebrations and entertainment, decadence and tradition - everything is mixed in a whirl of impressions that is your everyday life. However, it's not a life without worries, even if you never appear to be under stress. Behind all the gloss and pomp hides a growing amount of dirty play and hard choices. For intertwined with dancing, drinks and performances, are politics, intrigue, debts, services and silent agreements. A Morningstar is an artist and a host, as well as a crucial force among the rulers of Elysium's underground world.

Constantine Morningstar sits on the Council, and has been the family's leader for decades. His formal role as Supreme Historian makes him responsible for the archives of the enclave. In reality, everyone knows that he mostly cares about what appears on the stages and screens of the enclave theaters and cinemas. It is whispered that no performance can be shown without Constantine's approval.

Other Morningstars with prominent roles include Sofia, Alessio, Valentino, Minerva, Marco, and the twins Serena and Bianca.

House Color: Green

CONSTANTINE MORNINGSTAR

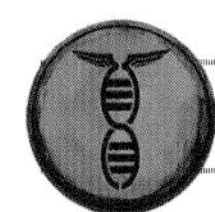

KILGORE

A Kilgore is a thinker, a researcher, or scientist seeking answers and new questions. It was a Kilgore who created the first xenogenetic creatures and gave humanity several of the new and wonderful building materials that made the enclaves possible.

It was also Kilgore scientists who took the decisive steps to combine man and machine. The first reconstructed human was created in a Kilgore laboratory. As a Kilgore, there is always another question to find the answer to. There is power in knowledge, and for every new discovery you make, your influence grows.

The current leader of the House is Antonia Kilgore. She controls both the Council of Sciences and the Academy, and has a finger in almost all crucial research projects. Many believe that her son Aston, the Chief Scientist of the enclave, will one day inherit

ANTONIA KILGORE

her role. Other Kilgores of significance are Marsden, Ashley, Castor, Leslie, Osmond, and Lindsay.

House Color: Red

OTHER FAMILIES OF NOTE

In addition to the four ruling Houses of the enclave, there are other families that wield considerable influence in Elysium I. They are the heirs of people who stood by the founding rulers. Before the fall of civilization, some of them were as influential as the great families, but as the dust settled their significance waned.

Around 3,000 of the enclave's 10,000 inhabitants belong to these minor families. None of them have forgotten their origins and long for nothing more than to ascend and reclaim their lost glory. The power of the four Houses is so heavily cemented that something extraordinary would be required for this to occur.

THE LESSER FAMILIES

The lesser families of Elysium I are Acton, Arundell, Battenburg, Bentick, Calvert, De Vere, Fairfax, Montague, Loftus, Poulette, and Somerset.

COMMON FIRST NAMES AMONGST THE NOBILITY

Afton, Agrona, Aida, Aiken, Aislinn, Alden, Aldrich, Allard, Allston, Alvina, Ariana, Arleigh, Arlo, Ashley, Audrey, Avon, Bailey, Ballard, Bancroft, Beldon, Beverly, Blaine, Blossom, Blythe, Brea, Brenda, Brewster, Brinley, Buckley, Burne, Cade, Calhoun, Calvert, Cameron, Carleton, Carlyle, Carvell, Chilton, Claiborne, Clifford, Colbert, Colter, Corliss, Creighton, Dale, Dayton, Demelza, Digby, Donald, Douglas, Doyle, Duncan, Dustin, Eartha, Edda, Edgar, Edith, Edmund, Edward, Edwin, Egerton, Eldon, Eldridge, Elmer, Emerson, Esmond, Ethel, Farley, Farrah, Fern, Fiona, Gilford, Godiva, Golda, Gordon, Hadley, Haley, Halsey, Harlan, Harmony, Hayden, Haywood, Hazel, Hedwig, Hendrick, Henley, Herbert, Hertha, Hollace, Holly, Hope, Horton, Humphrey, Idina, Isolda, Ivy, Jocelyn, Kenley, Kenton, Kimberley, Kyla, Layton, Leigh, Leslie, Lindsay, Locke, Luella, Lyndon, Maida, Manley, Marsden, Millard, Milton, Misty, Nara, Nelson, Nyle, Ogden, Osmond, Oswin, Payton, Penley, Preston, Radella, Ransford, Ransley, Reginald, Remington, Ridley

OVERVIEW OF ELYSIUM I

Elysium I is far more than a simple shelter. Close to a mile from top to bottom, and almost half as wide at its widest point, it resembles an ancient skyscraper buried under the earth. Its vaulted ceiling is a dome reaching high above the Winter Garden, the only truly spacious area in the enclave.

The further down you get into the enclave the narrower the inverted tower becomes. People, homes, hydroponic farms, factories and everything else are given less space, and the ceilings are lower. Down here, repairs are low priority, and the lower you go, the worse it gets, a testament to decades of neglect.

SECTIONS, SECTORS, AND LEVELS

Elysium I is a single enclave, but its three distinct sections represent three different sections of society. The top of the enclave is called the Crown. It got its name for two reasons – because it is the top of the tower-like underground facility, and because most buildings here have ceilings of copper that once glistened like golden crowns. The middle section of Elysium I is the Core, the largest part of the enclave. At the bottom is the Deep. The Core and the Deep are divided into seven and five different sectors, respectively. The Crown has only one sector.

THE SHAFT

The Shaft runs down through the center of Elysium, connecting all levels. The Shaft is roughly square in shape and about 70 yards wide. Its opens into the Winter Garden in the Crown and ends at the bottom of the Deep. In each corner of the Shaft, there is an elevator restricted to authorized personnel only. There are also metal spiral staircases which see a lot of traffic. Workers, messengers, and couriers can be seen running up and down almost 24 hours a day.

THE CROWN

The uppermost part of Elysium I belongs to you and to the rest of the enclave elite. It is here that each of the four ruling Houses has its palace. Each such complex is a massive structure of glass and stone with sloping, ornamented facades. Each palace occupies a corner of the section and runs up to the ceiling. Every palace is about 75 yards wide at the base and forty floors high. On the outside of each palace, glass elevators travel up and down the sloping walls.

The Crown is covered by a dome that extends from each of the corner palaces. Its highest point is 250 yards above the "floor" of the Crown, creating a sense of space that cannot be found anywhere else in the enclave. The walls lean outwards, 400 yards

MEMORIAL DAY

On the annual celebration of Memorial Day, Elysium's fallen soldiers are honored. According to tradition, the Council of Elysium always convenes to discuss and decide on issues pertaining to the future of the enclave. Also on Memorial Day, leaders of the Houses host large crowds in the Winter Garden. A select number of workers and others coming from the lower sections are permitted into the Crown to attend the ceremony.

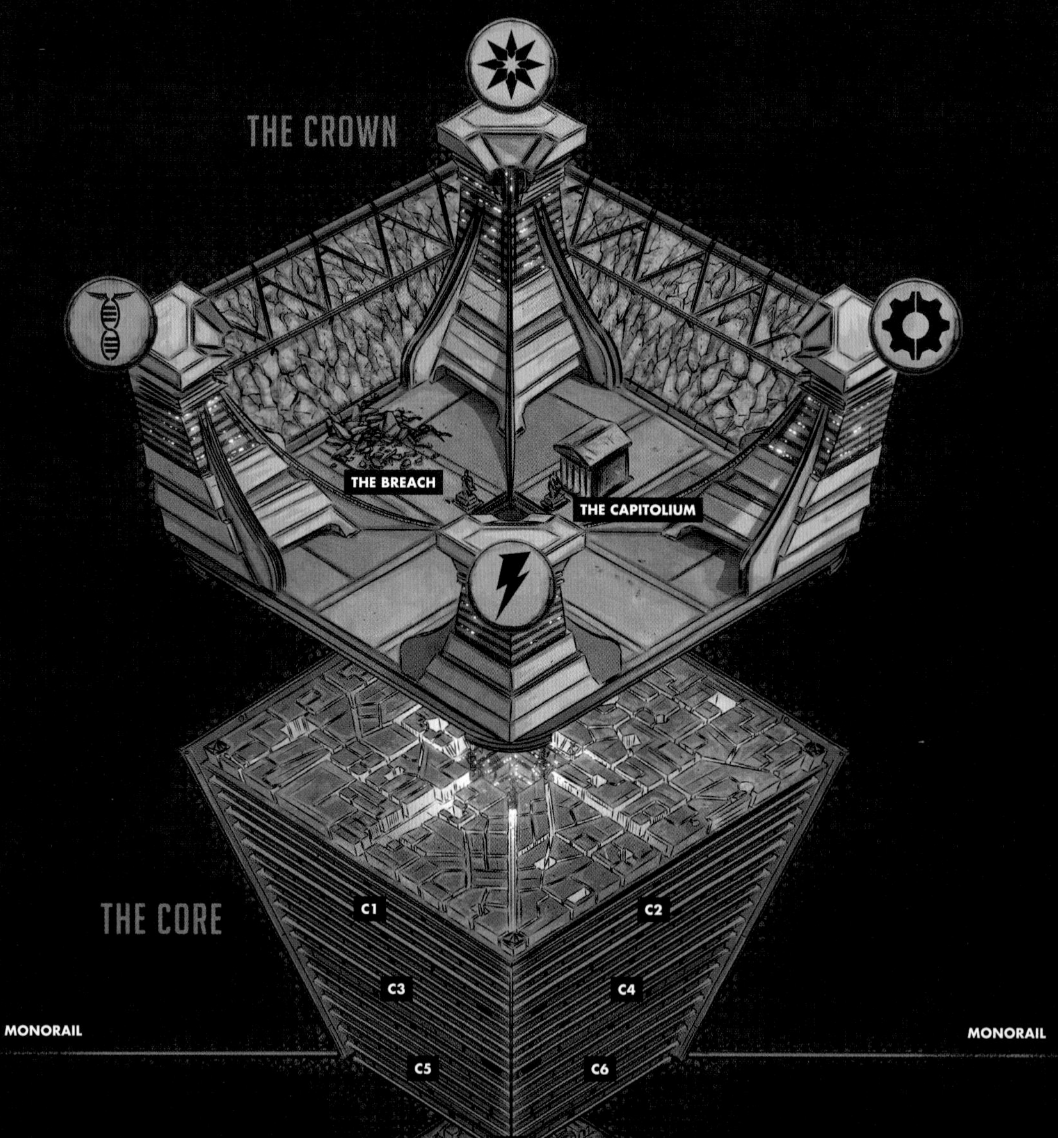

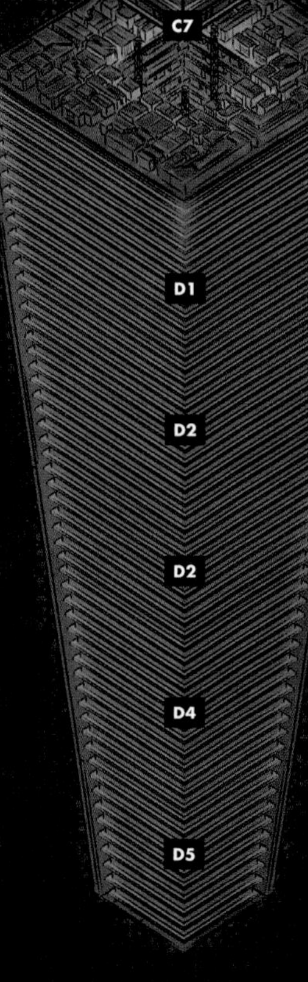

ELYSIUM I

THE CORE

C1. Nova Paloma
C2. Old Koly
C3. Pirius
C4. Tindertuft
C5. Northolme
C6. Calista
C7. Hindenburg

THE DEEP

D1. Mosel
D2. Laborum
D3. Arcadium
D4. Cinderfalls
D5. Cogs of Hel

wide at the bottom, widening to almost 500 yards at the base of the dome that covers the Crown.

Only members of the ruling Houses (Security Class III and above) normally have access to the Crown. The exception to this is during Memorial Day (see the boxed text on page 93).

The Winter Garden: Between the vast palaces of the Crown lies the Winter Garden – a large park where fallen soldiers are honored. This was the site of the last stand of the Enclave Wars, and where Elysium won its most bloody victory. The park area in front of each palace belongs to, and is maintained by, its respective House. The Winter Garden is adorned with war memorials throughout the field. The Winter Garden is currently unkempt, its once-trimmed plants looking withered and sick. In the center of the park is the opening to the Shaft – a square abyss. The stairs and elevators that are located here can take you all the way down to the Deep.

The Breach: At one location in the Winter Garden, below the point in the dome where the robot armies of hostile Titan Powers broke through and entered the enclave, the rubble still remains. The huge and rusty wrecks of battle robots were left here, as an eternal reminder of the desperate battle fought, and the sacrifices made to save Elysium I from destruction. This place is known to the public as the Breach.

The Capitolium: Near the Shaft, one of very few free-standing buildings in the enclave can be found: the Capitolium. It's a decaying multi-story mansion in rust-brown bricks that still carries scars inflicted by bullets and beam weapons during ancient battles. The copper roof is worn and on the columns along the front are engraved the names of all fallen soldiers. It is in the Capitolium that the Council gathers to make decisions for the enclave. The Capitolium also contains the headquarters of the

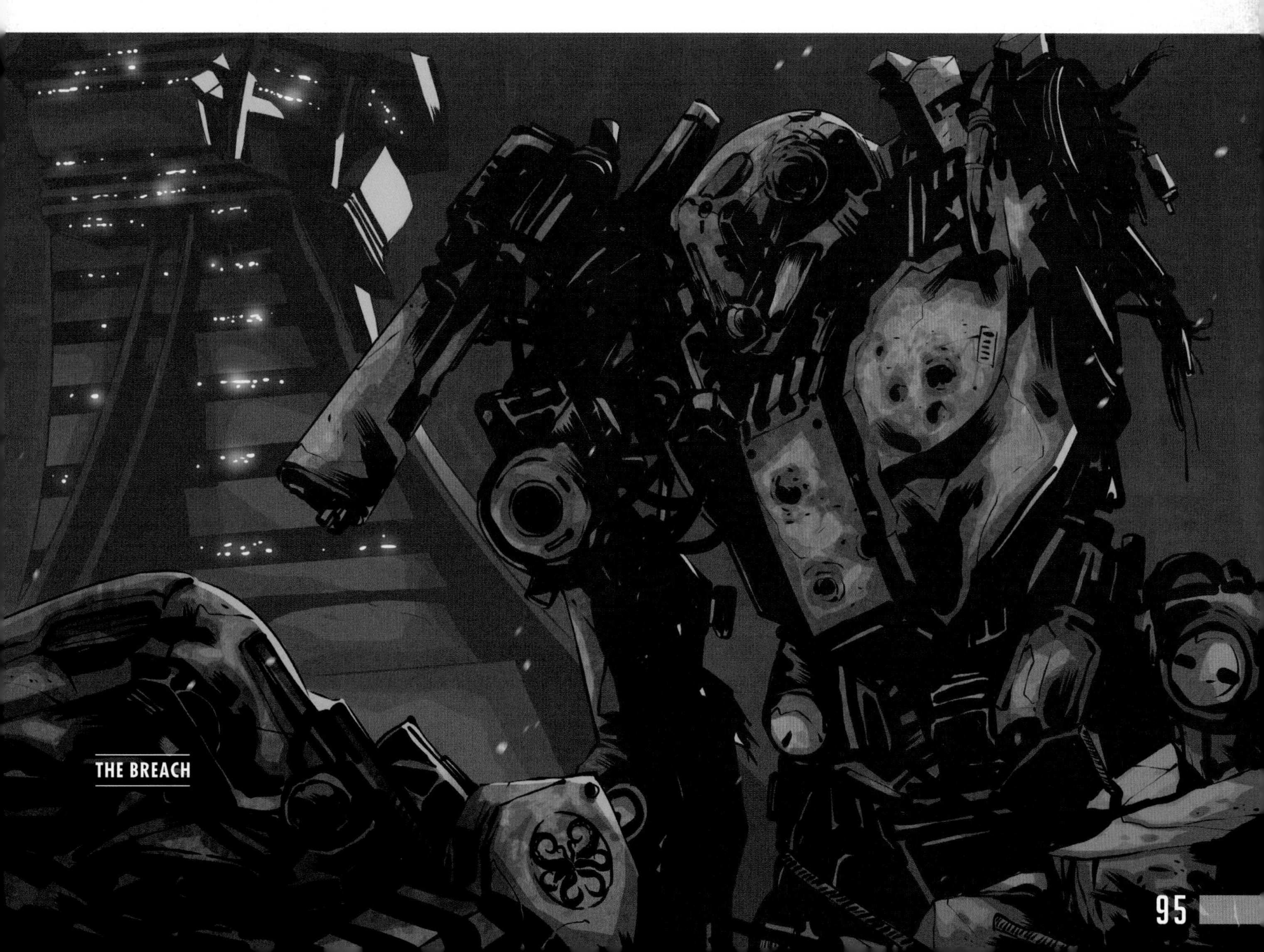
THE BREACH

HYDROPONIC PLANTATION

judicators. This is where you go to make reports and get new orders. Read more about your HQ on page 107.

THE CORE

Unlike the Crown, the Core is not an open space. Instead, it is divided into 20 main levels, each about 10 yards high. The huge Shaft runs straight through the section and continues further into the Deep, all the way down to the bottom of the enclave.

In each corner of the Core, there is a large freight elevator that slowly moves goods and work teams to all levels, from the Crown all the way down to the Deep. The trip from top to bottom takes several minutes and the noise inside the lifts is deafening.

The uppermost levels of the Core are about 400 yards wide, while those nearer the bottom narrow to about 250 yards. Each level consists of several sections, which in turn are divided into blocks. Multistory buildings run from floor to ceiling. Between them are the streets and alleys that demarcate the blocks. Some of the buildings house homes, shops, and taverns. Others contain work facilities such as factories, workshops, farms, and offices.

The Core has seven sectors:

- Nova Paloma
- Old Koly
- Northolme
- Pirius
- Tindertuft
- Calista
- Hindenburg

Nova Paloma: Two things make Nova Paloma different from other sectors. The first is the amount of light, emitted by neon signs and ornamental facades, and the other is the sense of space and freedom. The area has a high ceiling, with only the

THE ACADEMY

The enclave's only institute of higher learning is called the Academy. Its 20 floors in the Core run through three levels, surrounded by footbridges and small, decayed parks. The sculpted ceramic facade and huge nano-glass windows of the Academy contrast sharply with the dark and often dirty composite tile walls around the compound. The library in the Academy once contained much knowledge collected by ancient human civilizations, but decay and internal strife have unfortunately led to the loss of large parts of the collection.

Winter Garden giving a greater sense of space. The shops and bars here always have licenses for their goods and proudly display them in windows and on shelves. You can find everything from savory foods and pure spirits to precious luxury products and costly fun in Nova Paloma. There are also plenty of street stalls and wagon cafes where you can get a simple meal or a mug of beer.

Old Koly: In this sector many students, academics, artists and actors have their homes. There are enclave theaters, a few smaller cabaret scenes, as well as a handful of galleries and studios. A few places proudly display signs that state they have been open since the enclave was first populated. The artists and students, as well as the nearby Academy, all contribute to making Old Koly the cultural center of Elysium.

Pirius and Tindertuft: A few decades ago, structural deficiencies were detected in parts of one of the large residential districts. The damaged sections were torn down and what was left untouched soon became known as Old Koly. The new parts formed the sectors of Pirius and Tindertuft, an architectural chaos of alleys, archways and columns in ceramic and plate glass. The ornate parks and plantations found here are airier than in other sectors and sometimes seem to be as much decoration as they are practical. No enclave workers have their homes in these sectors. All families with influence, apart from the ruling Houses, have their palaces in Pirius or Tindertuft.

Northolme and Calista: Most of the licensed food in Elysium I is produced in Northolme and Calista. Aside some living quarters and service facilities, these sectors are dominated by large hydroponic plantations with carefully controlled water and lighting systems. In addition, there are vast ponds with fish farms, huge vats for growing synthetic meat, and dark, mile-long tubes used to grow mushrooms.

Hindenburg: The residential sector called Hindenburg is as old as Old Koly. The age of the sector is immediately apparent, as signs of heavy wear and tear are all around.

THE BAZAAR

Under the narrow and dark arches of the Core that make up the Bazaar there are lots of small shops, workshops, and shacks. Here you'll find simple as well as expensive crafts, foods, and drinks. The bazaar has become a popular gathering place, even for those who cannot afford the offered goods. The crowds and the atmosphere make it a popular haunt for many enclave dwellers. On the outskirts of the Bazaar lies the Exchange – a large hall where everyone can exchange goods with each other, whether licensed or not. The requirement is that the trade takes place on site and under the oversight of the Exchange Notary Office. Anyone who wants to shop must first register their name and goods. When the business is concluded, both parties must declare what was traded and with whom. It is not much of a secret that the Council encourages the trade in the Exchange – it makes it very easy to track and update records of both assets and people in the enclave.

HINDENBURG

THE CLINIC

The only hospital in the Enclave is called the Clinic, and it is also located in the Core. Officially, all inhabitants are entitled to free healthcare. However, in practice, members of the Houses are given a completely different level of care than those of lower status.

THE DATA WORKS

The area where the Data Works is located is under heavy and constant surveillance. Guards, cameras, and alarms secure the place. The monitors they watch are secret to all but the Council and their most trusted confidantes. The data collected by the different departments is crucial for Elysium I to exist. Everything is controlled from one of the most unassuming buildings in the area – the headquarters of the Central Data Agency. While many sectors are almost quiet at night, the activity in the Data Works never ceases. The staff work around the clock feeding data on everything that occurs in the enclave into massive but very old computer servers.

THE DEEP

The bottom section of the enclave consists of 57 levels. The height of the ceiling varies between the levels but is usually about ten yards. At the top of the Deep, the levels are approximately 250 yards wide, but narrow down to about 150 yards at the bottom. Because the enclave is so narrow here, you are never far from the Shaft. On some floors there is not much more than freight lanes and walkways. Those spaces are littered with sheds and dwellings crowded up against the walls, as if they were afraid of the darkness and the depths.

There is only one passenger elevator that reaches all the way down to the bowels of the enclave and it runs along the Shaft. The larger lifts available may only be used to transport goods, unless otherwise authorized by a judicator or the Council.

The Deep is where energy is produced and goods are manufactured for the entire enclave. Aside from the plantations in the Core, it is in the

INDUSTRY IN THE ENCLAVE
Today, the factories in the enclave are mostly only capable of repairing what is broken, not creating new goods. Elysium I simply lacks the resources. Equipment, buildings, and vehicles are patched up time and time again, made to last almost infinitely, but in spite of this, the number of things that need replacing grows each year. The focus of all large-scale manufacturing is towards this effort. Goods for decoration and pleasure are created only by licensed craftsmen.

Deep where the majority of the workers toil. Factories, power plants and mines occupy large parts of the sections. Tucked in between them are cramped and miserable housing quarters where the workers and their families have their homes.

A number of smaller plantations are also located here. The artistic sensibilities common to the Crown and the Core are absent in the Deep – here there is only concrete and steel, function over form being the rule.

There are five sectors in the Deep:

- Mosel
- Laborum
- Arcadium
- Cinderfalls
- Cogs of Hel

Mosel and Laborum: The oldest residential areas of Elysium I are found in the Mosel and Laborum sectors. Here, the majority of the reconstructed workers live alongside others while toiling away at the harshest and least wanted jobs in the enclave. The streets are dirty and crowded. It is well-known that some inhabitants grow vegetables and breed animals without permits in the narrow alleyways and courtyards here.

In Mosel, there is a path commonly known as the Stench. It runs along the dam that the Canal (see the boxed text) opens into. However, after its journey through the enclave, the water is sometimes closer to that of the Sewer, and the smell of the pond is what gives the promenade its nickname. Along the Stench, several smaller power plants and factories that utilize the easy access to water can be found.

Arcadium is the oldest factory sector by far. When more modern facilities were built in Cinderfalls, parts of Arcadium were converted into walkways and parks filled with plants to generate oxygen. The homes in Arcadium are therefore sought after. There is a strong contrast between the relatively airy Arcadium and the floors below, in the sector Cogs of Hel.

Cinderfalls: The industrial sector of Cinderfalls was built after Arcadium, but it is still over a hundred years old. The decay and wear are evident on its facades, ceilings, and corridors – everything is covered in soot and dirt. The air is toxic, and the stench of chemicals and waste follows you wherever you go. The small number of homes and farms found here are as gloomy as the factory buildings.

Cogs of Hel: In the factory sector of Cogs of Hel, at the very bottom of Elysium I, the Reconstruction Works can be found. It's just as drab and somber as the rest of the area, not very different from the miserable and tormented creatures that stumble out of its halls.

THE CANTINA
The Cantina is the place where workers and others with limited funds gather to eat. It is a column-filled hall with a vaulted ceiling, with hundreds of tables filling the space. You eat with your ilk – engineers with engineers, farmers with farmers and so on. At the far end of the hall there is a large table without chairs. Here, reconstructed convicts and other individuals without work can eat whatever their very few credits can afford to buy.

TYPICAL WORKER FIRST NAMES
Abner, Ada, Aggie, Aldus, Aram, Baltus, Barb, Berton, Bessie, Birdie, Burch, Callie, Celia, Clane, Cleon, Daisy, Derris, Dolly, Dottie, Ebbon, Elma, Elos, Enid, Festus, Flossie, Garnet, Ginny, Grizzie, Haskel, Hattie, Heran, Ivey, Jobe, Josey, Lent, Lindy, Lissie, Lulu, Lyman, Lynk, Mallie, Molly, Morrie, Mott, Nettie, Odell, Ona, Peachie, Pell, Pimm, Quitman, Rena, Roxie, Sadoc, Suvia, Taron, Trixie, Willon, Winnie

TYPICAL WORKER LAST NAMES
Abram, Alton, Badger, Barlow, Barton, Benson, Bing, Brady, Budd, Coombs, Dudley, Hale, Harlan, Holton, Merton, Morley, Norton, Ogden, Reed, Skelton, Tenley, Tickle, Tinley, Vance, Weld

THE CANAL

The Canal is a waterway that runs throughout the enclave and provides its different floors with clean and fresh water. In a few places in the Core, the Canal flows in the open, but otherwise it is well protected by thick walls. Its counterpart is the Sewer, a fully sealed system where all sewage is collected and transferred to the extensive wastewater treatment plant in the Deep.

THE CATACOMBS

In addition to the mines that are drilled down into the bedrock beneath the Deep, there is a part of Elysium I that is not part of the central structure: the Catacombs. Once, it served as a spaceport and terminal for transportation to other Elysium enclaves and bunkers. It was also the headquarters of the military forces of the enclave.

Near the end of the Enclave Wars, geotorpedoes hit the facility and destroyed it. All but a few tunnels to the area collapsed. By now, all that

COGS OF HEL

remains therein has been stripped clean of anything valuable.

The Catacombs serve today as the enclave's maximum-security prison. Criminals not sentenced to death or reconstruction end up here. Among the inmates of the Catacombs, referred to as the Exiles, survival of the fittest is the rule of law. Neither you nor any other judicator needs to care what happens to a convict after they are sent to the Catacombs. The criminals and enemies of the enclave who end up here grow their own food and get by as best they can. If sent to the Catacombs, you will never return.

A heavily guarded tunnel opening out of Hindenburg connects the Catacombs with the main enclave. Those living in the vicinity of the tunnel avoid it, as if only daring to look down the tunnel leading to the prison would result in being tossed in among the criminals there.

IS THE ENCLAVE DOOMED?

Computer simulations clearly show that the population of Elysium I is very vulnerable. This is taught to every child in school. Failure of individual systems can have a ripple effect that may very well lead to the whole enclave falling into chaos. When the Elysium enclaves were built, their leaders were aware that even without war or direct sabotage, it would be difficult for the isolated settlements to survive. Every person living in Elysium I knows that survival depends on doing your job with complete accuracy, no matter what function you serve. A single mistake by a single person could spell doom for the entire enclave.

THE OUTSIDE WORLD

Beyond the enclave there is only death and destruction. Earth's surface was turned into a devastated wasteland many generations ago. The only creatures that can survive out there are the abominations created during the Enclave Wars – creatures capable of coping with the infections, poisons, and radioactive fallout that kills everything else. No human can survive outside the enclave for longer than it takes for the seal of a hazmat suits to fail, or for an oxygen tank to run empty.

Once a year, the Exploration Institute, a department of the Academy, sends a probe to measure the levels of hazardous material in the soil and any other changes of interest. The results are always the same, always depressing – the Earth remains just as toxic as ever. According to the more optimistic forecasts, the world will one day be populated by humans again, but it is a day that will be many generations in the future.

LONGING FOR THE SURFACE

It does not happen often, but every now and then some individual develops the urge to escape the enclave, driven by the belief that survival is possible in the outside world. According to these fantasies, there are places free of radiation and sickness, places where intrepid individuals can make new lives for themselves. The longing for a different life on the surface is easy to understand but also extremely dangerous. Strict laws require immediate action against all such dangerous dreams. For milder cases therapy is often enough, but some individuals engage in subversive activities and must be handled swiftly and forcefully. Some are reconstructed, but most are sentenced to death.

THE STRUCTURE OF ELYSIUM

The enclave's society has been developing for generations. The power of the ruling Houses, the focus on the family as the key pillar of society, scarce resources, and total isolation are factors that have been decisive in establishing order, rules, traditions, and the habits that shape Elysium I.

HIERARCHY

The society in the enclave rests primarily on the sense of devotion to family and secondly on the role each inhabitant fills. Each family provides their members with a status that rarely changes. One can win or lose influence, but an individual can never reach a status beyond that which is held within their own family. The only exception is those who break away and become lawless in one way or another in the eyes of the enclave.

The fact that four mighty dynasties created the Elysium Titan Power, and still hold sway over the enclave, is the reason for this heavy focus on the role of family. For you, as a member of one of the four ruling Houses, this means that you are born to the status and rights only afforded to the wealthy and powerful. You have unbelievable privileges, the same as those fortunate enough to have been born under any of the other three Houses.

Everything in society revolves around the concepts of family and bloodlines. They are the social foundation on which the enclave was founded. Of course, your family also requires service from you, and it is unwise to ignore your family's responsibilities for long. Everyone carefully keeps track of their family ties as well as everyone else's. Even the most wretched servant in the Deep knows their ancestry in detail, just like you do. Not belonging to a family is to stand outside society. Most of the Exiles in the Catacombs have been ostracized by their families. Among the worst things you can imagine is to fall from grace and end up in the same situation, without a family.

In other words, your lineage controls what rights you have and also what your duties are. The family educates and protects you, but it also demands responsibility and duty. You must always care for and obey your family. It is the family after all, that has final word on the life choices that will impact you the most, be it career, love, or anything else. If you commit a serious mistake, your entire

CRIME & FAMILY

When someone commits a crime in the enclave, the family is responsible. Most often, the perpetrator is punished personally for the crime, but a family can choose other means to atone for the misdeed. Someone must pay for the crime, but it is not always the person who committed it. For a powerful family, the laws of Elysium are not absolute, but rather a framework for negotiations. When you mete out punishment as a judicator, make sure you consider what your family stands to gain, not only the nature of the crime itself. Perpetrators belonging to a family without influence are dealt with quickly and harshly – the actual perpetrator almost always the one who is punished, and their family will often suffer for the crime as well.

family will suffer for it. The only way for your family to exonerate itself from your misdeeds is to shun you forever.

The work task assigned to each resident of the enclave is another important part of society. This is true for all inhabitants of Elysium I. Everyone is needed and depended upon for the enclave to survive. Workers make sure the factories keep running, technicians are responsible for maintenance, information management and research knowledge, physicians take care of the medical needs, and so on. The size and hierarchy of the work teams vary, but they are all important and are controlled, directly or indirectly, by the Council.

There is often a strong link between family and the work task assigned to you. For example, as a child of a technician and a teacher, you are expected or even required to take one of those two jobs. It does happen that children are assigned to a different service than their parents, but it is not common. Personal qualities and talents weigh in, but the individual's family and its status always weigh heavier. For example, a child from a working family in the Deep can hardly expect a job in a particularly high position, no matter how talented the person is. For you and others of noble birth, the opposite applies – a high position is given, no matter how useless or inexperienced you are.

SECURITY CLASS

Residents of Elysium I are divided into security classes that determine which areas in the enclave they have access to. Only class III and above have access to the Crown. Security classes are identified using Roman numerals, from I to VII. Each resident is assigned an ID card indicating their security class, and it is mandated for everyone to always carry it. The ID card is also used for electronic payments.

SECURITY CLASS	SOCIAL CATEGORY
I	Proles
II	Security Guards
III	Civilian House Members
IV	Judicators
V	Military
VI	High Command
VII	Heads of the Houses

LAWS AND REGULATIONS

The resources of Elysium are limited and must therefore be used as efficiently as possible. For the sake of the enclave, sacrifices must be made, including some of the inhabitants' own liberties. This has necessitated a system of harsh and absolute laws. Originally the laws were created to secure the resources of the enclave and give the next generations a chance to survive. Nowadays they are the tool to secure the power and influence of the ruling Houses. Many laws are open to different interpretations, affording judicators the opportunity to use their own discretion.

LICENSES AND PERMITS

In Elysium I everything is controlled. Life in the enclave is only possible if resources are managed carefully and nothing is wasted. Shielded from the world and left without the ability to easily gather more resources, the residents have no other choice.

A limited amount of raw materials comes from mines that are dug deep below the enclave. Likewise, crops are grown in the hydroponic farms, but in very limited quantities. Recycling, repairing, and hard resource control are what make life possible. To maintain that balance, everything must be registered and regularly accounted for, a responsibility that rests with the Central Data Agency, or CDA. Its responsible manager, currently Valeria Fortescue, reports directly to the Council. Her reports can have major consequences for life in the enclave.

Getting a license varies in difficulty. The approval process for making a small garden at your home or selling some handmade craft is relatively easy. A license that allows something more than a small-scale operation is significantly harder to obtain. If a person is not assigned to a task considered essential for the enclave, it is possible to obtain a license to operate a small business, as long as what is sold is carefully controlled and monitored. Innovative ideas or desirable products are rarely licensed. Instead, the creator or creators will be employed at an appropriate production or research facility.

Business licenses can be inherited. A background check is supposed to be performed by the CDA, however, they will not dig too deep if the licensee has a clean criminal record. There are shops and other establishments that families have owed for generations, often a great source of pride.

The right to procreate is one of the most sought after and difficult licenses to obtain. The enclave's resources and space are monitored to calculate sustainability. The wait can be very long, and is sometimes in vain. Most, however, are eventually granted permission. The average amount of children authorized per household is two, more in larger partnership units. Although everyone knows the risks of having illegal children, some do it anyway. The penalty for an unlicensed birth is reconstruction, and all licenses currently held are immediately withdrawn. The child is taken from those who birthed it and given to a new partnership unit.

FAMILY STRUCTURE

The core of the family are the bloodlines. There is more to it however, than mere genetic heritage. Children registered as kin in a household do not need to share blood with all parents. Larger partnership units often combine their genetic heritage in different ways, an opportunity that comes with the license to acquire children. This makes the family a broad concept in Elysium.

Who you will register partnership with is important, and often determined by consultations with your entire family, and that of your partner. Couples of two are still the most common, but partner collectives of up to a dozen individuals exist. Adoption also occurs, which in some cases may be the only way for a newborn to move up in society.

For you and any of those belonging to a ruling House, a license to have children is a given, but your choice of partner is strictly controlled. A lot is riding on the children born into the families after all.

MILITARY AND LAW ENFORCEMENT

Once, Elysium had a huge army of both machines and humans. Only a small fraction of that force remains today. Called the Deep Watch, it consists of about 200 well-trained soldiers under the command of General Margot Fortescue. The four ruling Houses have always been protected by their private forces, called the Honor Guards. You and other judicators are the judicial system of the enclave, along with the support provided by the Tribunal in the form of advice. Finally, there are various units of security guards who serve at important facilities or have the task of enforcing public order and calling for judicators if necessary.

JUDICATORS

You and the other judicators are responsible for ensuring that the laws of Elysium are maintained.

You are the first and last line of defense in the fight against criminals, traitors, and spies. If a security guard spots a crime, it is you who they call for. It rests on your shoulders not only to arrest those who violate the law but also to judge – and when necessary – punish them. It is your duty to sift through allegations and lies to find the truth and enforce the law.

The laws of Elysium are numerous and often contradictory, and you will face hard moral choices in your work. However, you are not without support. For help, you have the Tribunal, four old and highly experienced judicators who, after many years of experience, received the title of Judge. These Judges possess a wealth of knowledge acquired over their long years of service in Elysium I, but remember, like everyone else, their first loyalty rests with their family.

JUDICATORS AND THE TRIBUNAL

As a judicator of Elysium, it is your primary task to protect the enclave and to enforce its laws. You seek to both prevent and resolve crimes, but you can also impose punishment. The most common crimes, such as illegal gambling or trade, disobedience or theft, are to be dealt with on the spot. For more serious crimes, you have the support of the Tribunal. This is a panel of four judges who deliberate and propose appropriate punishments. The Tribunal never passes judgment itself – it only offers suggestions based on precedence, leaving it up to you and your patrol to deliver the final sentence.

THE DEEP WATCH

The enclave's military force is named the Deep Watch, the only regiment left from Elysium's once powerful army. General Margot Fortescue is the commander of the approximately 200 soldiers of the Watch. Slowly, as years pass and resources dwindle, some are concerned that the enclave will soon not be able to maintain a military force at all.

In addition to the command of the Deep Watch, General Fortescue has the right to commandeer large parts of the enclave's population in case of war. According to the ancient defense plans, the population is divided into local defense units with different tasks. Earlier generations practiced drills at least once a year for such an event, but it's been years since an exercise alert was issued and today the organization mostly exists on paper only.

SECURITY GUARDS

Simple security jobs in the enclave are handled by the numerous units of local guards. There is no single organization for these, instead every unit has its own local command and uniforms. The authority granted to the security guards is limited. Their task is to report incidents, issue warnings, and to provide a presence of security for the residents. Armed with a comm radio and a stun baton, the security guards are sufficiently equipped to handle most troublemakers. When the situation demands it, judicators are never more than a radio call away.

The security guards are obligated to follow orders given to them by judicators, even if they contradict orders from their own superiors, a fact that sometimes leads to frictions between the two groups.

In total, there are approximately 200 security guards in Elysium I. They generally wear simple uniforms with name tags and a comm radio.

EVERYONE IS A CRIMINAL

The many and sometimes arbitrary laws and regulations of Elysium mean that a judicator can almost always find something that an individual is doing wrong. Illegal plantations, unauthorized items, and unlicensed trade are all commonplace infractions. If you want to nudge someone into doing what you want, just look for leverage. Should you not find something, you can always make it up – your word weighs heavier than that of the common citizen. How to wield this power is up to you and your conscience.

WEAPONS

Elysium has very strict weapon laws. For all but military personnel, judicators and members of the Honor Guard, carrying weapons is forbidden. Security guards are allowed to carry stun batons and stun guns only. Even improvised weapons are strictly forbidden. Severe punishment awaits anyone caught violating this law, with penalties that range from immediate execution to a one-way ticket to the Catacombs. However, the exact definition of "weapon" is somewhat open to interpretation (and abuse, if you are that kind of judicator).

THE HONOR GUARD

The four ruling Houses of Elysium are protected by a force known as the Honor Guard. Formally, they belong to a single organization, but they have no higher authority to report to, and everyone knows that there are actually four separate Honor Guards, one for each of the ruling Houses. The Honor Guards are very disciplined and drill regularly, but their equipment fits better in a parade than on the battlefield. They wear colorful uniforms with gaudy emblems, and they are armed with a saber and a gyrojet gun. Saber fencing is the Honor Guard's forte, and they are immensely proud of their skills with the weapon and the fact that they are the only ones in the enclave with the right to bear them. The practical use of the sabers is debatable, but they do look quite stylish.

THE JUDICATOR HEADQUARTERS

The headquarters of the judicators is located in the Capitolium building, in the Winter Garden. The judicators are divided into patrols, generally with four people each. In total there are 24 patrols, divided into two shifts. When one shift is active, the other is on-call. Each shift is led by a Chief Inspector, currently Astride Fortescue and Castor Kilgore. The Chief Inspectors are in turn subordinate to the Supreme Commander of the Judicators, Superintendent Minerva Morningstar, who reports directly to the Council.

The active patrols gather for a roll call and briefing before each shift. There, the Chief Inspector goes over any current incidents in the enclave and decides which of the patrols to send to handle them. A shift is typically twelve hours long but may be longer if the situation on the scene demands it. After five shifts you receive two days of rest, then a new shift begins. Normally, you alternate between day shifts and night shifts, but the distinction between the two has lost much of its meaning after decades underground.

In addition to the judicators themselves, the headquarters houses some assistants to the commanders, three communications officers, and a procurator who manages the archives of all legal matters you handle. The latter has the help of the ancient protocol robot TXS-012, nicknamed Texas Twelve. In addition, there is an old couple who manage various janitorial tasks such as washing and repairing your uniforms, cleaning, and cooking.

HQ PERSONNEL

- **Chief Inspectors:** Astride Fortescue and Castor Kilgore
- **Superintendent:** Minerva Morningstar
- **Assistants:** Eldon Montague and Audrey Battenburg
- **Communication Officers:** Godiva De Vere, Carleton Somerset, and Reginald Arundell
- **Procurator:** Luella Acton
- **Procurator's Assistant:** Unit TXS-012
- **Janitors:** Ada and Aldus Budd

Assembly Hall. A barren, run-down hall with benches made of artificial dark wood. This is where the judicators have their briefings before each shift. There is sitting space for about 100 people. At the front of the hall there is a stage, where the Chief Inspector stands. On the wall behind there is a large data screen, where maps of selected parts of the enclave are displayed as needed.

Communication Central. Wide screens cover one wall, next to a worn wooden table stained by decades of coffee mugs. The screens show maps of the enclave indicating the positions of judicators in the field, and where incidents have been reported. There is text flow with status reports. At least one person is sitting here at all times.

Workspaces. A large hall with small desks of artificial wood. Each is equipped with keyboards and shelves for data plates. Portraits of Council members hang on the walls.

The Superintendent's Office. A comparatively spacious room with a worn desk, metal storage cabinets, and pictures on the walls.

Warehouse. Naked light bulbs hang from the ceiling and illuminate a room filled with shelves and packing boxes. Everything from weapons and armor to uniforms can be found here, virtually all bearing signs of wear and use. The desk is usually littered with thick folders.

Locker Room. Two rows of tall, narrow lockers made of artificial dark wood are located along the walls in this room. Copper name tags on each cabinet indicate who its contents belong to. There are also baskets for labeled uniforms, towels or dirty laundry to be thrown in. A shelf next to the shower door always has clean towels. Even personal weapons can be stored in the lockers.

Training Hall. The ingrained sweat from generations of physical exercise permeates this space. Heavy and worn sandbags hang from the ceiling. There are slabs and weights available, as well as a mat used for practicing hand to hand combat.

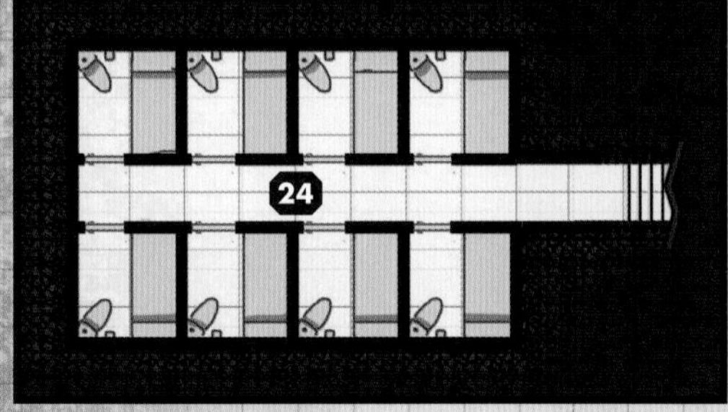

1 × 1 meter

THE JUDICATOR HEADQUARTERS

1. Reception
2. Administration
3. Archives
4. Assembly Hall
5. Communication Central
6. Workspaces
7. The Superintendent's Office
8. Chief Inspectors' Office
9. Procurator's Office
10. Classroom
11. Warehouse
12. Armory
13. Food Storage
14. Locker Room
15. Training Hall
16. Showers
17. Toilets
18. Cantina
19. Lounge
20. Kitchen
21. Laundry Room
22. Interrogation Room
23. Stairs to Cell Block
24. Cell Block

Cantina. Three long tables with benches are in the middle of the room. The walls consist of dark wood panels. Brass lamps are mounted on the walls and lamps with yellowish glass hang from the ceiling.

Lounge. One of the most frequented rooms in the headquarters. Run-down sofas, a couple of hologram pinball machines, and a small table with chairs can be found here.

Kitchen. Almost everything here is made of polished steel or solid artificial wood. The kitchen is spotlessly cleaned every night, no matter how messy it gets during the busy hours.

Laundry Room. A damp and warm room where a massive washing machine runs almost 24 hours a day. Two large drying stations are located along one wall. A workbench stands along another wall. Large fans are mounted on the ceiling above the drying stand.

Interrogation Room. A bare room with a solid metal table welded to the floor, with a chair on each side. A pair of handcuffs can be locked to the table.

Cell Block. Reinforced cells with thick metal doors. The doors have a sliding slit. A metallic folding bunk, a pair of blankets and a hole in the floor for a toilet is all that can be found in each room.

LIFE IN THE ENCLAVE

Life in Elysium consists largely of hard labor in the name of duty. For most, there are at least a couple of hours of leisure time each day, and most weeks have one or two days of rest.

LIVING QUARTERS

When an enclave dweller turns 15 years of age, either further studies in the Academy or a first work task will be assigned. Simple accommodations are provided, either a bunk in a dormitory or sometimes even a small apartment. Registered families are generally provided with an extra room for the children. An individual who rises in the ranks can, over time, expect the opportunity to move to larger

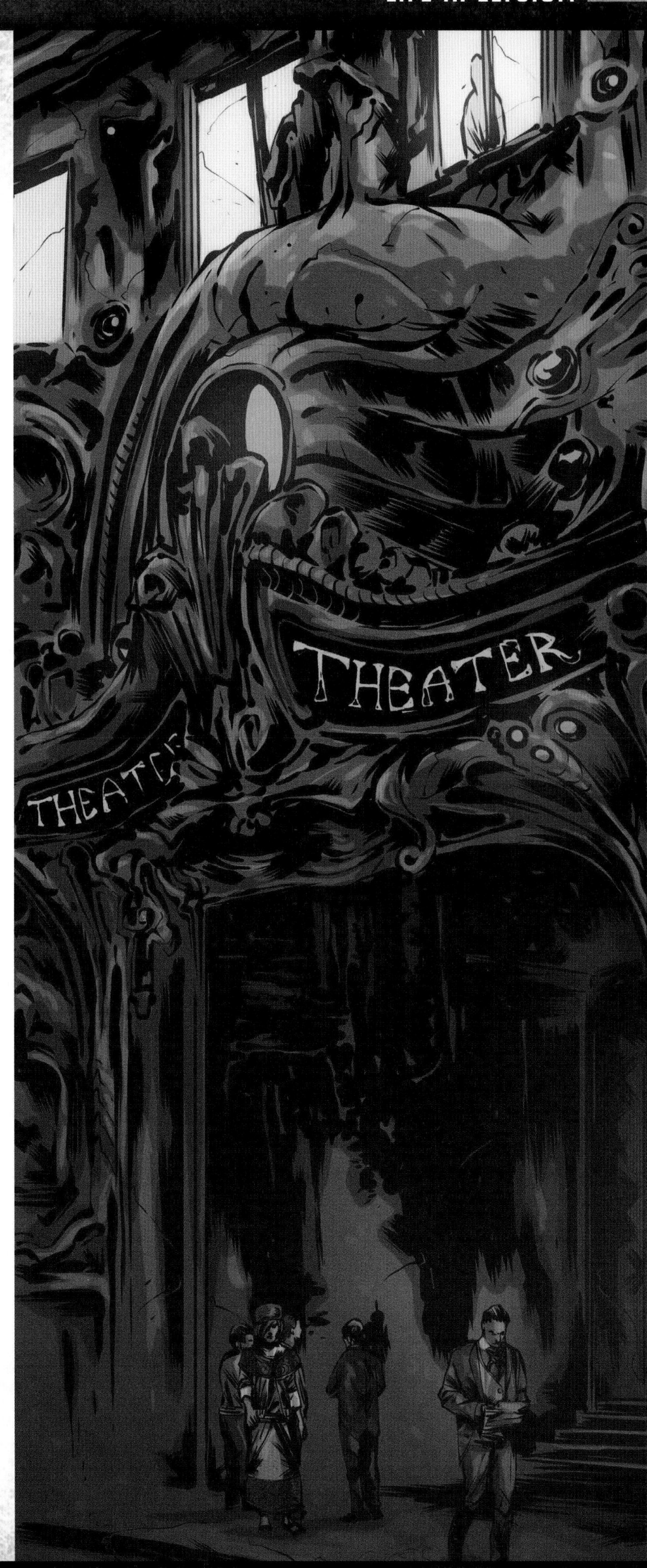

and more comfortable accommodations. However, most people stay in the neighborhood where the rest of their family lives.

A private apartment is typically about 50 square feet in size, rarely over 100 square feet. At best, there is room for a bed, a closet, a chair, and small table. Most apartments have a simple computer terminal used to receive radio and text messages – most often decrees from the ruling Houses, but also some carefully controlled forms of entertainment.

THE DATA NETWORK

Most of the data transmitted via the enclave computer system is text-based. Image and video material are very limited. Reports are written, sent digitally, in some cases read, and then archived. Almost all information in the enclave is digitally stored. Books and paper are very rare and expensive.

The founders of the enclave believed that storage capacity would be almost infinite. But damage caused during the Enclave Wars, combined with the enormous amounts of data gathered throughout the decades, have turned storing data into a huge challenge.

All data is now preserved at the Central Data Archives at the Data Works (see page 98), but not everything has fared throughout the years. Much data has been corrupted or degraded, and as a result of the limited storage capacity, a large amount of data has been compressed as much as possible. For example, a video file might first be compressed into a series of image files, then later into a single image file, and then into a text file.

COMMUNICATION

Most communication throughout the enclave is done via text messages and voice calls, using the network of cables connecting most levels. A robot-controlled switchboard monitors all communication, flags any suspicious traffic and reports it to the judicators.

There is also a network of radio transmitters and receivers, but only the Deep Watch, the judicators and security guards are allowed to transmit radio messages. For civilians, radio transmitters are strictly prohibited.

MEDIA

Most homes in Elysium are fitted with a simple receiver for radio and text messages. There is only one radio channel on air, the rest of the bandwidth is just white noise. In case of an enclave-wide emergency these devices can be remotely activated to broadcast emergency messages, but it has been so long since it needed to be used that no one around today is certain of how it works. A few hours of music and a limited number of entertainment shows are aired every week.

In numerous plazas around the enclave, and in some of the homes of the elite, terminals that also receive video can be found. The video shows are broadcast directly from a decaying old television studio in Old Koly. Every evening, there is a short video news bulletin, and every Saturday at seven, the three-hour entertainment show Voice of Dawn is broadcast. The host, Valentino Morningstar, always draws large crowds to the streets during these shows, but he is not popular among the workers of the enclave. The Voice of Dawn is a mix of community information, propaganda, and entertainment.

In many sectors there are also cinema theaters that show movies for a few credits. Most cinemas show documentaries about the enclave's glorious history, although sometimes feature films are shown – a few newly recorded, but mostly classics from the Old Age. The cinemas are subject to strict censorship and cannot display any films that might have a negative impact on the moral values of the citizens or be considered subversive. However, some underground salons do take the risk of showing unauthorized movies.

VEHICLES AND TRANSPORTATION

Civilian vehicles in working order are rare in Elysium I, with the exception of simple kick bikes. A few sectors of the Core also have old, wired streetcars in working order. In some of the industrial sectors of the Deep, freight trains and cargo lifts are used for heavy transports.

The most advanced vehicles are restricted for use only by the military and law enforcement. As a judicator on patrol, you will often use the distinctive four-seat patrol hovercraft or a two-seat hoverbike, equipped with sirens and flashing lights.

DEALING WITH MONEY

As long as you live in the enclave and work as a judicator, you do not have to worry about keeping track of your salary and your daily expenses. Assume your salary is enough for your living expenses – if you want to buy something in addition to this, you need to access credits in another way, for example through contacts.

For transporting commons goods, elevators and sheer muscle power are used. Loads are drawn on wagons or carried, on foot or on kick bikes. Bicycle taxis are also used, but riding one is a privilege for the elite, or those who have plenty of credits to spare.

The Deep Guard has other vehicles, such as heavily armored hovercraft of different sizes. Armored troop transports with advanced weapons systems are rumored to be available for expeditions outside the enclave. As far as you know, these vehicles haven't been used for decades now.

CREDITS

The enclave still uses its ancient currency, the Elysium Credit. A credit is divided into 100 cents. Residents are given accommodation and equipment required for their service – everything else must be purchased with credits. For proles, pay is just enough for bare necessities, while the members of the ruling Houses can live well – some even in abundance. Salary is usually paid weekly, see the table on page 112. Payment is usually done electronically via the ID card that specifies your security class, and which you are required to always carry with you. On page 119, there is a price list for common goods and services available in the enclave.

Cash: Because many resources in the enclave are hard to come by and thus restricted, a black market has emerged in Elysium I. Electronic transactions are not used by these shady businesses, as they can be tracked. Instead, traders in the Bazaar (see page 97) have started to use an improvised hard currency – small pieces of metal with the Elysium eagle icon embossed on them. The Houses tried to combat this illegitimate currency but have since given up, and the trade of these coins is now tolerated.

Even as a judicator, sometimes it may be useful to spend some cash to pay informers without leaving an electronic trail.

SALARIES IN ELYSIUM I

CITIZEN	WEEKLY SALARY
Worker	1 credit
Foreman	2 credits
Security Guard	3 credits
Judicator	5 credits

FOOD, DRINKS, AND DRUGS

For most people in the enclave, food and drink are a necessity, not a joy. Most workers, and others with little credit, eat their meals in the Cantina (see page 99). This limits the diet to whatever is being served there, which is mostly mushroom-based products and root vegetables supplemented with crushed cakes of insect meat. Farm laborers in the plantations of Northolme and Calista are luckier, as they get to eat what they produce and thus have a diet more akin to what the elites eat.

Higher status means more credits, along with access to the restricted eateries at most factories, offices, and facilities. The food is not always much better than what is served in the Cantina, but it is more varied and real fish or seafood sometimes

ENCLAVE FOOD
The range of food available in the enclave is adapted to the limited supplies. Fish and shellfish are farmed, as are insects, but the main source of protein is artificially grown meat. This meat mass is sponge-like in taste and texture, more of a necessity than a tasty meal. Vegetables – specifically root vegetables – are genetically modified to grow faster and be more nutritious, but they are not always tasty. Fruits are harder to grow and are thus an expensive luxury. There are no real slaughter animals. Should you come across a real piece of meat, it has either been kept in a cryo freezer for centuries or it comes from someone who has slaughtered one of the dogs in the enclave without a license.

appears on the plate along with vegetables or even fruit. For you and others in the elite, there are exclusive dining rooms few others even know about. A kitchen can be found in each House palace as well as in the Capitolium. You eat better than most in the enclave and do so at no cost.

Those with a lower status can only afford variations to their diet in the form of synthetic coffee, tea, or fermented drinks purchased at simple diners in the Core and the Deep. You and others with plenty of credits can visit a number of decent restaurants in the Core, but they can rarely match the meals served in the four palaces. The best chefs and ingredients go almost exclusively to the four Houses.

Alcohol is heavily regulated in the enclave, hence always sought after on the black market. Calming or soothing drugs, which are usually smoked, are more tolerated. Working under the influence of any stimulant is strictly prohibited, but this law is hard to enforce among workers with the hardest and dirtiest jobs in the enclave. Stimulants that increase wakefulness and focus are sometimes used by researchers or work teams with extremely long and demanding assignments but are otherwise prohibited.

RECYCLING

Everything in the enclave must be recycled. The resources are limited and everything from feces and urine to broken appliances and machinery are collected, sorted, and reused in some way. Even the inhabitants themselves are part of this cycle. Over the years in sectors like Calista and Northolme it has become commonplace for farm workers who die to be buried there, becoming part of the mill, which gives residents so much of their food.

Two main facilities handle recycling on a large scale: the Recycle Works and the Night Hall smelter, the latter staffed by convicts sentenced to hard labor. However, many of the resources used by enclave dwellers come from items recycled at home.

Everyone knows the benefit of reusing anything possible. Children and the elderly perform the tasks of sorting, storing, and fixing everything that can be used again, as well as making sure that as much as possible gets into the family compost. If the latter is not used for a small plantation, it can be sold for some profit in Calista or Northolme. Groups of toddlers and elderly rummaging for scrap or compost are common, even though doing so is not strictly legal. Everyone must do their part in Elysium, no matter how small or tired they are.

WASHING, CARE AND TOILETING

If you live in the Crown or the Core, your home may have its own bathroom. Most, however, share toilets and showers with a limited number of people. In the Deep, an entire floor or a whole building can share a single bathroom. The reason is partly to conserve space, but mainly due to the scarcity of water. Showers in the enclave drip rather than spray water, and toilets are emptied using vacuum pressure.

For the elite, a proper shower or even a private bath are available if you can afford it. Strictly controlled bathhouses offer luxurious baths at expensive prices. It can also be a privilege that comes with a very high position within the hierarchy.

For the ordinary enclave dweller, there are other establishments that may be visited. Finding a place to get a haircut, delousing, or health check is easy in the residential areas of the Deep and the Core. If you are looking for something more congenial than impersonal and fast treatment, you can visit one of the few licensed barbers or clinics available, but of course, such services cost more.

Laundry is handled in a similar manner. Workers submit their dirty overalls once a week to the laundry facilities and receive a washed and mended one in return. Everyone is responsible for keeping their private garments clean as best they can. For managers, administrators, and others with higher status, there are laundry facilities available, but the individual is responsible for the care of their own garment. For you and others within the elite there are servants who handle such tasks. As a judicator, a clean and pressed uniform always awaits you in your quarters at the start of a shift.

SHOPS

There are quite a few shops in the enclave. Workers rarely have many credits to spend and getting a business license for anything other than selling food and drink in the Deep is difficult. Workers generally go to the Exchange and the Bazaar, where they can find a range of goods and gadgets if they have something to offer in return.

For those with more credits, there is a limited but varied range of shops and craftsmen available. Fine clothes, jewelry, utensils, art, home appliances, tools and anything else you want can be found in the trade districts of Nova Paloma. In the residential districts, there are less sophisticated stores that offer an assortment of general goods.

RUMORS OF MEAT

Stories and rumors of meat are common in the enclave. It is said that gangs in the Deep or Exiles in the Catacombs are hunting mutant beasts coming in from the Outside, or that they have turned to cannibalism. There are even rumors of hidden breeding halls in the palaces of the Houses, and secret laboratories where hundreds of different species are kept in cages. It is alleged that these are meant to be used to repopulate the surface one day, but are also used as a source of luxury food for the highest ranks of the Houses.

There is no large-scale production of items for private consumption in Elysium I. Anything you buy is crafted in small workshops, usually by hand. These items are often beautiful, take a long time to create, and cost a lot of credits. Few enclave residents can buy anything beyond the simplest of items. Instead, many treasure ancient family heirlooms from the Old Age.

Illegal trade is common, especially among workers in the Deep. Some see the black market as a necessity that gives people what they want, but if unchecked for too long it can lead to a waste of precious resources. Much of the illegal trade is controlled by various criminal gangs who exploit weakness for profit. Stopping those who engage in black-market trade on a larger scale is difficult, not least because the trail sometimes leads back to high-ranking people in Elysium I, even to members of the Houses.

ILLEGAL PLANTATIONS

To determine which residents of the enclave should be allowed to grow their own crops or vegetables is a difficult assessment for the rulers of the enclave, and often you as a judicator will have to make the call. A few plants for spices or decoration are generally allowed, as are small patches used to grow mushrooms or insects. Anything beyond that increases the risk of unwanted attention.

For many, credits are not the main incentive, it is simply a matter of growing plants for personal use. Despite the risk and the challenge, some entrepreneurs do take the chance to expand their crop patches. The laws are unclear and many judicators choose to look the other way when an otherwise good citizen is just trying to secure an extra meal.

SPORTS IN THE ENCLAVE

Because many in the enclave have sedentary jobs, practicing sports is encouraged. Sporting events are good for keeping the inhabitants busy. The only arena in the enclave is called the Palace of Light, and it is located in Tindertuft. It can seat a thousand individuals but is rarely filled to its limit. Instead, residents view their favorite sports in smaller venues scattered throughout the enclave.

Most of the popular sports in the enclave were inspired by sports from before the Apocalypse.

CRIMINAL GANGS
Criminal gangs like the Sooty Hand and the Cravats have been around for years in Elysium I. Rumors say that some are based in the Catacombs. Open conflict between the gangs and the law is uncommon – the gangs know that direct confrontation with judicators will not end well – but it does occur from time to time. Squabbles between the gangs for control over different sectors of the Deep, or over the control of the trade of drugs and alcohol, are more common.

Betting is widespread and all but impossible to snuff out. Below are the most common sports:

Saber Fencing is popular among the Houses and other influential families. The most famous fencer today is the masterful Beatrix Morningstar, who spellbinds the audience with her dance-like moves. Biomechatronic implants are strictly forbidden in this sport. Tournaments are arranged every Sunday in the Palace of Light, with the results broadcast by the Voice of Dawn.

Dawn Race: A yearly running contest that starts on level 50 in Arcadium and ends on level 2 in Nova Paloma. The race is as much about tactics as it is about endurance, because the contenders need to use the transport lifts designated for the runners. In recent years, the event has become popular among the workers as the miner Marton Reed has won three consecutive races.

Velodrome Racing: This is a sport for the wide masses. Both high and low born meet in the Palace of Light at the end of each month to enjoy the races. These occasions are one of the rare instances that the stadium is fully packed, with opportunists selling fake tickets for the finals.

Sling Ball is a widespread sport in the Deep. It is played between two teams on a small rectangular plane with H-shaped goals. Each player is equipped with a long club. You score by either shooting the ball under the bar (three points) or over the bar (one point). This sport can get very violent and players often use the clubs to beat each other up.

Chain Lift: This is another popular sport among the proles. Played in or around factories, workers compete to lift the heaviest objects with the help of a chain and pulley.

Body Bombing: In this violent, no holds barred form of martial arts, biomechatronic implants are often used. The "sport" itself is not licensed by the Council and competitions are organized in secret locations around the Deep. The latest Body Bombing star is the wanted gang member Veronica Volt.

RELIGION

The Council does not allow another group in the enclave to threaten its authority. This includes religious communities. The only existing religion with many believers is the Temple, and its devoted followers are not seen as a threat to power. Some more radical cults have emerged in recent years, but they are have all been very small.

THE TEMPLE

The world's history is filled with wars triggered by faith in higher powers. When the people of Elysium fled from the surface, they left the old ways of worship behind. But religion did not die. During the many generations that followed, wrought with hardship and more war, remnants of different religions of old mingled together and became one: the Temple. It stands for unity and a belief that all people share a higher power which binds them together, and one day will deliver them to the surface again.

The Temple never demands any tribute, prayer, or sacrifice. Perhaps this contributes to its popularity. It only brings people together, offering a kind of meditative unity. After many decades, the temple has grown into a strong institution, but without any formal power. Its existence is tolerated by the Council, who sees the Temple as a way to keep the enclave workers under control.

The Temple is led by an Eminence. There are a total of ten Eminences, but only one is awake at any given time – the other nine are kept in deep cryosleep. The ten Eminences were chosen by the original founders of Elysium to ensure that enclave residents would not deviate from Elysium's original values over the many years in the depths.

Eminences change shifts once a year, generally around the time of Memorial Day celebrations. Then, a new Eminence is woken from his/her cryo bed and the current one goes back to sleep, to wake up again nine years later. All Eminences were born before the Apocalypse and bring with them the knowledge of what happened, to ensure that something like that never happens again. The current Eminence is named Creon.

Initially, the Eminences were formal advisors to the Council, but over time the focus of their work shifted to providing guidance to the enclave's inhabitants and leading the emerging Temple. This was a development welcomed by the Houses, who did not want the Eminences to meddle in their affairs.

The task of the Temple is to unify the people of Elysium, especially the workers, under the dream of a common future and to remind them of the horrors of the past. This is done in many ways, most often through informal gatherings in small chapels situated all around the enclave – at least one on each level. To help them carry out their work, the Eminences have around one hundred volunteer novices – they come from all strata of society in the enclave, but most often from the ranks of the workers.

Believers rarely stand out. Some bear the Temple's Sun and Moon symbols on their clothes, others carry a meditation mat to their workplace or have a small part of the home dedicated to calm contemplation. Around many gates and arches in the residential districts, there are small alcoves where simple gifts or food for the Temple can be left.

OTHER RELIGIONS AND CULTS

In comparison to the Temple, all other religious groups in the enclave are small and without influence. A dozen or so cults exist, but with very few adherents.

During the latest decade, it has become somewhat of a trend and status symbol for those with higher station in the enclave to be a member of an esoteric sect or quasi-scientific cult. Most are harmless, simply an excuse to meet, dress up, and participate in rites that are said to be secret. However, you have heard the whispered rumors of macabre rites including human sacrifice and cannibalism, but no concrete evidence has ever been presented.

There are also the fringe lunatics you always have to watch out for. For example, the fools who speak of spirits in the machines and of robots being equal to humans, or even worse, the lunatics claiming that it is possible to live on the surface and that the Houses keep the enclave in ignorance about this fact.

TECHNOLOGY AND SCIENCE

For many years, Elysium focused most of its time and resources into the discipline known as xenogenetics, the research that gave rise to different mutant creatures. You have heard of remote genlabs, research stations where remarkable progress was made, before the Enclave Wars brought it all to an end.

The progress made by Elysium in the manufacture of robots was limited and the artificial intelligences they created never reached the level that those of the Noatun Titan Power did. Instead, the success of xenogenetics led Elysium to further advances in biomechatronics, the science of linking living tissue with machines.

XENOGENETICS

Almost all research regarding xenogenetics occurred in enclaves other than Elysium I, particularly in Elysium IV. The laboratories in Elysium I once used for researching xenogenetics are today used almost exclusively for the study of biomechatronics.

The usefulness of xenogenetics is significant but it is a double-edged sword. The dangers are great and therefore there are strict bans on any alterations that can be inherited by, or affect, human offspring. As a result of this, very limited progress has been made during the latest generations.

Strange pests occasionally appear in the Deep that seem to be either xenogenetically modified or completely unknown to science. Those who live there claim that these are creatures from the surface world that managed to burrow into the enclave. For you and the Council, however, such problems seem to solve themselves – the residents do their utmost to kill the critters.

ILLEGAL CLINICS
You are aware of the existence of xenogenetic clinics, focusing mostly on cosmetic changes. Such sites sometimes function as a cover for unauthorized facilities that dabble in unsanctioned experiments.

BIOMECHATRONICS

Biomechatronic implants come in many forms. They can be subtle and sleek, or they can be big, ugly, and cumbersome. For Elysium's elite, unseen implants are the only option. To bear no outward sign of alteration is a sign of belonging to the upper echelons of society.

For Elysium's workers, some jobs may require one or several implants. The more expensive the service is, the better and less visible the implant will be. Many simple implants are relatively common and cheap. In some circles, they have even become a symbol of subtle rebellion against the old hierarchies of the enclave.

BIOMECHATRONIC IMPLANTS
How biomechatronic implants work is explained in Chapter 9.

The most intrusive biomechatronic implants are called reconstructions. Those who bear them have undergone very radical alteration to their bodies. To be reconstructed is to be sentenced to a life of suffering.

People are reconstructed for a variety of reasons, most often as a punishment for some crime. Reconstructive implants are generally bulky and ugly, with little consideration given to what the patient will look like. Many reconstructed suffer not only physical pain, but also mental trauma after having their bodies so radically changed.

ROBOTS

The robots found in Elysium I are comparable to many simpler models that the other Titan Powers created. The enclave's scientists failed to create more advanced variants of thinking machines, such as the Noatun Titan Power's artificial intelligences, powerful entities known as constructs (see *Mutant: Mechatron*).

However, Elysium's researchers of biomechatronics have created experimental entities that can compare to constructs in terms of intelligence and processing capacity. Such an entity is called a cyber and is a fusion of a human and a robot brain.

There are not many robots in Elysium I today. A few military units that are still in working order are kept in storage, in case Elysium I should ever need to go to war again. The Clinic and the Academy each have a number of medical units and lab robots, some farming robots work in Calista and Northolme, and the Central Data Network employs a number of protocol models. In addition, there are industrial robots in the enclave factories, most in very poor condition.

DEVELOPMENT LEVELS

Elysium I is a society in decline, despite the proud words of the ruling Houses. To measure the state of the enclave, four Development Levels are used, just like in the Ark of *Mutant: Year Zero*. Unlike in the Ark, the Development Levels in Elysium I start high, but then decrease during the game.

The Development Levels used in *Mutant: Elysium* are Production, Security, Science and Culture. All Development Levels start the game at 80. The levels drop during play as a result of the Incidents that occur in the enclave – read more in Chapter 10. The efforts of you and the other judicators can slow down the decline, but you cannot stop it.

Fill in the Development Levels on the enclave sheet, found in the back of this book, and available for download at the Free League website.

PRODUCTION

The Development Levels in Production affect prices for goods and services in the enclave.

60+	Production shuffles along and provides most of the enclave inhabitants with what they need. Prices are unaffected (see page 119).
40–59	Some items are becoming harder to find. Prices in the enclave rise to twice as high as normal. Power outages are becoming more common. The black market grows, with increasing crime as a result.
20–39	The shelves are empty and there is a shortage of most items in the enclave. Residents begin to hoard food. Looting occurs in the Deep. Power outages are getting longer. Prices in the enclave are three times as high as normal.
0–20	There is a desperate lack of food and other basic necessities. Looting now breaks out even in the Core. Power is permanently cut to several sectors in the Deep. Prices are four times as high as normal, if the goods are available at all.

SECURITY

The level of Security development affects the ability of the judicators to resolve Incidents in the enclave. Read more in Chapter 10.

60+	Crime and other incidents are common, but security guards and judicators manage to maintain law and order overall.
40–59	Robberies, thefts, and protests are becoming more common. Street gangs in the Deep act openly and take over some blocks. Groups of vigilantes form among the workers.
20–39	Unrest spreads to the Core, where the gangs increasingly gain a foothold. Civilians avoid walking alone in the alleys, and all shops have guards at the door.
0–20	Looting and riots break out in the Core. Security guards and even judicators are openly attacked on the streets. The Deep is largely lawless, with gangs controlling the different sectors.

SCIENCE

The level of development in Science affects which artifacts can be manufactured by enclave factories. When the Science Development Level drops below the Technology level of an artifact, it can no longer be manufactured and is therefore no longer generally available for purchase in the enclave.

60+	Despite the lack of resources, the scholars of the Academy continue unwaveringly in their work to prepare humanity to return to the surface world.
40–59	Several research programs are shut down due to lack of resources and competence among the scholars. Parts of the Academy are now empty.
20–39	Only the most critical research projects carry on, but with less resources and staff.
0–20	The Academy is largely empty. Apart from a few exceptions, all research has been abandoned and the remaining skilled scientists try to save what little they can of the knowledge they have accumulated.

CULTURE

The level of development in Culture has no concrete effect in terms of game mechanics, but it can still have a big impact on life in the enclave.

60+	Books are a rarity and the salons are worn down, yet the enclave has a lively cultural life with literature, stage shows and cinemas.
40–59	Some theaters close due to increasing censorship, threats, vandalism, or just lack of resources. An increasing number of cinemas show unauthorized films in defiance, resulting in several of them being banned and closed.
20–39	Conformity increases and the few theaters and cinemas still in operation show almost only propaganda works that celebrate the Houses and Elysium's great history. People begin broadcasting illegal messages of protest over unauthorized radio stations, despite severe punishments.
0–20	Cultural life in the enclave has almost come to an end. Only the Voice of Dawn is still heard, continuously broadcasting a stream of propaganda for the few that continue to listen.

PRICE LIST FOR GOODS AND SERVICES

The list on the next page summarizes the prices in credits for common goods and services available in Elysium I. Prices may be affected by the current Development Level in Production (see above).

COMMON PRODUCTS AND SERVICES IN ELYSIUM I

PRODUCT	PRICE
Emergency ration of food	10 cents
Pack of cigarettes	5 cents
Cup of synthetic coffee	3 cents
Glass of fermented drink	5 cents
Glass of liquor (requires license)	10 cents
Sedating drug, smoked	5 cents
Stimulant, pills	5 cents
Kick bike	1 credit
Hoverbike (requires license)	6 credits
Patrol hovercraft (requires license)	10 credits
E-pack	1 credit
Data panel	1 credit
Comm radio (requires license)	1 credit
Electronic tool kit	1 credit
Flashlight	50 cents
Stun baton	2 credits
SERVICE	**PRICE**
Letter delivery by runners	2 cents
Package delivery by runner	4 cents
Bicycle taxi ride	5 cents
Carrier	20 cents
Bath house visit	10 cents
Haircut	10 cents
Shave	5 cents
Stylist	20 cents
Theater visit	25 cents
Cinema visit	10 cents
Simple meal in a diner	5 cents
Decent meal in a restaurant	20 cents
Lavish meal in fine restaurant	50 cents
Clothes washing and pressing	20 cents
Delousing	5 cents
Physical check-up	10 cents

1

YOUR JOB AS GAMEMASTER

The Council and the Houses may think they control Elysium I, but the enclave's true ruler is you, the Gamemaster. You control the workers, the higborn, and the Eminences – all residents of Elysium I except the player characters.

GAME PRINCIPLES

Just like in *Mutant: Year Zero* and its expansions, *Mutant: Elysium* is based on a number of principles. Their purpose is to help you create the right mood and themes in the game and to guide you when you are unsure how to handle certain situations during play.

1. THE HOUSE ABOVE ALL ELSE

Elysium I may very well be humanity's last bastion in the world, and it is up to the great Houses to make sure the flame of civilization is not snuffed out forever. It is up to each player to ensure that it is his or her own House who leads the way into the new dawn. Nothing is more important than the bond of blood, the family, the House.

2. JUDICATORS STILL HAVE A JOB TO DO

The Houses may be the most important thing for the characters, but judicators still have an important job to do. They must be very discreet when they put the family's interests before duty, because a judicator who is punished for misconduct is an embarrassment for the House. This balance between family and duty is central to the game.

3. JUDICATORS ARE NOT THE GOOD GUYS

Unlike, for example, the animals in the Paradise Valley struggling for freedom, the PCs in *Mutant: Elysium* can hardly be considered good guys. As judicators, it is their job to defend and maintain a system that is anything but fair or democratic. This can be perceived as a difficult or unwholesome task by the players, but it is also an interesting challenge. How do they use their power? Will they be oppressors, or will they try to do good within the limits of their duty?

4. THE ENCLAVE WILL FALL

Even though the Voice of Dawn does its best to deny it, it is obvious to everyone that the enclave's days are numbered. Raw materials are scarce while tools and even facilities are dangerously beyond repair. The leaders of the Houses would never admit it openly, but behind closed doors there are talks and plans for the day when Elysium I has to be abandoned.

5. THE SURFACE IS UNINHABITABLE

Every child born in Elysium has been told this over and over – the terrible weapons of the Ancients scorched the surface of the Earth. Venturing out will lead to certain death. Increasingly however, both members of the families and servants alike are beginning to doubt whether this is still the case, although few dare to talk openly about it.

6. NO ONE LIVES FOREVER

As in *Mutant: Year Zero* and its expansions, it's important that the players feel their characters are mortal. Life as a judicator is perilous. Do not deliberately kill the characters, but do not go out of your way to shield them from the harshness of their reality. It's easy enough to replace a dead judicator in a patrol with a new one, after all.

7. THIS IS STILL MUTANT

Mutant: Elysium differs a lot from *Year Zero, Genlab Alpha,* and *Mechatron.* But do not forget that we are still playing Mutant! Ruin and decay combined with black humor is still an important aspect of the game.

8. HUMANS ARE THE MASTERS OF THE WORLD

Sooner or later, Elysium I will fall, and when it does the characters will meet mutants, animals, and robots in the Zone. For the many enclave humans, it will be difficult to see these creatures as equals – most will regard them as lower beings that must be controlled or dominated. Certainly, some mutants and animals will oppose this social world view.

PLAYING THE CAMPAIGN

As in *Mutant: Year Zero*, the game in *Mutant: Elysium* can take many different directions, and how the story develops depends largely on the players' own choices. The *Guardians of the Fall* is described in detail in Chapters 10.

The campaign tells the story of the enclave Elysium I. The narrative is driven by Incidents the Houses themselves will set in motion – in most cases with the characters acting on their behalf.

INCIDENTS

Guardians of the Fall differs a bit from a typical roleplaying campaign. Although this may sometimes place higher demands on the GM, at the same time it opens up new opportunities for exciting gaming sessions. The campaign is comprised of Incidents. An Incident is a mini-scenario intended to be played during one or two game sessions.

An Incident resembles a Special Zone Sector (see *Mutant: Year Zero* and the various Zone Compendia), with the difference being that the PCs have a clearly defined task to solve. The other difference is that, for the most part, the players themselves – as representatives of their Houses – choose which Incidents they want to send their characters to solve.

This increases the players' freedom of choice but at the same time demands that you read up on all Incidents in advance. If you get into a situation where you feel you are not prepared, our tip is that you either break for the evening or take a short break before resuming the game. The Incidents are relatively short and easy to remember.

GAMES BETWEEN THE INCIDENT

Incidents are the core of the *Guardians of the Fall* campaign, but it can be enriched by inserting other events between the Incidents. After all, the judicators have free time, albeit in very limited quantities.

One tip is to play scenes where the PCs interact with their contacts (see Chapter 5). These scenes usually play out with one player at a time, and should therefore be kept very short. Of course, this kind of scene can be expanded into a whole mini-adventure involving several other players. The game sessions between Incidents can also be expanded using random events and missions unrelated to the campaign (read more below).

RANDOM EVENTS

Elysium I is a crowded and eventful place. This section describes a number of minor events that can occur whenever you want to spice up the action a bit – during an Incident or when the PCs are off duty and moving about the enclave.

Players can always choose whether to intervene or not. However, failing to intervene against an ongoing threat to enclave security can lead to a reprimand for misconduct (page 24).

Some Incidents do not cause conflict for PCs, while others may develop into smaller scenarios. The events are divided between the Core and the Deep. Roll on the table below or simply pick the event yourself.

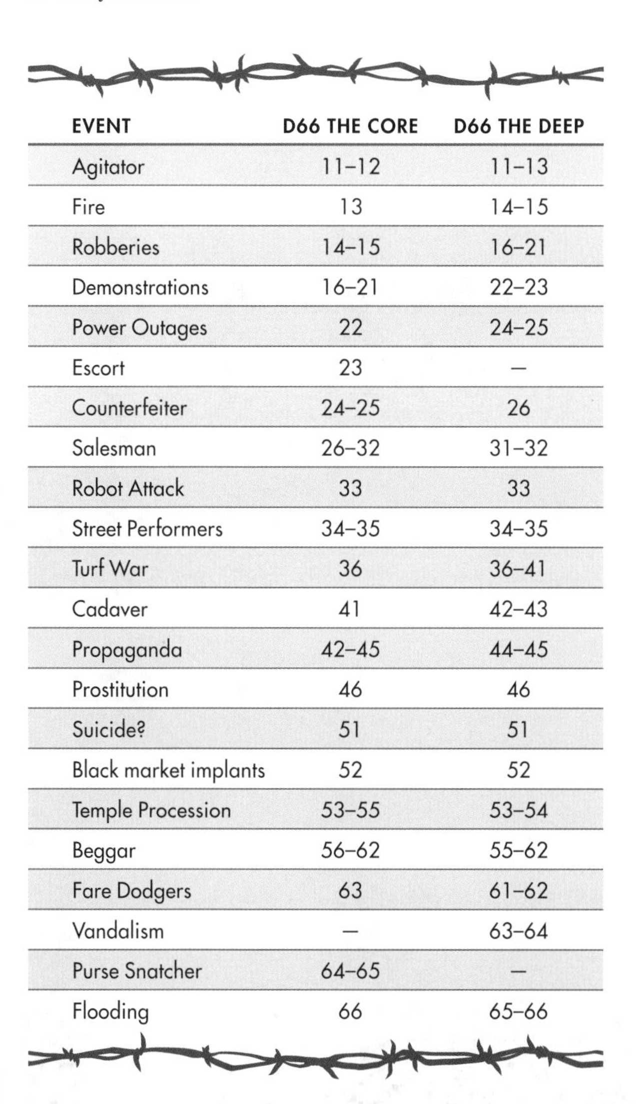

EVENT	D66 THE CORE	D66 THE DEEP
Agitator	11–12	11–13
Fire	13	14–15
Robberies	14–15	16–21
Demonstrations	16–21	22–23
Power Outages	22	24–25
Escort	23	–
Counterfeiter	24–25	26
Salesman	26–32	31–32
Robot Attack	33	33
Street Performers	34–35	34–35
Turf War	36	36–41
Cadaver	41	42–43
Propaganda	42–45	44–45
Prostitution	46	46
Suicide?	51	51
Black market implants	52	52
Temple Procession	53–55	53–54
Beggar	56–62	55–62
Fare Dodgers	63	61–62
Vandalism	–	63–64
Purse Snatcher	64–65	–
Flooding	66	65–66

AGITATOR

A man in worker's overalls stands up and screams "Down with the oppressors! We are living under a false sense of security!" This is followed by "Rise up against the Houses!" People hurry past, looking away nervously or shaking their heads.

Worker Willon Bing has lost everything and is tired of life in Elysium I. He walks around the streets screaming out his dissatisfaction, which is of course not allowed in the enclave. The problem is that Boris is not alone. If the PCs try to stop him too aggressively, other residents will intervene, with protests or even violence.

FIRE

The smell of smoke hangs in the air. Black clouds and fluttering ash can be seen coming from an alley further down the street. Somebody screams "Fire, fire!" Panic flashes in the eyes of the enclave inhabitants.

Some garbage containers in an alley caught fire and the flames quickly spread to the adjacent buildings. PCs can try to control the fire by organizing a water chain. This requires a successful Manipulate roll. To be able to stay close to the fire requires a successful Endure roll. The reason for the fire is unclear but a witness states he saw two individuals climb atop the containers just before the fire broke out...

ROBBERIES

Two loud bangs echo along the streets of the enclave, followed by screaming. Further down the street, people disperse outside a shop that sells canned foods.

The workers Burch and Haskel have tired of their jobs in the mine and are living on the street. They decided to rob a local small shop, but everything has gone wrong. They shot the shop owner by mistake, then panicked and took hostages. The PCs can try to talk them into surrendering by rolling Manipulate or use violence to handle the situation.

DEMONSTRATION

A crowd gathers with signs that read "Up to the Surface," "The World has Healed," "The surface is safe!" and "The Apocalypse is Over." They encourage people to accompany them or donate technology and supplies "for the final dig to the outside."

This type of procession is illegal, but is usually ignored by the Council. PCs can decide if they want to intervene or not.

POWER OUTAGES

The lights throughout the sector flash a few times and eventually die out completely. Somebody screams and then a salesman is heard shouting "THIEF! THIEF!"

The sector has suffered a power outage. It could be the result of willful tampering or just poor maintenance. The PCs are expected to intervene and maintain the peace until technicians arrive. In the dark, some of the poorer and unfortunate inhabitants of the sector take the chance to grab gadgets and supplies for themselves. See rules for darkness in Chapter 6.

ESCORT

A man calls out to the judicators from a luxurious bicycle taxi. The highborn Pernicus Warburg requires an escort to his destination because he finds that the surroundings are threatening.

Pernicus will not proceed unescorted and threatens to report the PCs if they do not comply. Pernicus is on his way to a nearby restaurant, club, theater, or game hall.

COUNTERFEITER

A woman with a biomechatronic jaw meanders through the alleys. She discreetly approaches and talks with the people she passes. Some stop and exchange credits for large envelopes full of who knows what.

Grizzie sells all kinds of fake licenses. She can offer anything from a home nursing license to a license to procreate. If she spots the judicators,

she immediately makes a run for it. Forging fake licenses (see Chapter 7) is strictly forbidden and punished severely. If the PCs manage to Manipulate Grizzie, she can reveal an unauthorized license printing facility located in the Deep.

SALESMAN

A street vendor working out of a bicycle stand decorated with colorful lights crosses the street. He shouts "Fresh insects, fresh insects. Fried mushrooms, fried mushrooms. Great products! 50 cents for a pound!" When he sees the PCs, he becomes very silent and speeds up.

Pimm sells home-grown mushrooms and insects without a license, which is strictly prohibited in the enclave. He will try to evade the judicators. His bike stand gives a -2 modification to Move because it is so heavy. If he fails, he leaves his wares and runs away on foot.

ROBOT ATTACK

The screams of horrified enclave dwellers can be heard from further down the street. People scatter in panic as an industrial model robot storms into view. It pummels and slashes everything within reach of its mechanical tool-arms.

The robot TBL-401, nicknamed Table-For-One, is malfunctioning and has gone berserk. The only way to stop it is to permanently shut it off.

STREET PERFORMERS

Melancholic music echoes along the street. At a crossing there are many performers, including a man and a woman in knitted sweaters dancing to the music. The performance is a dramatized interpretation of Elysium's history.

The actors perform shows with names like "Atomic Bomb" and "Towards the Deep." Some onlookers watch with respect while others spit on the floor as they pass.

TURF WAR

The street is suddenly devoid of people. An eerie quiet descends over the sector. Only a distant child crying is heard. Something is wrong. Suddenly, two groups violently clash against each other. As they collide the silence is broken by the noise of screams, broken bones, and iron pipes.

The PCs are in the middle of a turf war between the Sooty Hand and Cravats gangs. They can try to interrupt the fighting themselves or call for reinforcements. A patrol of security guards is nearby but the PCs must Manipulate them to convince them to intervene.

CORPSE

A group of kids gathers around something in a narrow alley. In a pile of illegally dumped garbage there is a well-dressed but lifeless man. He has no visible injuries but is clearly dead.

Who the man is and how he died is up to the GM. Perhaps he witnessed something he shouldn't have, or jealousy or some other drama led to his demise. Perhaps he has fallen victim to the conflict between the Houses.

PROPAGANDA

A floating jumbotron glides through the bustling alleys of the sector, its screen showing Voice of Dawn. The host, Valentino Morningstar, explains that the enclave is filled with happy inhabitants in humanity's last outpost. Pictures of people in an Elysium I untouched by the ravages of time fill the screen. These are soon replaced by clips of mushroom clouds exploding, disease-ridden people, and ruins left behind after the fall of civilization. The narrator's voice assumes a serious tone that warns of the dangers of the surface world and explains that it is likely that it will remain uninhabitable forever. The program closes with a decree, calling on all people to obey the judicators, be loyal to the Council, and always follow the Elysium creed of "Tradition, Resolution, Courage!" A bang is heard and the jumbotron shuts off for a few seconds, then replays the same message.

It is evident that someone on the dirty street below threw an object at the floating machine. The judicators may have to intervene against the vandal.

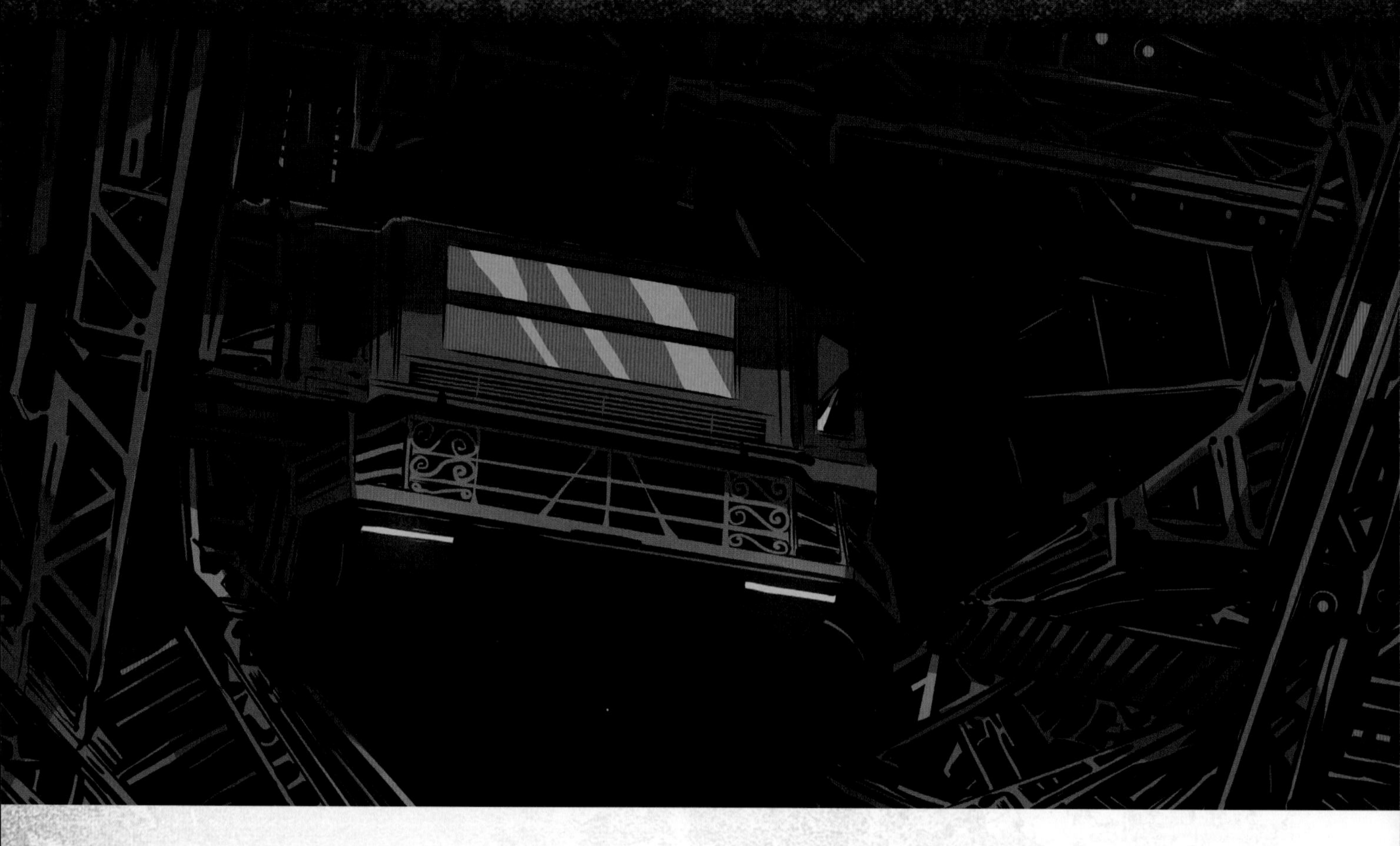

PROSTITUTION

A man with a trendy, bright-green hairstyle and revealing latex clothes offers his services to passersby.

The gigolo Redmond has lost all hope for his life and tries to sell his body to anyone who walks past – judicators as well as ordinary citizens. He is in a noticeably drug-induced state. Prostitution is illegal in the enclave, but it is nonetheless commonplace.

SUICIDE?

A whistle echoes through from the Shaft. It increases in volume and is followed by a loud thud. A woman shouts and people gather around a ledge at the edge of the Shaft.

The young highborn Chester Fairfax has thrown himself – or was pushed – to his death from a sector higher up in the enclave. He sought a license to start a family with the young highborn Vendela Warburg, but got denied. It is known that the girl is pregnant. He could have been driven to suicide, or perhaps someone important wanted him dead.

BLACK MARKET IMPLANTS

A man stands on a street corner and discreetly distributes small brochures to onlookers. Some ignore him while others stay and ask questions about the contents of the brochures.

The man's name is Ebbon. If he sees the judicators, he releases the brochures and takes flight with his very fast machine legs (page 140). The brochure has the heading "Time for a Change – Remake Yourself" and is about the "Reconstruct" clinic that offers biomechatronic implants and "reasonable loans" to pay for them. The truth is, the loans are not particularly reasonable. Interest rates are high while unlicensed operations are both dangerous and illegal. The clinic's director, Dr Remius, is violating a number of enclave laws. Read more about so-called black market implants on page 139.

TEMPLE PROCESSION

A procession of women and men in drab attire moves slowly through the sector. Under the hoods are tired but friendly faces. People on the street stop and lower their heads as a sign of respect. Someone holds an amulet with the Temple's sun and moon symbol.

Noises come from a chapel devoted to the Temple. The sect is popular within the enclave and is approved by the Council.

BEGGAR

A single man approaches the judicators, walking on crutches made of scrap. He is bearded and has worn out clothes. He presents himself as Odell and asks for some credits.

If the PCs refuse to give Odell money or threaten him with an arrest (begging is illegal) he says he has important information to sell. The details of the information are up to the GM to determine.

FARE DODGERS

Close to the Shaft, children are laughing loudly and playing. A few of the little ones cling to the ropes and are dangerously jumping between the lifts and stairs in the Shaft.

Neighborhood youths compete to see who can come closest to the Crown by climbing through the lifts. This is not only forbidden but also potentially fatal.

VANDALISM

A bunch of teenagers with colorful hairstyles are running along the street. People scream, and someone runs after them and shouts threats while waiving a weapon. One of the youngsters stops and writes something with a spray can on a wall. A girl with wild eyes stops and makes a hand gesture showing three fingers – the symbol for belonging to the third section of the Deep.

The youths have vandalized a nearby transport elevator. Perhaps they are guilty of some of the power outages elsewhere, or the flooding. They could be acting on their own or else were hired by someone to start trouble. Whichever the case, the crime is serious. The youngsters try to flee from the judicators and will turn violent if engaged.

PURSE SNATCHER

An old woman on the street shouts loudly. A little girl has stolen her bag and takes off on a scooter. The woman shouts "My bag, my bag, she stole my bag!" and falls to the ground.

The girl is named Ginny, and she flees on a kickbike (page 83). The PCs can chase after with a Move roll.

FLOODING

A stream of wastewater flows through the sector. The flow increases and soon everyone is ankle deep in it. People try to protect their property the best they can. Some can't keep themselves from vomiting while the rest loudly complain about the stench.

A pipe of the Sewer (page 100) has broken. The PCs can locate the leak with a successful Force roll. Failure means the smell becomes overpowering and they must give up. In order to fix it, a technician is required to make a Tinker roll. Perhaps during repairs someone can help determine the cause of the rupture.

NPC GAME DATA

OCCUPATION	NAME	REPUTATION	ATTRIBUTES	SKILLS	DESCRIPTION	GEAR
Agitator	Willon Bing	1	Strength 2 Agility 3 Wits 3 Empathy 4	Manipulate 3	Piercing stare, loud, spits when he talks	
Robbers	Burch and Haskel	0	Strength 4 Agility 3 Wits 2 Empathy 2	Force 4 Fight 3 Shoot 2	Shaved heads, noticeable scars on face and scalp	Burch is armed with a scrap pistol and Haskel with an iron pipe
Demonstrator		1	Strength 3 Agility 3 Wits 2 Empathy 3	Manipulate 1 Fight 1	Loud and agitated	

NPC GAME DATA

OCCUPATION	NAME	REPUTATION	ATTRIBUTES	SKILLS	DESCRIPTION	GEAR
Heir	Pernicus Warburg	6	Strength 2 Agility 3 Wits 4 Empathy 4	Manipulate 4	Refers to himself as "we"	Palanquin
Forger	Grizzie	1	Strength 3 Agility 4 Wits 4 Empathy 2	Fly 1 Shoot 1 Scout 2 Manipulate 2	Biomechatronic jaw	Scrap knife, reinforced skull, forged licenses
Salesman	Pimm	1	Strength 3 Agility 3 Wits 3 Empathy 4	Move 2 Fight 1 Manipulate 4	Wide toothless smile, plastic hat	Sales stand with colorful lights
Malfunctioning Robot	TBL-401	0	Strength 3 Agility 3 Wits 3 Empathy 4	Force 3 Fight 3	Four-legged machine with a small and glowing blue head	Mining drill (Gear Bonus +2, Weapon Damage 2)
Street Performers		1	Strength 3 Agility 4 Wits 2 Empathy 5	Manipulate 4	Black and white tights	
Gang Members		0	Strength 4 Agility 4 Wits 2 Empathy 5	Fight 3 Move 1	Hates judicators	Blunt instrument
Biomechatronic dealer	Ebbon	1	Strength 3 Agility 4 Wits 2 Empathy 4	Move 4 Shoot 2 Manipulate 3	Green plastic poncho, machine leg	Machine leg, brochures
Prostitute	Redmund	0	Strength 2 Agility 3 Wits 3 Empathy 5	Manipulate 5	Stylish hair, brightly colored contact lenses	
Vandals		0	Strength 3 Agility 4 Wits 3 Empathy 2	Fight 2 Move 1	Cocky, but will flee if confronted	Armed with a scrap knife
Temple Novices		2	Strength 3 Agility 3 Wits 3 Empathy 3	Manipulate 1	Hardened workers with friendly smiles	
Beggar	Odell	0	Strength 2 Agility 4 Wits 4 Empathy 3	Shoot 2 Manipulate 3	Missing a leg, uses a scrap crutch	
Street children		1	Strength 2 Agility 4 Wits 3 Empathy 3	Move 3	Unruly kids who enjoy teasing judicators	
Purse-snatcher	Ginny	1	Strength 2 Agility 4 Wits 3 Empathy 3	Fight 1 Move 3 Manipulate 1	Dirty clothes, sleek smile	Kickbike

MISSION GENERATOR

Incidents are the core of the *Guardians of the Fall* campaign, described in detail in Chapter 10, but nothing prevents you from reinforcing the campaign with other missions to experience more of the judicators' everyday life.

As the GM, you can simply roll on the following generator to create an exciting case for the PCs to investigate. Unlike the campaign's core Incidents, these minor events do not affect the Development Levels of the enclave or the Control of the Houses.

The tables are meant only as a source of inspiration. Expand or alter these cases as you see fit. Sometimes the tables will create unreasonable situations. If this happens feel free to adjust the results so that they work well within your game.

1. Roll or choose the type of crime.
2. Roll or choose a crime scene.
3. Determine if the case should encompass more than one location, and if so, how many. One or two usually suffices. The perpetrator is found at the last location.
4. Roll or choose other locations.
5. Roll or choose a clue for each location.
6. Roll or choose victims, witnesses, and perpetrators as well as motives.
7. Roll or choose an unexpected twist in the case.
8. Play the case.

CRIME

D66	CRIME
11–12	Fraud
13–16	Burglary
21–22	Sexual Assault
23–24	Extortion
25–32	Assault
33–35	Drug Trafficking
36–41	Rioting
42–43	Robbery
44–46	Kidnapping
51–54	Sabotage
55–64	Murder
65–66	Treason

CLUES

D66	CLUES
11–15	Anonymous Tip
16-31	Witness
32-42	Evidence
43-53	Forensic Evidence
54-56	Recording
61-62	Documents
63-66	Rumors

SECTOR

D66	SECTOR	SECTION
11–12	Cogs of Hel	The Deep
13–14	Laborum	The Deep
15–16	Arcadium	The Deep
21–22	Cinderfalls	The Deep
23–24	Mosel	The Deep
25–32	Hindenburg	The Core
33–34	Calista	The Core
35–40	Northolme	The Core
41–43	Tindertuft	The Core
44–51	Pirius	The Core
52–55	Old Koly	The Core
56–63	Nova Paloma	The Core
64	Winter Garden	The Crown
65	The Breach	The Crown
66	House Palace	The Crown

CRIME SCENE/THE CORE

D66	LOCATION
11	Gallery
12–14	Shop
15–23	Park
24–26	Restaurant
31–34	Residence
35–42	Office
43–44	Alley
45–52	Bar
53–55	The Bazaar
56	Theater
61	Food stalls
62–63	The Academy
64–66	Data Works

CRIME SCENE/THE DEEP

D66	LOCATION
11–12	Waste Station
13–15	Dam
16–21	Power Plant
22–25	Warehouse
26–34	Factory
35–43	Residential Area
44–45	Shop
46–51	Bar
52–53	Alley
54–55	Cantina
56–62	Farm
63–65	Mine
66	Control Center

MOTIVE

D66	MOTIVE
11–14	Hatred
15–22	Love
23–26	Ideology
31–32	Pleasure
33–41	Money
42–46	Revenge
51–66	Family

VICTIMS, SUSPECTS, AND WITNESSES

Roll once to generate a random NPC. To get more variation, roll once for each column.

D66	FIRST NAME	SURNAME	PROFESSION	QUIRK	WHEREABOUTS
11	Aram	Badger	Reconstructed	Murmurs	The Deep
12	Haskel	Block	Penal Laborer	Dirty	The Deep
13	Garnet	Coombs	Gang Member	Loud and rowdy	The Deep
14	Taron	Bing	Criminal	Sneaky	The Deep
15	Max	Tinley	Enforcer	Grins	The Deep
16	Molly	Reed	Bartender	Bored	The Deep
21	Festus	Vance	Waste Management Worker	Pungent odor	The Deep
22	Leida	Hale	Cultist	Stares	The Deep
23	Mallie	Benson	Prostitute	Fearful	The Deep
24	Berton	Tickle	Drug Dealer	Drugged	The Deep
25	Clane	Brady	Worker	Tired	The Deep
26	Abner	Weld	Foreman	Angry	The Deep
31	Bruno	Budd	Fighter	Tall	The Deep
32	Gunny	Norton	Pest Control	Ill-tempered	The Deep
33	Baltus	Ogden	Store Clerk	Sleepy	The Core
34	Hertha	Bentick	Actress	Vain	The Core
35	Creighton	Montague	Doctor	Arrogant	The Core
36	Boris	Barlow	Security Guard	Drunk	The Core
41	Sonya	Skelton	Server	Stressed	The Core
42	Kenley	Loftus	Researcher	Curious	The Core
43	Moro	Holton	Clerk	Secretive	The Core
44	Milly	Merton	Student	Hiding Something	The Core

D66	FIRST NAME	SURNAME	PROFESSION	QUIRK	WHEREABOUTS
45	Heran	Dunkle	Pensioner	Tired	The Core
46	Sadoc	Benson	Poet	Talkative	The Core
51	Mott	Dudley	Errand-boy	Cocky	The Core
52	Cleon	Carp	Conveyor	Sweaty	The Core
53	Ariana	Acton	Scholar	Meticulous	The Core
54	Kenton	Arundell	Technician	Sly	The Core
55	Aislinn	Battenburg	Soldier	Stares	The Core
56	Emerson	Fairfax	Officer	Arrogant	The Core
61	Manley	Montague	Honor Guard	Cavalier	The Crown
62	Demelza	Bentick	Surgeon	Irritable	The Crown
63	Natasha	Fortescue	Highborn	Restless	The Crown
64	Pandora	Morningstar	Highborn	Charming	The Crown
65	Hendrick	Warburg	Highborn	Angry	The Crown
66	Ransford	Kilgore	Highborn	Cold and detached	The Crown

PLOT TWISTS

D66	TWIST
11–33	None
34–35	The victim is the perpetrator! Roll again for the victim's crime.
36–41	The perpetrator is a scapegoat, someone else is behind the crime.
42–43	The crime is a ruse. Somebody orchestrated everything from beginning to end.
44–46	The perpetrator is innocent and is being compelled by someone else.
51–52	It's a trap! The perpetrator is waiting to ambush the judicators.
53–54	Serial criminal! The perpetrator is much worse than suspected. He is behind a lot of other crimes.
55–62	The tip of the iceberg! The perpetrator belongs to an organized group performing similar crimes.
63–65	The perpetrator is insane and completely unpredictable.
66	The perpetrator is a member of one of the Houses in disguise!

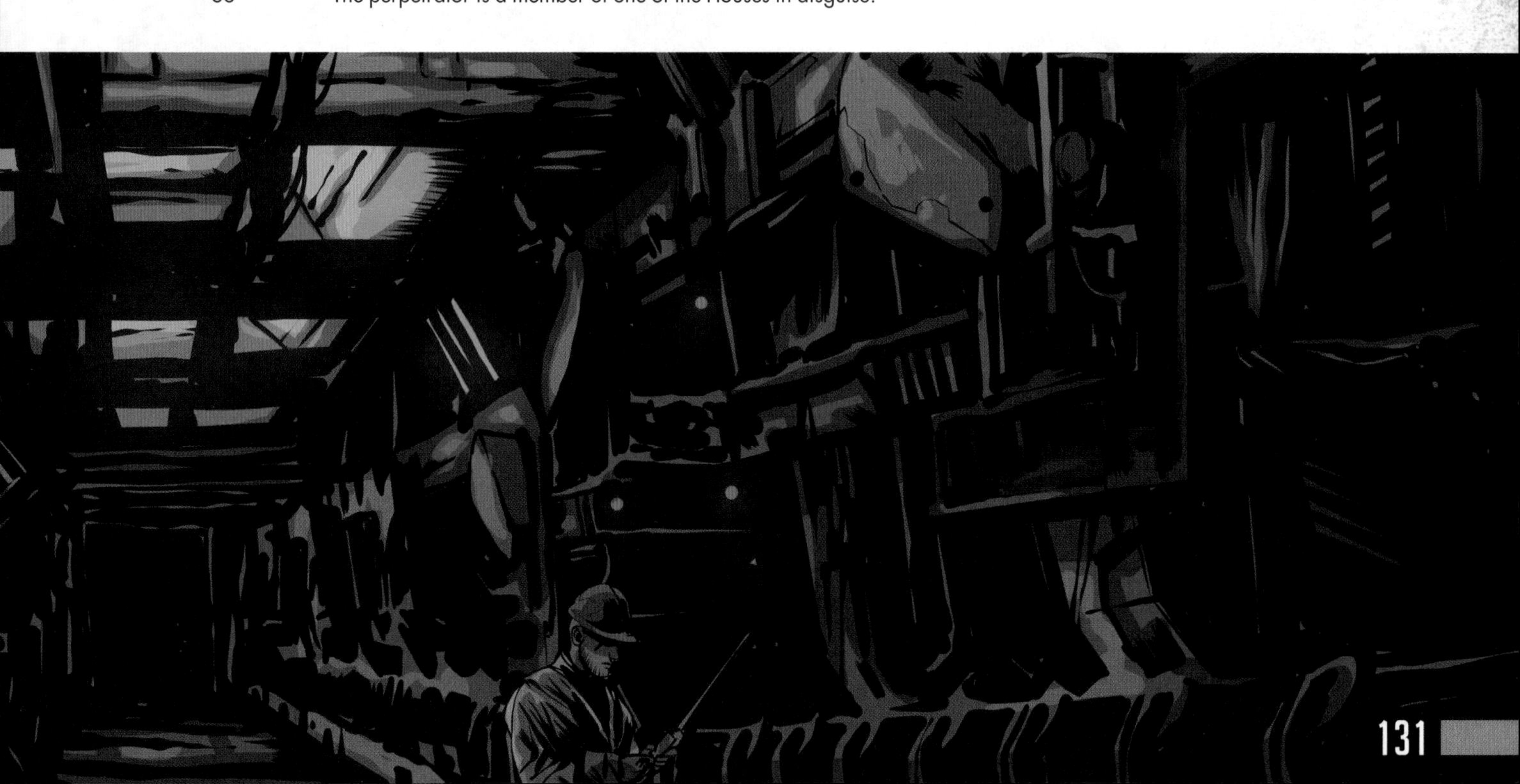

ARTIFACTS & BIOMECHATRONICS

Elysium I is full of high-tech objects called artifacts. Artifacts are not an unusual sight but part of everyday life in the enclave. In recent years, the production of new artifacts has begun to slow, and it is becoming increasingly important to maintain and repair these items – even for the judicators.

In the outer world, which Elysium's inhabitants call the Zone, artifacts are very rare and only the luckiest explorers will ever find one.

This chapter describes 17 specific artifacts in detail.

Electronic Artifacts: Some artifacts are noted as *electronic*. Any attempt to repair an electronic artifact (which is a separate artifact) gets a -3 modification.

Energy Weapons: Artifacts noted as *energy weapons* require large amounts of electricity to function and must be loaded with an E-Pack (separate artifact) or have access to an alternative supply of electricity. Read more on page 73.

PURCHASING ARTIFACTS

Artifacts can be purchased with credits in the enclave. The basic price of each artifact is stated in this chapter. The price will be affected by the current Development Level of Production (see page 118).

As a judicator, each PC is assigned starting equipment. Beyond that, they are responsible for buying any additional equipment they might want. They are also responsible for replacing lost or damaged equipment.

UNDERSTANDING ARTIFACTS

PCs automatically understand how to use artifacts they purchase in Elysium I. If, on the other hand, they find a foreign artifact outside in the Zone, they must study it to discover its purpose and how it works before they can use it. This requires a successful Comprehend roll. A PC who succeeds on such a roll understands the artifact and can now also show others how it works.

Development Level requirements specify the lowest Science Development Level (see page 118) required for an artifact to be manufactured and generally available in Elysium I. If the Science score falls below the requirement, it will only be possible to acquire the artifact through barter. The Development Level requirements are also used when playing outside in the Zone, see *Mutant: Year Zero*.

The **Development Level bonus** for each artifact has no effect while in the enclave – these values are only used when building a new settlement out in the Zone.

LIST OF ARTIFACTS

ARTIFACT	COST
Bellicin	4
Combat Armor	5
Comm Radio	1
Electronic Tools	3
Energy Armor	15
E-Pack	1
Frag Grenade	2
Gauss Pistol	3
Gauss Rifle	5
Gyrojet Carbine	6
Gyrojet Pistol	4
Hoverbike	6
Patrol Hovercraft	10
Reconnaissance Armor	12
Stun Gun	3
Stun Baton	2
Ultrasonic Carbine	7

BELLICIN

An experimental combat drug developed during the Enclave Wars to make soldiers more aggressive and resistant to pain. It is only available in pill form. Unfortunately, the side effects are severe.

Effect: Lets you make skill rolls with your full attribute score regardless of any trauma suffered. The effect lasts for D6 hours. Then, you suffer from severe chills and suffer D6 points of fatigue. The pills are enough for D6 doses – after you have taken all, you must discard the card. Tiny item.

Cost: 4

DEV Requirement: Technology 50

DEV Bonus: –

COMBAT ARMOR

A full-body, dark gray overall with plates of bulletproof material covering the groin, arms, and legs. Gloves, sturdy boots and a helmet with gas filter included.

Effect: Armor Rating 6 against both damage from attacks and Zone Rot.

Cost: 5

DEV Requirement: Technology 20

DEV Bonus: Technology +2D6

COMM RADIO

A black, fist-sized device with a small antenna and a microphone. Can be fastened to a belt or a sleeve.

Effect: Allows wireless communication between user and the base, or another person also equipped with a comm radio. About 10 kilometers range. Needs to be charged after a week's use by connecting it to an E-pack, a battery, or some other power source. Light electronic item.

ARTIFACT CARDS

The custom card deck for *Mutant: Elysium* contains an Artifact Card for each of the 17 artifacts described in this book. If a PC finds a certain artifact, you can simply hand them the card. If a PC finds artifacts out in the Zone, you can let them draw a card from the pile or choose which card they will receive.

Artifact Cards for *Mutant: Elysium* are fully compatible with the cards from *Year Zero*, *Genlab Alpha*, and *Mechatron*. Once a PC has left the enclave and ventured into the Zone, you can shuffle together the Artifact Cards from all the games to create a really massive deck of Artifact Cards.

Cost: 1
DEV Requirement: Technology 40
DEV Bonus: Technology +D6

ELECTRONIC TOOLS

A small kit with high tech tools for repairing and caring for electronic devices, such as energy weapons and robots.

Effect: Gear Bonus +2 when repairing electronic items. All attempts to repair such items without these tools suffer a -3 modification to the roll.
Cost: 3
DEV Requirement: Technology 50
DEV Bonus: Technology +D6

ENERGY ARMOR

An advanced experimental armor created for combat in extremely hazardous environments. The armor is made of a black composite material that covers the entire body including the head. Electrodes in the helmet read the wearer's brain signals and amplify all movements automatically. The helmet also contains a light intensifier.

Effect: Armor Rating 12 against both damage and Zone Rot. Gear Bonus +3 to Force, Fight, and Move. Eliminates all negative effects of darkness. Energy weapon. (requires E-pack, if all Gear Dice for the armor show ✷ after a roll the artifact is discharged). Electronic item.
Cost: 15
DEV Requirement: Technology 80
DEV Bonus: Technology +D6, Defense +D6

E-PACK

A fist-sized power capsule with a plastic cover.

Effect: Supplies electricity to energy weapons (see page 73). Can also be used to charge the internal energy source of a robot with D6 Energy Points (see *Mutant: Mechatron*) but will then be exhausted. Tiny item.
Cost: 1
DEV Requirement: Technology 60
DEV Bonus: Technology +D6

FRAG GRENADE

A lump of plastic and metal, as big as a fist with a spring release at the top. Handle with Care!

Effect: Light item. Throw the grenade with the Force skill. Extra ☢ beyond the first have no effect. Short range. No Gear Bonus. If the attack is successful, the grenade lands at Near range from the target (in a random direction), and detonates, otherwise it lands at Short range from the target. The explosion has Blast Power 12 and Weapon Damage 1.
Cost: 2
DEV Requirement: Technology 40
DEV Bonus: Technology +D6

GAUSS PISTOL

A long, narrow pistol made of metal with light diodes on the covers. The weapon generates a powerful magnetic field that fires very small projectiles (caliber 1 mm) at extremely high speeds.

Effect: Light weapon with Gear Bonus +2 to Shoot and Weapon Damage 2. The target's Armor Rating counts as 3 points lower than normal. Long range. Energy weapon. Electronic item.
Cost: 3
DEV Requirement: Technology 70
DEV Bonus: Technology +D6

GAUSS RIFLE

A long rifle made of metal with light diodes on the covers. The weapon generates a powerful magnetic field that fires very small projectiles (caliber 1 mm) at extremely high speeds.

Effect: Gear Bonus +2 to Shoot and Weapon Damage 2. The target's Armor Rating counts as 3 points lower than normal. Distant range. Energy weapon. Electronic item.

Cost: 5

DEV Requirement: Technology 70

DEV Bonus: Technology +D6

GYROJET CARBINE

A large firearm made of gray composites and metal. It requires the use of two hands to operate. Fires small rockets that explode on impact.

Effect: Loaded with gyrojet rockets. Gear Bonus +3 to Shoot. Long range. Weapon Damage 3 at Short range or further, Weapon Damage 1 at Near range or closer (the rocket must travel some distance before it can detonate. Capable of full auto fire. Ignores all negative range modifications.

Cost: 6

DEV Requirement: Technology 60

DEV Bonus: Technology +D6

GYROJET PISTOL

A bulky pistol in gray composites and metal. Fires small rockets that explode on impact.

Effect: Fires gyrojet rockets. Gear Bonus +3 to Shoot. Short range. Weapon Damage 3 when used at Short distance, Weapon Damage 1 at Near range or closer (the rocket must travel some distance before it can detonate). Ignores all negative range modifications.

Cost: 4

DEV Requirement: Technology 60

DEV Bonus: Technology +D6

HOVERBIKE

A small and highly maneuverable vehicle that carries the driver and no more than one additional passenger. The vehicle is propelled with a pair of small but powerful turbines.

Effect: The hoverbike can carry two people and doubles movement in combat. It grants a +3 Gear Bonus to Move when you try to escape from combat. You can also use the hoverbike as a weapon. No Armor Rating, Resilience 1. Requires special fuel. Read more on page 83.

Cost: 6

DEV Requirement: Technology 60

DEV Bonus: Technology +2D6

PATROL HOVERCRAFT

A typical patrol vehicle used by judicators in Elysium I. The vehicle flies with the help of small but powerful turbines that are controlled by the driver to create forward motion and lift.

Effect: This vehicle can carry five people and doubles movement during combat. It grants a +3 Gear Bonus to Move when you try to escape from combat. You can also use the patrol hovercraft as a weapon. Armor Rating 3, Resilience 2. Requires special fuel. Read more about vehicles on page 83.

Cost: 10

DEV Requirement: Technology 70

DEV Bonus: Technology +2D6

RECONNAISSANCE ARMOR

A prototype armor designed for fast exploration of hazardous surface environments. The armor consists of gray overalls with insulated, bullet-proof plates, a helmet with visor, and a small rocket engine on the back with fins on the arms and legs to enable steering while in the air.

Effect: Armor Rating 6 against both damage from attacks and Zone Rot. The suit also grants the ability to fly. It counts as a vehicle which doubles movement during combat and gives Gear Bonus +3 when you try to escape from combat. Requires special fuel.

Cost: 12

DEV Requirement: Technology 60

DEV Bonus: Technology +2D6

STUN GUN

A small pistol made of light plastic that fires a strong electric charge designed to temporarily immobilize the target without causing lasting damage.

Effect: Light weapon with +2 Gear Bonus to Shoot and Weapon Damage 2. Short range. Inflicts fatigue instead of damage on living targets. Armor does not provide protection against these attacks, although natural armor still offers its bonus as normal. Energy weapons. Electronic item.

Cost: 3

DEV Requirement: Technology 60

DEV Bonus: Technology +D6

STUN BATON

A high-tech, close combat weapon built to incapacitate the target without killing it.

Effect: Gear Bonus +2 to Fight, Weapon Damage 1. On a hit, the weapon inflicts D6 points of fatigue in addition to damage. Armor does not protect against the fatigue suffered, although natural armor still provides the usual bonus. Energy weapon. Electronic item.

Cost: 2

DEV Requirement: Technology 60

DEV Bonus: Technology +D6

ULTRASONIC CARBINE

A high-tech firearm of white, bright plastic with a large barrel shaped like a funnel. Several handles and illuminated diodes adorn the covers. The weapon vibrates vigorously when it is fired, but the beam of concentrated ultrasound is invisible and cannot be perceived by human ears. Damage is caused by powerful micro-vibrations.

Effect: Gear Bonus of +2 to Shoot and Weapon Damage 2. Inflicts fatigue in addition to damage, in the same amount. Armor has no effect against the fatigue. Short range. Energy weapon. Electronic item.

Cost: 7

DEV Requirement: Technology 80

DEV Bonus: Technology +D6

BIOMECHATRONICS

Over the decades of isolation, Elysium researchers have been working to modify and improve humanity in order to one day survive on the desolate surface. Two research fields made great leaps forward:

Xenogenetics seeks to create new, stronger lifeforms by isolating the best traits, in the form of DNA, of different species and incorporating them into others. Elysium started Project Genesis (see *Mutant: Genlab Alpha*) and other projects in the Elysium IV genlabs. Mimir's Project Eden (see *Mutant: Year Zero*) is also part of this research field.

Biomechatronics seeks to enhance and improve mankind with mechanical implants. This research made incredible advances in Elysium I during the early years of the enclave.

BIOMECHATRONICS IN ELYSIUM

Due to the risk of machine fever (below), biomechatronic implants are relatively uncommon among the highborn. Most members of the Houses usually avoid biomechatronics altogether or have very discreet implants.

By contrast, biomechatronics are very common among the enclave workers. Many of them have large and rough implants – entire body parts can be built from metal and ceramics, either to replace those lost to damage or simply to make the worker stronger and more durable.

Over time, large biomechatronic implants have become a trend among the workers, who show off their implants with pride.

IMPLANTS

Twenty common implants are described below and summarized in the table on the next page.

Using Implants: Biomechatronic implants function as artifacts and usually have an associated Gear Bonus. A reduced Gear Bonus can be fixed by a Technician in the same way as artifacts. All implants count as electronic items. When a skill roll using a bonus from an implant is made, there is also a risk of triggering machine fever (see below).

Player Characters who are Soldiers or Technicians may take a biomechatronic implant during character creation (see Chapter 2). Any PC can buy biomechatronics throughout the course of the game. The cost in credits is shown with each implant. This cost covers both the implant itself and the surgery required to attach it.

Grafting Implants: Grafting an implant requires a surgical procedure. This is risky. The patient is automatically broken (see page 77) by the procedure and suffers a critical injury (considered non-typical damage). This means that the patient risks dying if the surgeon fails his Heal roll.

MACHINE FEVER

Elysium researchers initially had major plans to strengthen all enclave residents with biomechatronic implants. But they soon understood the drawbacks of the technology. Replacing large parts of the human body with artificial machine prosthetics could trigger violent side effects. The researchers came to call these symptoms machine fever.

Pushing the Roll: Biomechatronic implants usually have a gear bonus, just like other artifacts. They differ in what happens when the dice roll is pushed and one or more comes up – in addition to the decreases in Gear Bonus (-1 per) the characters is also affected by machine fever. The more rolled, the worse the effects will be.

ROLL	EFFECT
1	The patient suffers severe trembling and takes 1 point of fatigue.
2	The patient suffers from chills, difficulty breathing, and uncontrollable shaking. They also lose all Agility and are thus broken by fatigue. The patient can Recover as normal.
3+	Machine psychosis! The patient suffers a violent psychotic episode and attacks any living targets within Near range. This violent outburst lasts until the patient is broken by damage. During the rage, the patient will foam at the mouth and is immune to all other forms of trauma. If no person is within Near range, see 2 above. After the psychotic rage ends, the patient's Empathy score is *permanently* reduced by 1 point.

BLACK IMPLANTS
On the black market in Elysium I, biomechatronics are available at half price. However, purchasing them entails major risks. Less qualified surgeons who offer the so-called black implants often have a low Heal skill. In addition, a separate Gear Die must be rolled whenever a black implant is used – this die only determines whether machine fever occurs or not.

LIST OF IMPLANTS

IMPLANT	COST
Air Tank	3
Communicator	2
Data Banks	7
Heat Vision	4
Interface	5
Laser Eye	9
Machine Arm	5
Machine Legs	6
Monofilament	5
Overdrive	7
Pain Inhibitors	6
Polygraph	4
Reinforced Skull	2
Rot Protection	6
Shock Grip	4
Targeting Scope	7
Tool Hand	5
Trash Gut	3
Voice Amplifier	2
Weapon Mount	3

AIR TANK
An internal air reserve tank, enough for 15 minutes of breathing. During this time, the user has no need for air and is immune to toxic gases. Provides a Gear Bonus of +2 to Move in water or vacuum. When depleted, the tank can refill itself in a few minutes with access to a supply of air.
Cost: 3

COMMUNICATOR
Built-in comm radio. Functions exactly as the artifact comm radio on page 134.
Cost: 2

DATA BANKS
The brain is enhanced with a large digital storage capacity, which grants a +2 Gear Bonus to Comprehend rolls. Up to 40 hours of visual and audio recordings with full accuracy can be saved. Data can be played back on an external device via an Interface. The user can also upload and store other digital data in the Data Banks.
Cost: 7

HEAT VISION
A red biomechatronic eye that can detect heat and various spectrums of radiation. Heat is highlighted and looks brighter than cold, which easily lets the user distinguish living creatures. The eye provides a Gear Bonus of +2 to Scout when detecting living creatures. The implant also eliminates all negative effects of darkness, up to Short range.
Cost: 4

INTERFACE

Built-in receptors in the neck or arm allow the user to connect directly to digital data networks. When attempting to influence or understand advanced technical systems, this implant grants the wearer a +2 Gear Bonus to Tinker and Comprehend rolls. This implant is also required to fully utilize some other implants, such as Data Banks.

Cost: 5

LASER EYE

A small but powerful laser is installed in an eye socket. It can be used as a weapon with Gear Bonus +2, Weapon Damage 1, and Short range. With a successful Shoot roll, the laser can also cut through metal, such as bars, chains, or a lock.

Cost: 9

MACHINE ARM

A powerful arm made of metal and composite materials. The arm grants a Gear Bonus of +3 to Fight (only unarmed) and Force rolls.

Cost: 5

MACHINE LEGS

Both legs are replaced by powerful robotic ones. These give a +3 Gear Bonus to Move and Force rolls when the legs can be used. With a Move roll, the user can jump up to 15 feet vertically or 30 feet horizontally.

Cost: 6

MONOFILAMENT

Hidden in the thumb is a small weight attached to an extremely thin and strong wire, wound around an internal coil. The weight and wire can be thrown like a yoyo up to Near range. This is considered a normal attack in close combat, with a Gear Bonus of +2. The wire can cut through meat and bones like a hot knife through butter. It's so dangerous that it automatically inflicts a random critical injury if the attack hits its target. It does not cause regular damage. Extra ☢ have no effect.

Cost: 5

OVERDRIVE

Modified nerve and muscle systems allow the user to perform incredible feats of speed. Grants a Gear Bonus of +2 to Move rolls and allows the user to make initiative rolls using the Move skill instead of a single D6. In this case, the highest number rolled with the Move skill is used for the initiative score.

Cost: 7

PAIN INHIBITORS

The body is enhanced with external synthetic glands that numb pain and fatigue. Skill rolls using Strength or Agility are always made with their full attribute scores, regardless of how much damage or fatigue has been suffered.

Cost: 6

POLYGRAPH

Implanted sensors that detect subtle changes in another person's heart rate, breathing, and blood flow in the skin – signs that can reveal if someone is lying. Gives a Gear Bonus of +2 to Sense Emotion, but can only be used at Arm's Length.

Cost: 4

REINFORCED SKULL

The skull is reinforced with a blend of metal and protective composite materials. The implant provides Armor Rating 3 against attacks in addition to any armor worn. Additionally, the user may re-roll the result of 66 on the table of critical injuries on page 78 (crushed skull). The re-roll can only be made once.

Cost: 2

ROT PROTECTION

Built-in sensors and chemical barriers that both detect and protect against what is commonly known as the Rot out in the Zone. Allows the user to immediately determine the Rot Level in an area (see page 85). The implant grants Armor Rating 5 against the Rot.

Cost: 6

SHOCK GRIP

Powerful electrodes built into the hands that enable the user to subdue living creatures. Shock grip

provides a +2 Gear Bonus and Weapon Damage 1, but causes fatigue instead of damage.
Cost: 4

TARGETING SCOPE
Built-in advanced optics in one eye grant a Gear Bonus of +2 to Shoot, but only at Short range or more and only when the user is aiming carefully.
Cost: 7

TOOL HAND
One hand is replaced by an advanced multi-tool kit. It is treated as the electronic tools artifact (see page 135) and grants a Gear Bonus of +2 to Tinker or Jury-Rig for all types of repairs. The tool hand can also be used as a weapon in close combat – unarmed attacks using the tools have Weapon Damage 2.
Cost: 5

TRASH GUT
The efficiency of the mouth, throat, and digestive system are vastly improved so that nutrition can be extracted from rubbish. The taste buds are removed, and the sense of smell is significantly dampened. The user can eat almost anything in the Zone and will therefore never need grub if there is organic matter nearby. The implant does not provide protection against the Rot.
Cost: 3

VOICE AMPLIFIER
An implant in the larynx that allows the user to speak with an extremely loud voice, like using a megaphone. Provides a Gear Bonus of +2 to Manipulate or Intimidate, but only in situations where raising one's voice is useful.
Cost: 2

WEAPON MOUNT
Any (portable) weapon can be mounted in the arm. This allows the user to draw the weapon without spending a maneuver. It also conceals the weapon – others must actively look for the weapon and make a Scout roll to spot it. The weapon itself must be purchased separately. This implant can be obtained several times, once for each weapon to be mounted.
Cost: 3

10

GUARDIANS OF THE FALL

Everything you have read so far in this book has been leading up to this story. The main campaign of *Mutant: Elysium,* called *Guardians of the Fall,* will be presented in detail in this chapter and the next. The campaign is comprised of two major components.

- Open campaign mechanics, where players themselves control the power struggles between Houses within the enclave, generating the assignments the player characters will be sent on.
- A series of crucial key events, which are woven into the campaign mechanics and lead up to an epic campaign finale.

Combining the player-influenced and predetermined elements, you create a unique sequence of events that is largely controlled by the players themselves, while simultaneously weaving an epic story about the fall of Elysium I.

BACKGROUND

When Elysium was founded, the leaders of the Houses realized that it would take many decades, perhaps centuries, before the surface of the Earth could be inhabited again. They feared that in the meantime, the citizens of the enclave would forget their purpose and lose their values, just as they believed the Ancients had done.

THE EMINENCES

To ensure that Elysium's moral compass remained intact, the leaders of the great families appointed ten "Eminences." These men and women were carefully selected for their high moral upbringing. The Eminences, who were all meant to embody the Elysium motto of "Tradition, Resolution, Courage," were placed in cryosleep. Each year, one of them would arise to offer counsel to the enclave leaders. At the end of that year, the Eminence was placed into long, cold sleep again, with one of the others emerging to take on the same duty.

In this way, the lifespans of the Eminences were extended tenfold – enough to preserve the memories of the world's fall and Elysium's foundation until the time came to return to the surface and forge a new world. At least, that was the plan.

THE TEMPLE

Initially, the waking Eminence was a part of the Council, with considerable influence over the four ruling Houses. Over the decades however, the role slowly changed. Step by step, the Houses came to view "the Gray" – as the Eminence came to be known – primarily as a spiritual guide for the less fortunate inhabitants of the enclave: the workers.

Reluctantly, the Eminences accepted their new role, having no choice in the matter. In order to give guidance to the inhabitants of the enclave, the Eminences brought in helpers. Selected servants called "novices" would assist waking Eminence with their work. This led to the birth of the Temple. Over the decades since, the Temple has grown in followers and influence.

CRYOLAB DELTA

A hundred years ago, during the raging Enclave Wars, the Elysium enclaves suffered greatly. Elysium IV was destroyed, and even Elysium I was attacked by waves of battle robots from the Mimir

Titan Power. The enclave survived, but a ring of smaller facilities outside the central enclave shaft sustained heavy damage.

These external facilities, connected to each other and the main shaft by kilometers of monorail tracks, are today known as the Catacombs (see page 100). They include the main enclave reactor, the Port Mendel spaceport, and the headquarters of the Eminences: Cryolab Delta.

While Port Mendel was mostly destroyed by the Mimir attacks, Cryolab Delta remained functional. However, the cryobeds were damaged, resulting in all Eminences waking up at the same time – something that has never happened at any point since the foundation of the enclave.

THE SLEEPING COUNCIL

When the Eminences gathered face to face for the first time, they realized how Elysium I had decayed throughout the years. They decided to act, to save humanity from its final destruction. But the Eminences could not challenge the power of the ruling Houses directly.

Instead, the Eminences chose to act slowly and carefully, increasing the power and influence of the Temple over a long period of time, until the day came when the enclave would be ready for a revolution. In order to avoid arousing suspicion from the Houses, and to buy time, the Eminences agreed to once again go into cryosleep.

Only one Eminence at a time would remain awake, but with one significant difference to how things were before. Thanks to the advances in biomechatronic technology developed by the enclave, the Eminences could connect their brains to the central computer of the cryolab.

This link operated perfectly despite most of those connected being in deep cryosleep. A waking Eminence could benefit from the brain capacity of all the sleeping brethren, together achieving superhuman intelligence. As a side effect, the active Eminence sometimes suffers from strong visions, which originate from the dreams of those colleagues that are still sleeping.

All the while, the Eminences slowly created a small army of very powerful biomechatronic warriors, known as machine guards.

THE ENDGAME

The Eminences' plan is simple. After decades of maneuvering in the shadows, the time for action is almost here. Blinded by their power struggles, the ruling Houses are carelessly pushing the enclave toward its destruction.

The day when all ten Eminences will rise from their cold sleep, to lead the enclave workers to revolution against the Houses, is fast approaching. After taking over Elysium I they aim to lead mankind on the right path into the new dawn.

The player characters, tasked to maintain law and order in the enclave, will end up in the middle of a fierce ideological storm. The final battle of Elysium I is drawing near.

PLAYING THE CAMPAIGN

As mentioned previously, this campaign is comprised of two parts: an open campaign mechanism controlled by the players themselves, and a series of key events woven into the narrative that drive the campaign toward an epic finale.

INCIDENTS

Both parts of the campaign use what are known as Incidents. Incidents are events in the enclave that the PCs, as judicators, are sent to handle.

All the campaign's Incidents are described in the next chapter. An Incident is like a short scenario, but most are open-ended and lack a predetermined outcome. Instead, it is a situation that the PCs can handle in many ways.

Most (but not all) Incidents occur in a geographically confined location, and each Incident has an accompanying map. An Incident is meant to take about one gaming session to complete.

The campaign contains eleven Incidents in total. Of these, eight are normal Incidents – the order in which they are played is determined by the players themselves, and it is not even necessary to play all eight. The three special Incidents are key campaign events controlled by you as the GM.

DEVELOPMENT LEVELS

Incidents will often affect the Development Levels of the enclave (see page 118). As the GM, you are responsible for recording the current Development Levels on the enclave sheet (found in the back of this book, and available for download at the Free League website).

SPECIAL INCIDENTS

The three Special Incidents are described in detail on page 215 and onward. Here is a brief summary of them:

1. **Signal from Genlab Alpha.** Elysium I receives an unexpected transmission from the Elysium IV enclave, which was attacked and thought destroyed over a century ago. The signal comes from an external facility called Genlab Alpha. The PCs are sent to investigate and discover the truth about the outer world.
2. **A Day to Remember.** Led by the Eminences, the workers of Elysium I rise en masse against the ruling Houses. The revolutionaries are supported by a small army of biomechatronic warriors, so called machine guards, activated by the Eminences. The PCs end up in the middle of the mayhem.
3. **Attack on Cryolab Delta.** The Houses realize who is orchestrating the revolt and send the PCs to storm the headquarters of the Eminences – Cryolab Delta. Can they save Elysium I from its final fall?

CONTROL

The strategic power struggle between the Houses is a battle for Control. Control is measured on a scale from zero to 2 in each of the twelve sectors of the Core and the Deep. The Winter Garden and the headquarters of the Houses in the Crown are not part of the strategic game.

STARTING LEVELS

At the beginning of the campaign, each of the four Houses has a total of 4 points of Control. These four points are assigned in secret – each player writes on a piece of paper which sectors he wants to have Control in, and how much (1 or 2 points). These choices are then revealed at the same time.

ASYMMETRIC START

An interesting option is to start the game with an imbalance in the power distribution between the Houses. This leads to conflicts and pact formation quicker. If you want to try this option, One House begins with 5 points of Control, two Houses start with 4 points each, and the fourth House starts with 3 points.

Everyone gets the Control they wanted, with one exception:

If two or more players have assigned 2 points of Control to the same sector, they each get only 1 point of Control in that sector. The extra point is lost. Note that it is therefore possible for some players to start the campaign with less than 4 total points of Control.

TRACKING CONTROL

Control is recorded by you, the GM, on the enclave sheet (available at the end of this book or for download on the Free League website). If you like, you can place tokens of any suitable form on the enclave map to represent Control points.

TOTAL CONTROL

The most important numeric score in the strategic game is the total Control of each House – that is, the sum of the Control points a House has in all enclave sectors. Total Control has a number of important in-game effects:

- **Influence Points.** The total Control of a House determines how many Influence Points (IP) each player gets at the beginning of each gaming session. See page 59.
- **Choose Incidents.** When voting on which Incident the PC patrol is to be sent on, each player will vote with the total Control of their House. See page 150.
- **Appoint Patrol Leader.** When voting to appoint a new patrol leader, each player votes with the total Control of their House. See page 23.

DOUBLE AGENTS

A House's Control can be changed by events outside the strategic round. When a double agent is exposed after an Incident (see page 24), the Control of the double agent's House is decreased by one in the sector where the Incident occurred. If the House has no influence in the sector, it loses one point of Control in a randomly selected sector instead.

SECTOR CONTROL

CONTROL	EFFECT
0	**No Control.** The House has no presence in the sector aside from possibly a few informants.
1	**Weak Control.** The House has some presence in the sector, via groups or individuals under the family's control. Several Houses may have weak Control in the same sector at the same time. However, if one or more other Houses have Control 1 in the same sector, all attempts to stage an Incident in that sector suffer a –1 modification.
2	**Strong Control.** Through its agents, the House now controls most of what happens in the sector. Only a single House can have Control 2 in a sector at any given time. When a House achieves strong Control, the Control of all other Houses in the sector drops to zero. It's still possible for other Houses to stage Incidents in the sector, but with a –2 modification. If several players would reach Control 2 in the same sector in the same strategic round, all of them stay at Control 1.

THE TWELVE SECTORS

The table to the right summarizes the twelve sectors of the enclave. Each sector has a listed difficulty level. This is a modification to the number of dice rolled when a House tries to stage an Incident that judicators other than the PCs are sent to handle. Such Incidents are resolved with a single roll of the dice, rather than by role-playing the events. See below.

SECTORS AND DIFFICULTIES

SECTORS IN THE CORE	CODE ON THE MAP	DIFFICULTY
Nova Paloma	C1	–2
Old Koly	C2	0
Pirius	C3	–1
Tindertuft	C4	0
Northolme	C5	0
Calista	C6	0
Hindenburg	C7	0
SECTORS IN THE DEEP		
Mosel	D1	0
Laborum	D2	+1
Arcadium	D3	0
Cinderfalls	D4	+1
Cogs of Hel	D5	+2
OTHER MODIFICATIONS		
Other Houses have Control 1		–1
Other House has Control 2		–2

SELECTING STARTING SECTOR

At the beginning of the game, what sectors should players choose to have Control in? Technically speaking, it is advantageous to have Control in sectors of tougher difficulty, such as Nova Paloma or Pirius, as it will be more difficult for other players to stage Incidents in these sectors during play. On the other hand, there is the risk that several players choose to have Control in these sectors – thus, it may be wise to choose easier sectors instead.

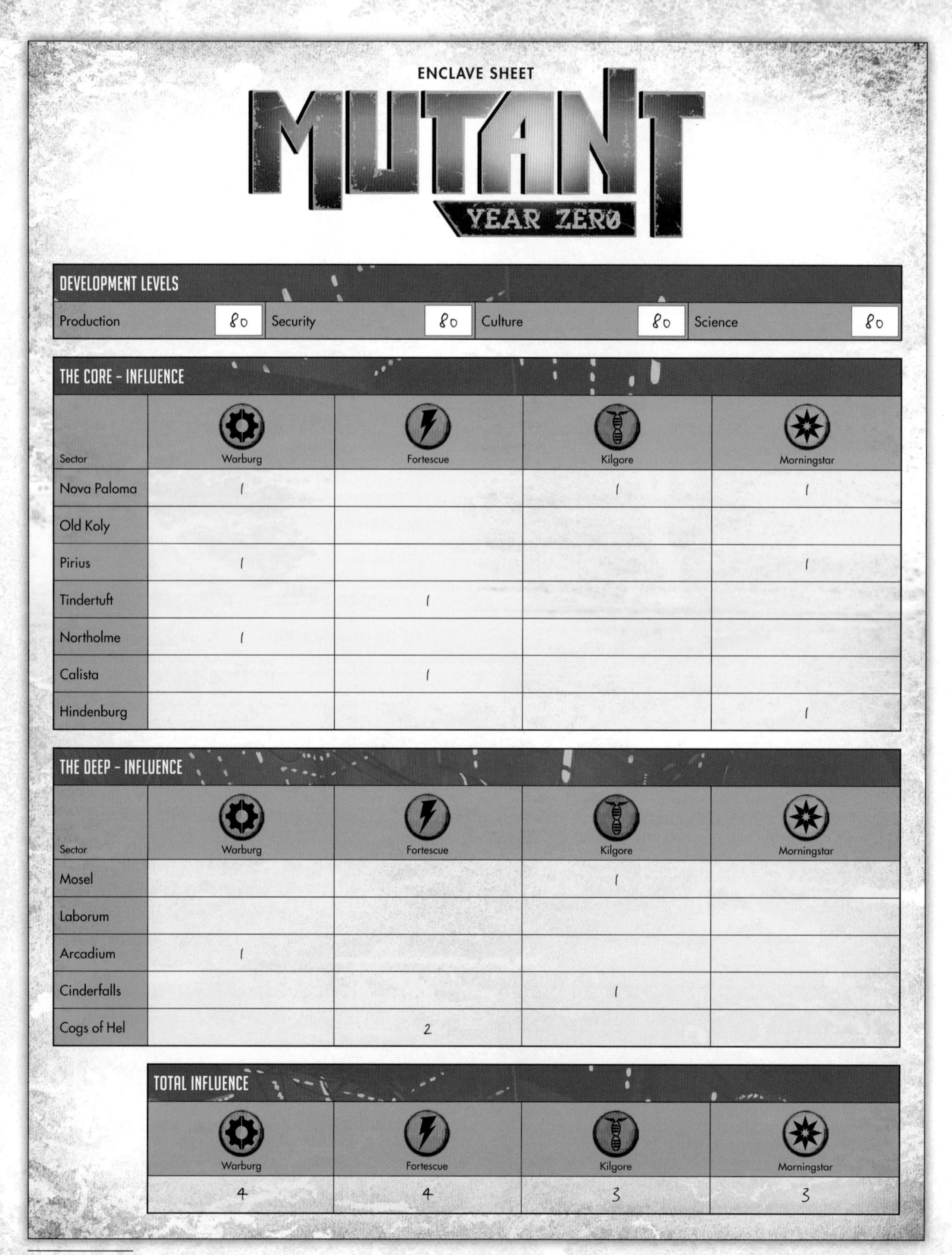

ENCLAVE SHEET

MUTANT YEAR ZERO

DEVELOPMENT LEVELS

Production	Security	Culture	Science
80	80	80	80

THE CORE – INFLUENCE

Sector	Warburg	Fortescue	Kilgore	Morningstar
Nova Paloma	1		1	1
Old Koly				
Pirius	1			1
Tindertuft		1		
Northolme	1			
Calista		1		
Hindenburg				1

THE DEEP – INFLUENCE

Sector	Warburg	Fortescue	Kilgore	Morningstar
Mosel			1	
Laborum				
Arcadium	1			
Cinderfalls			1	
Cogs of Hel		2		

TOTAL INFLUENCE

Warburg	Fortescue	Kilgore	Morningstar
4	4	3	3

SEE EXAMPLE 1

EXAMPLE 1

The players Sylvia (House Kilgore), Jack (House Warburg), Yasmine (House Fortescue) and Richard (House Morningstar) are about to start the strategic game. All secretly choose the sectors that they want to have Control of at the beginning of the gaming session.

House Kilgore gambles and assigns 2 points of Control to Nova Paloma and 1 point to both Mosel and Cinderfalls. House Warburg decides on 1 point of Control in Nova Paloma, Pirius, Northolme and Arcadium. House Fortescue assigns 2 points to Cogs of Hel and 1 point to Calista and Tindertuft. Finally, House Morningstar wants Control 2 in Nova Paloma and 1 point each in Hindenburg and Pirius.

Because both House Kilgore and House Morningstar chose to put 2 points of Control in the same sector (Nova Paloma), they only get Control 1 in this sector. Thus, Kilgore and Morningstar both start the game with a total Control of 3, while Warburg and Fortescue start the game with total Control 4.

See the filled-in example enclave sheet to the left.

STRATEGY VERSUS PERSONAL INFLUENCE

The total Control of a PC's House determines how many Influence Points (IP) he gets to activate contacts with (see Chapter 5). At the beginning of every game session, each PC's pool of IP is renewed – they get new IP equal to the total Control of their respective House. Any leftover IP from the previous session are lost. PCs can win additional IP by cultivating their contacts. Read more in Chapter 5.

STRATEGIC ROUNDS

The player-controlled elements of the campaign are managed during strategic rounds. Typically, a strategic round is played at the beginning of each gaming session, but it can be done less frequently, or at the end of sessions if you and your group prefer that.

During the strategic round, each player represents not their PC but their entire House. The players secretly plan and stage Incidents in the enclave on behalf of their families. The goal of this game is to increase the House's Control in the sectors of the enclave, or to reduce the Control of other Houses.

The Incidents staged in the strategic rounds then become cases for the judicators to handle – either the PCs themselves or other patrols. More on that later.

STAGING INCIDENTS

The *Guardians of the Fall* campaign contains eight normal events that are staged by the players themselves during the strategic rounds, and three special Incidents which are controlled by you, the GM. All eleven incidents are described in detail in the next chapter of the book. Also, the eight normal Incidents each have an accompanying summary card in the custom card deck for *Mutant: Elysium.* Each Incident is an event that one way or another threatens law and order in the enclave. These events do not appear by chance – there is always a House behind each one of them.

Sectors: Each Incident is staged in a specific sector. Five of the Incidents can only occur in the Core, while the other three can only be staged in the Deep.

Effects: Each Incident has two separate strategic effects: a starting effect and a final effect.

The starting effect occurs immediately when the Incident is revealed (see below). The final effect only occurs if the judicators fail to resolve the Incident – regardless of whether it was handled by PCs and roleplayed or handled by other judicators and resolved with a single roll of the dice (more on this below). If the PCs handled the Incident themselves, the GM will have the last word when judging whether they were successful or not. Sometimes it will be obvious, sometimes more of a judgment call.

Typical Incident effects are decreased Development Levels (see page 118) and changes in the Control of a House in the sector. Remember, Control in a sector can never go above 2 and never below zero.

MORE THAN FOUR PLAYERS?

If you have more than four players in the group, it means that one or more Houses will have two representatives among the players. During the strategic round, only one player can represent each House. Players whose characters belong to the same House can either take turns managing the strategic affairs of the House or work together during strategic rounds.

LESS THAN FOUR PLAYERS?

If your gaming group has three players, you as the GM must assume control of the missing House during the strategic round. The strategic game won't be affected too much, as all players (and you) still plan their Incidents in secret. You simply become a player during the strategic game.

With just one or two players in the group, the strategic game does not work as intended. In this case, we recommend that you simply determine which Incidents occur in the enclave and which the PCs are sent to handle. One aspect of *Mutant: Elysium* will be lost, but the *Guardians of the Fall* campaign can still be played this way.

THE FIRST STRATEGIC ROUND

In the first strategic round of the game, each player is randomly and secretly assigned two Incidents. If you have access to the custom card deck for *Mutant: Elysium*, simply deal two random Incident Cards to each player. If not, use any random method to assign the Incidents. Only reveal the following information about each event (the same as on the Incident Cards):

- The title of the Incident
- Where it can be staged (a sector in the Core or the Deep)
- The starting effect
- The final effect

The players must keep their assigned Incidents secret from one another as well as from you. Then, follow the steps below.

1. Choose Incident and Sector. Each player secretly decides which of his two available Incidents to stage, and which sector to stage it in. The players secretly note this information on a piece of paper and hand it to the GM. If you are using the custom card deck, each player should hand the Incident Card he intends to stage in this strategic round to the GM as well.

2. Fill in the Incident Sheet. As the GM, take an Incident Sheet (available at the end of this book and for download on the Free League website) and mark on it – without the players seeing it of course – what Incidents each House will stage and in what sectors.

3. Activate the Incidents. Reading from your Incident sheet, announce to the players which Incidents are occurring and in which sectors – but of course not which House is behind which Incident. These four Incidents are now *active*. If you are using the Incident Cards, place the cards for the active Incidents directly on the game map, on the sectors in which the Incidents are staged.

4. Resolve Starting Effects. Immediately resolve the starting effects of each active Incident.

5. Vote on Where to Go. Each active Incident is a task for the judicators to solve, a potential mission for the PCs. But the PCs can't solve all the problems in the enclave by themselves. They can only be sent to one of the four active Incidents – the other Incidents are handled by different groups of judicators.

INCIDENTS IN THE SAME SECTOR
It's entirely possible that multiple Incidents can occur in the same sector in the same strategic round. In this case, any increases or decreases of Control in the sector are cumulative. Any reduction of Control to zero has precedence over a numerical increase or decrease, however. Also, more than one House can never have Control 2 in the same sector – if this would occur due to the effects of multiple Incidents, immediately reduce the Control of both Houses to 1.

To determine what Incident the PCs are sent to handle, the players hold a secret vote. Each player simply writes down the name of the Incident they vote for on a piece of paper and hands it to you. It is not the PCs themselves that are voting, but rather their Houses, influencing the judicator command. Each player votes with the total Control of their House. Any tie is broken by the patrol leader. Also note that the Powerful Mother contact (see page 65) can affect the outcome.

The winning Incident is assigned to the PCs and is roleplayed in detail. Read more on each Incident in the next chapter. Incidents that don't win the vote become the responsibility of other judicators, see below.

OTHER JUDICATORS

When the player characters are sent to an Incident, any other Incidents staged in the strategic round will be handled by other judicators. A roll of the dice will determine whether they successfully handle the Incident or not. This roll is made at the beginning of the next strategic round.

The player whose House staged the Incident makes the roll. The number of dice rolled depends on the enclave's current Security Development Level (see the table to the right). The number of dice is modified by the sector in question, as well as the Control of other houses in the sector – see the tables on page 147. At least one die is always rolled.

If the player rolls one or more ☢, the judicators fail to handle the Incident and the final effect of the Incident is triggered.

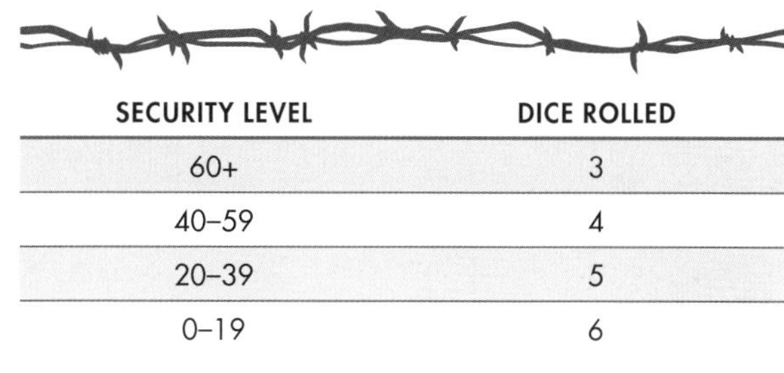

SECURITY LEVEL	DICE ROLLED
60+	3
40–59	4
20–39	5
0–19	6

EXAMPLE 2

It is time for the first strategic round. Each player draws two Incident Cards. Kilgore draws Censorship and Murder, Warburg draws Strike and Sabotage, Fortescue gets Riot and Kidnapping, and finally Morningstar draws Epidemic and Hostage.

Kilgore decides to stage a Murder in Nova Paloma, Warburg chooses a Strike in Arcadium, Fortescue stages a Kidnapping in Tindertuft, and finally Morningstar triggers an Epidemic in Pirius. Each player secretly notes their choice on a piece of paper and hands it to the GM.

Using the information from the players, the GM secretly fills out the Incident Sheet, and then reveals the four Incidents. Thus, the players now know which Incidents occur and where, but not which Houses are behind them (except their own). The map on page 154 shows the situation – each House symbol represents one point of Control

The GM then determines the starting effects of each Incident. The murder in Nova Paloma lowers the Science Development Level by 3 (to 77), the Strike in Arcadium reduces Production by 5 (to 75), the Kidnapping in Tindertuft reduces Culture by 2 (to 78), and the Epidemic in Pirius reduces Production by an additional 3 (to 72). Security remains at 80.

Now it is time for the Houses – that is the players – to vote on which Incident to send their PCs to. They write their choice on another piece of paper and hand it to the GM. Kilgore votes for the Strike in Arcadium, Warburg for the Kidnapping in Tindertuft, Fortescue

INCIDENT SHEET

MUTANT YEAR ZERO

Round 1	THE CORE - INCIDENTS							THE DEEP - INCIDENTS				
Sector	Nova Paloma	Old Koly	Pirius	Tindertuft	Northolme	Calista	Hindenburg	Mosel	Laborum	Arcadium	Cinderfalls	Cogs of Hel
Warburg										STRIKE		
Fortescue				KID-NAPPING								
Kilgore	MURDER											
Morningstar			EPIDEMIC									

Round	THE CORE - INCIDENTS							THE DEEP - INCIDENTS				
Sector	Nova Paloma	Old Koly	Pirius	Tindertuft	Northolme	Calista	Hindenburg	Mosel	Laborum	Arcadium	Cinderfalls	Cogs of Hel
Warburg												
Fortescue												
Kilgore												
Morningstar												

SEE EXAMPLE 2

for the Epidemic in Pirius, and Morningstar for the Murder in Nova Paloma. No player picks their own Incident. Both Fortescue and Warburg have a total Control of 4, so it is a draw. The Warburg player's PC has the Powerful Mother contact and chooses to activate it. The total Control of Warburg now counts as 5, and the House wins the vote. The PCs are sent to handle the Kidnapping in Tindertuft.

Now, the strategic round is over and normal play resumes.

SUBSEQUENT STRATEGIC ROUNDS

The second and subsequent strategic rounds begin with each player revealing what Incident their House staged in the previous strategic round. Then, each player who staged an Incident that the PCs where not sent to rolls dice to determine if the other judicators sent to handle it were up to the task or not (see below).

Trigger Final Effects: For each Incident that the judicators failed to handle in the previous strategic round – including the PC's Incident – the final effects of these Incidents are triggered and resolved. You as the GM have final say on whether the PCs were successful in handling their Incident or not. Most times, it will be obvious.

Assign New Incidents: Next, all normal Incidents *except* the ones that have been played out in detail by the PCs are secretly and randomly assigned to the players. Incidents not staged in the previous round are not kept – all Incidents that have not been played out by the PCs are re-assigned now.

ENCLAVE SHEET

MUTANT YEAR ZERO

DEVELOPMENT LEVELS

Production	Security	Culture	Science
72	80	78	77

THE CORE – INFLUENCE

Sector	Warburg	Fortescue	Kilgore	Morningstar
Nova Paloma	1		1	1
Old Koly				
Pirius	1			1
Tindertuft		1		
Northolme	1			
Calista		1		
Hindenburg				1

THE DEEP – INFLUENCE

Sector	Warburg	Fortescue	Kilgore	Morningstar
Mosel			1	
Laborum				
Arcadium	1			
Cinderfalls			1	
Cogs of Hel		2		

TOTAL INFLUENCE

Warburg	Fortescue	Kilgore	Morningstar
4	4	3	3

SEE EXAMPLE 2

SEE EXAMPLE 2

HOUSE BEFORE ENCLAVE
Note that many of the Incidents will have a negative impact on the enclave's Development Levels. This is a price that the Houses are prepared to pay in order to gain power and leverage over each other. Only the Security level has a concrete impact on the campaign mechanics (see page 151), but the other Development Levels will affect life in the enclave in different ways. See the table on page 118.

If you are using Incident Cards, simply remove the cards for Incidents that the PCs have been sent to handle. This means there will be one Incident less to assign in each new strategic round. Assign the Incidents as evenly as possible, starting with the player whose House has the highest total Control and going down. Break any ties with a random dice roll.

Choose New Incidents to Stage: From this point, follow the same steps as if it were the first strategic round. Start by having the players choose their Incidents and where to stage them, vote on where to send the PCs, etc. Note that as the campaign progresses, players will have fewer and fewer Incidents to chose from. From the fifth round on, some players will not get to stage any Incidents at all.

EXAMPLE 3

The PC have finished the Kidnapping Incident, and it's time for the second strategic round. All players reveal which Incident their Houses staged in the previous round.

Then the players roll the dice to determine if their Incident succeeded or if they were stopped by the other judicators – except House Fortescue, as the PCs were sent to handle that Incident. The PCs succeeded in resolving the Kidnapping Incident, and thus the final effect of the Kidnapping is not triggered.

Kilgore rolls for the Murder in Nova Paloma. The Security development level is over 60, which gives three dice to roll. But Nova Paloma has a difficulty of -2, and in addition to that there are other Houses with Control 1 in the sector, for a total modification of -3. However, at least one die is always rolled. The player rolls no ☢ however, and therefore the Murder was solved by the other judicators. The final effect is not triggered.

Warburg rolls for the Strike in Arcadium. The sector has a difficulty modification of zero and no other Houses have Control there. Three dice are rolled and the Warburg player gets one ☢. The House succeeds! Warburg's Control in Arcadium increases to 2, and the total Control of House Warburg rises to 5. The final effect of the Strike is triggered, and the Production level is decreased by another 5 (to 67).

Morningstar rolls for the Epidemic in Pirius. The sector has a difficulty of -1 and another House has Control 1 in the sector, which means the total number of dice rolled is one. The roll fails, and the final effect is not triggered.

Next, using Incident Cards, the GM randomly assigns all Incidents except Kidnapping to the players. Warburg (with total Control 5) gets the first card. Both Warburg and Fortescue (which has total Control 4) will be assigned two Incidents in

SELECTING INCIDENTS
Players should think carefully when voting for what Incident the PCs will be sent to solve.

It is often best for each player to try and send the PCs to the Incident with the final effect that would be most detrimental to their House, as the players generally have a good chance of solving that Incident. For the same reason, a player generally will not want to send the PCs to an Incident staged by his own House.

Adventurous players can bring it up a notch and try to send the PCs to the Incident whose final effects would benefit his House, and then sabotage the patrol from the "inside" to make sure the group fails. However, this is a risky tactic, as the PC will be at risk of admonishment for misconduct (see Chapter 2).

this strategic round. Morningstar and Kilgore (both have total Control 3) roll off to determine who gets two Incidents in this round and who gets one, as only seven potential Incidents now remain in play.

The strategic round then continues in the same way as the first one.

THE STRATEGIC ROUND

A strategic round follows the below steps. Skip steps 1–3 in the first strategic round.

1. Each player reveals which Incident they staged in the previous strategic round.
2. Players roll dice to determine the success or failure of any Incidents the PCs were not sent to handle.
3. For each Incident that the judicators failed to handle in the previous strategic round – including the Incident that the PCs were sent to – the final effect is triggered.
4. The GM randomly and secretly assigns all Incidents to the players, except Incidents previously played out by the PCs. Start with the player whose House has the highest total Control.
5. Each player chooses an Incident to stage and the sector in which to stage it. Each player notes this on a piece of paper and hands it to the GM.
6. The GM fills in the information from the players on the Incident Sheet.
7. The GM announces which Incidents are occurring in which sectors. The starting effects of all Incidents are immediately triggered.
8. The players, as representatives of their Houses, vote with their total Control to determine which Incident the PCs should be sent to investigate.

PACTS

If two or three Houses wish to cooperate during a strategic round, they can form a Pact. This must be declared before the players decide which Incidents to stage. The members of a Pact can show each other which Incidents are available to them and coordinate their plans. The members of a Pact may not show each other the notes they give to the GM however – it's entirely possible to betray a Pact. A House can only be part of one Pact at a time. A pact can at the most have three members, never all four Houses. A pact only lasts for a single strategic round, but nothing stops the Houses from reforming the same pact in the next round.

RE-USING INCIDENTS

Incidents that were activated but not handled by the PCs personally are re-used in later strategic rounds. This does not mean that the exact same event happens again, only that a similar type of event occurs. When an Incident has been played out in detail by the PCs however, it cannot occur again and is removed from the game.

SPECIAL INCIDENTS

In addition to the eight normal Incidents in the campaign, there are three special Incidents. These three Incidents are entirely governed by you as the GM and are described in detail in the next chapter.

Whenever it is time for a strategic round, you can choose to activate a special Incident. The strategic round is then immediately canceled, and the PCs are automatically assigned to the special Incident. No normal Incidents are assigned or activated, and no vote is held.

Double Agent: After a special Incident, there is no vote to reveal the double agent (see page 25).

Timing: The first special Incident, called "Signal from *Genlab Alpha*" should be activated approximately halfway into the campaign. The two final

ENCLAVE SHEET

MUTANT YEAR ZERO

DEVELOPMENT LEVELS

Production	67	Security	80	Culture	78	Science	77

THE CORE – INFLUENCE

Sector	Warburg	Fortescue	Kilgore	Morningstar
Nova Paloma	1		1	1
Old Koly				1
Pirius	1	1		
Tindertuft				
Northolme	1			
Calista		1		
Hindenburg				1

THE DEEP – INFLUENCE

Sector	Warburg	Fortescue	Kilgore	Morningstar
Mosel			1	
Laborum				
Arcadium	2			
Cinderfalls			1	
Cogs of Hel		2		

TOTAL INFLUENCE

Warburg	Fortescue	Kilgore	Morningstar
5	4	3	3

SEE EXAMPLE 3

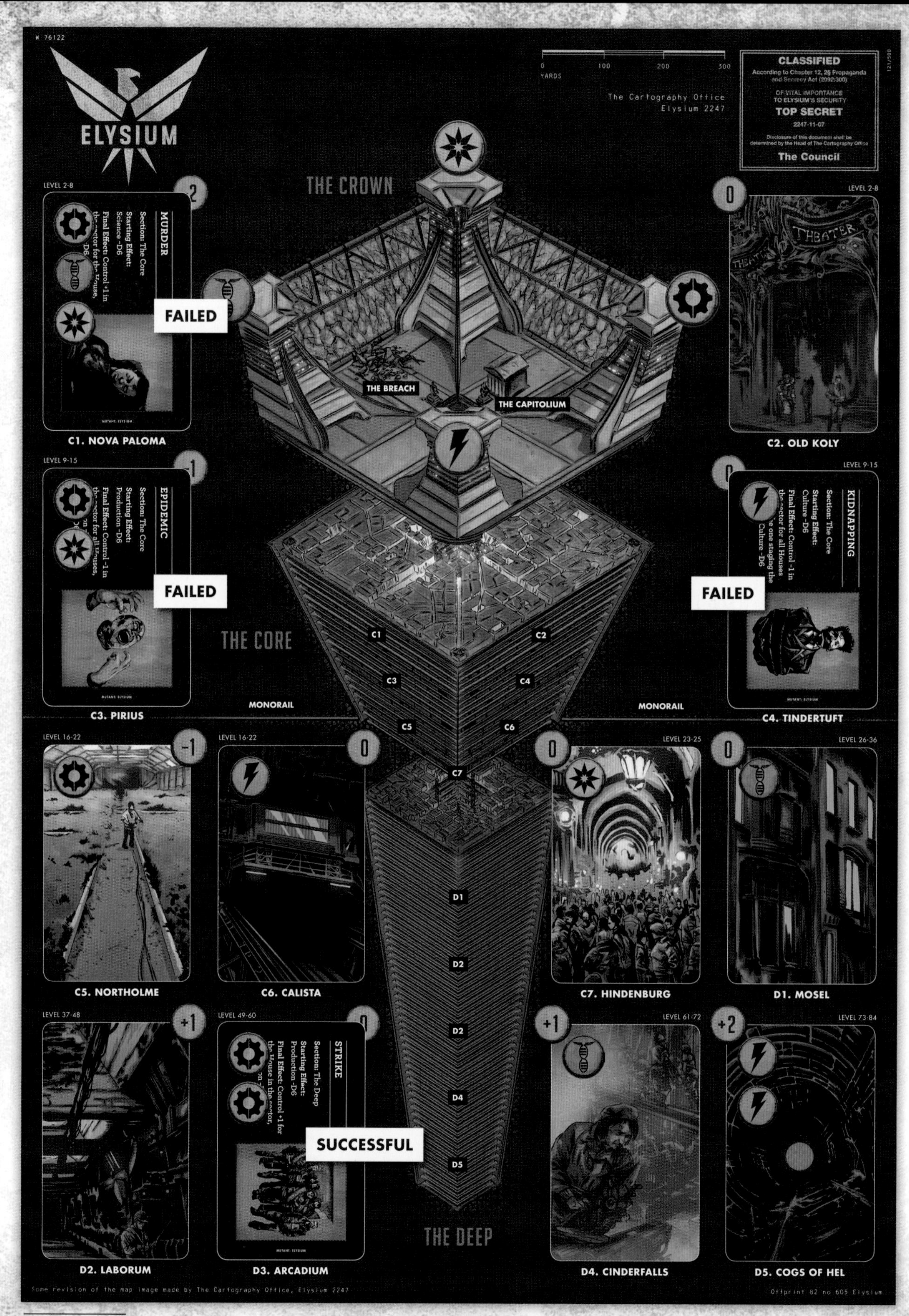

SEE EXAMPLE 3

WHEN TO LAUNCH THE ENDGAME?

Note, you as the GM can choose to start the endgame of the campaign before running out of normal Incidents. It all depends on how long you want the campaign to run. However, we recommend that the PCs play at least four of the eight normal Incidents before launching the endgame.

special Incidents, "A Day to Remember" and "Assault on Cryolab Delta," constitute the finale of the campaign and should be saved until you have played all the normal Incidents that you intend to play. You don't need to play all eight normal Incidents if you don't want to.

ENDING THE CAMPAIGN

The longer the campaign runs, the fewer Incidents there will be in play.

Three Incidents Remaining: When only three Incidents remain in play, one player will be left without an Incident to stage. The game goes on normally, except that this player will not activate an Incident.

Two Incidents Remaining: When only two Incidents are left in play, two players will be unable to stage Incidents.

One Incident Remaining: When only one Incident remains, it's assigned to the player whose House has the highest total Control. The PCs will automatically be sent to this Incident, no vote is held.

Final Round: After the eighth Incident has been played by the PCs, there is one last strategic round. If the patrol failed to handle the Incident, the Incident's final effect is triggered. After that, the strategic game ends immediately and it is time to launch the endgame of the campaign with the special Incident called "A Day to Remember."

KEY NPCS

The remainder of this chapter describes fifteen NPCs that are key to the *Guardians of the Fall* campaign and that can appear in several Incidents. If possible, try to prevent these NPCs from dying during the early stages of the campaign. If they do, be ready to replace them with other similar NPCs. NPC Cards: Each key NPC has a unique, illustrated NPC Card in the custom card deck for *Mutant: Elysium*. Show the NPC card when the NPC is introduced in the game. On the back there is game data that should not be displayed to the players.

ANTONIUS BLOCK

ANTONIUS BLOCK

- **Incidents:** Hostage
- **PC Relationships:** Soldier, Investigator, Procurator, Officer

A charismatic leader who was born to one of the Houses. He served as an officer in the Deep Watch. A few years ago, while on an assignment, his patrol was surrounded by angry workers. When another officer opened fire against the crowd, Antonius used force to stop him. The exchange resulted in the death of the colleague.

Only his prior years of spotless service allowed Antonius to escape the Catacombs. Instead, he was sentenced to a lifetime of hard labor in the Deep. Antonius was disowned by his House, and he took the name Block.

Over the years in the Deep, Antonius Block has become a leader among the penal workers in Night Hall, the dirtiest and most dangerous factory in the enclave. Block has also come into contact with novice Cassandra of the Temple and believes in her teachings. He is not a fanatic however, rather a clever realist who is ready to negotiate when he needs to.

Personal Goal: To transform Elysium I into an open and equal society – using violence if necessary.

Reputation: 3

Attributes: Strength 4, Agility 3, Wits 3, Empathy 5.

Skills: Force 3, Fight 4, Move 2, Shoot 2, Sense Emotion 5, Manipulate 3.

Equipment: Blunt instrument. During the Hostage Incident, Block also carries a stolen gauss pistol.

EPHRAIM DUNKLE

- **Incidents:** Epidemic, Strike
- **PC Relationships:** Investigator, Procurator

This scarred worker has toiled in the Reconstruction Works for most of his life. His body can no longer take hard manual labor, and he therefore spends most of his time drinking away the sorrow and pain.

Personal Goal: Drowning his sorrows in liquor and living one day at a time.

Reputation: 1

Attributes: Strength 4, Agility 2, Wits 2, Empathy 3.

Skills: Endure 4, Fight 2, Sense Emotion 3.

Biomechatronics: Air Tank, Machine Arm.

Equipment: None.

FLORIAN

FLORIAN

- **Incident:** Hostage
- **PC Relationships:** Procurator

A young and principled judicator. Florian is a man with a proud attitude. If Florian has a family relationship with a PC, they belong to the same family, otherwise he is a Warburg.

Personal Goal: First his freedom, then to arrest or kill Antonius Block at any cost.

Reputation: 4

Attributes: Strength 3, Agility 4, Wits 2, Empathy 3.

Skills: Fight 2, Move 2, Shoot 3, Press On 2.

Equipment: None during the Hostage Incident, otherwise he is armed with a gauss pistol.

EPHRAIM DUNKLE

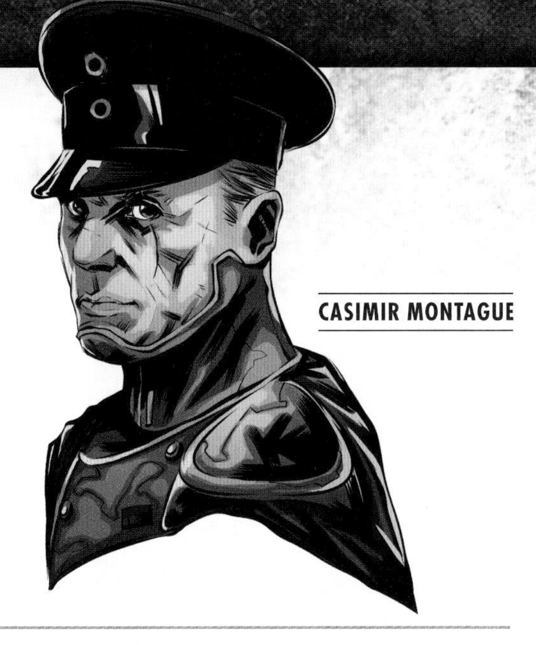

CASIMIR MONTAGUE

- **Incidents:** Riot, Epidemic, Censorship, Signal from *Genlab Alpha*
- **PC Relationships:** Officer, Soldier

Colonel Montague is a notorious officer in the Deep Watch, the military force of the enclave. He does not belong to any of the four families and therefore lacks the advantage of their influence. However, he more than compensates for this through rigorous discipline and ruthlessness.

The colonel is a middle-aged man with thick hair, a strong jaw, and is in very good physical shape. He lives alone and owns a large collection of ancient military strategy books. He is almost never seen without his uniform.

Personal Goal: To destroy any threat to the enclave without mercy or remorse.

Reputation: 8
Attributes: Strength 4, Agility 5, Wits 4, Empathy 4.
Skills: Fight 4, Move 3, Shoot 5, Sense Emotion 5, Manipulate 3, Command 5.
Equipment: Gyrojet rifle, 12 gyrojet rockets.

CASSANDRA

- **Incidents:** Hostage Drama, Murder
- **PC Relationships:** Technician

This young novice only recently joined the Temple. Unlike most other novices, she does not come from the ranks of the workers. Cassandra was born into one of the Houses – if she is the sister of a PC, she belongs to the same House. If not, determine randomly. Cassandra was once called Ashley and used to work in the Academy.

Ashley became sad and disillusioned after an event where a rival from her own House stole her life's work and took credit for the research. In disgust, Elisa turned her back on both the Academy and her own House, seeking refuge in the Temple. There, she changed her name to Cassandra.

She was quickly noticed by Creon and became his most trusted novice. Cassandra knows that Creon intends to overthrow the Council, but she does not know the details of the plan, or that Creon communicates with the sleeping Eminences.

Personal Goal: To be recognized for her work and make her own House pay for her suffering. Unlike Creon, she is not really interested in overthrowing the rule of the Houses.

Reputation: 5
Attributes: Strength 2, Agility 3, Wits 5, Empathy 3.
Skills: Sneak 2, Move 3, Sense Emotion 4, Manipulate 3.
Equipment: None.

CREON

- **Incidents:** Hostage, Kidnapping, Attack on Cryolab Alpha
- **PC Relationships:** Officer, Procurator, Investigator, Scholar

Creon is currently the waking Eminence and thus the driving force behind the clandestine revolt against the great Houses. In due time, all ten Eminences will rise, but until that time the responsibility rests on Creon's shoulders.

This is Creon's 25th shift awake; thus he has only aged 25 years since he first entered Elysium I. He was then 40 years old and his biological age is now 65. However, the long years in cryosleep have taken their toll on his body. Creon is a very thin and pale man.

Creon was born before the Red Plague, and centuries before all other waking inhabitants in the enclave. His speech seems old-fashioned and is sometimes difficult to understand. Creon's beard has whitened during the years of cryosleep and he wears the gray robes of the Eminences.

Personal Goal: To overthrow the great Houses and finally end his years of servitude.

Reputation: 12
Attributes: Strength 3, Agility 4, Wits 5, Empathy 5.
Skills: Fight 3, Move 3, Shoot 4, Comprehend 5, Sense Emotion 5, Manipulate 5.
Equipment: Gyrojet pistol with six rockets.

MELINA

- **Incidents:** Murder, Kidnapping, Censorship
- **Possible PC Relationships:** Scholar

A prominent Scholar at the Academy. What House Melina belongs to is decided during the Murder Incident.

Personal Goal: To be recognized in all of Elysium for her brilliance.

Reputation: 5
Attributes: Strength 2, Agility 3, Wits 5, Empathy 3.
Skills: Shoot 2, Comprehend 5, Know the Zone 3, Enlighten 5.
Equipment: Gauss pistol.

MOLLY FINKEL

- **Incidents:** Epidemic
- **PC Relationships:** Investigator

Molly runs the Scat Dobbling's bar in the Core, a simple but popular hole in the wall and retreat for both workers from the Deep as well as members of Houses from the Crown who want a taste of the underbelly of the enclave. Things can often get messy in Scat Dobbling's, which is why Molly always has her faithful scrap rifle hidden under the bar.

Personal Goal: To keep Scat Dobbling's open for business.

Reputation: 2
Attributes: Strength 4, Agility 3, Wits 2, Empathy 4.
Skills: Fight 2, Shoot 2, Sense Emotion 4.
Equipment: Scrap Rifle and three bullets.

RUPERT ACTON

- **Incidents:** Epidemic, Hostage Drama, Kidnapping
- **PC Relationships:** Soldier, Procurator

Rupert is the youngest of five siblings and has throughout his entire life been compared to his older and more successful brothers and sisters. During his service in the Deep Watch he was injured in the leg and was forced to retire from the active corps. Instead, he became a security guard and was eventually promoted to commander. He turned out to be well suited for his new role and is well-liked by all. Rupert is a very dutiful man and a good comrade.

Personal Goal: To one day stand in the spotlight as the enclave's greatest hero.

Reputation: 3
Attributes: Strength 4, Agility 2, Wits 3, Empathy 3.
Skills: Fight 3, Move 3, Shoot 3, Sense Emotion 2, Command 2.
Equipment: Stun pistol, stun baton, two E-Packs.

THE SCRAP KING

- **Incidents:** Kidnapping, Attack on Cryolab Delta
- **PC Relationships:** Soldier, Investigator

The leader of the Cravats gang, the Scrap King is a pale, fat man with a Biomechatronic right arm and lower jaw. He was a miner who was sentenced to the Catacombs for killing another worker. Being sent to the Catacombs was the best thing that has happened to him.

Personal Goal: To see pain and fear in the eyes of others.

Reputation: 5
Attributes: Strength 5, Agility 3, Wits 4, Empathy 4.
Skills: Shoot 3, Fight 4, Comprehend 4, Manipulate 3.
Biomechatronics: Metal Skull, Machine Arm.
Equipment: Spiked bat, gyrojet pistol with six rockets.

SONYA CARP

- **Incidents:** Riots, Strike
- **PC Relationships:** Technician, Scholar

Sonya Carp was born to a worker family in Cogs of Hel and all she knows of Elysium I is poverty and squalor. Like her parents, she has done her job and worked long days all of her life, grateful to the Houses for her place in the lifeboat of humanity.

But over the years doubt slowly found its way into her thoughts. Should the workers not have a better life than this? Without actively seeking a role as a leader, Sonja became a person that other workers looked to for advice and guidance.

Sonya is a middle-aged woman in worker's attire with a reconstructed left arm. She has gallows humor and often has a smile on her lips.

Personal Goal: To give the enclave workers a better life.

Reputation: 4
Attributes: Strength 4, Agility 3, Wits 3, Empathy 4.
Skills: Force 4, Fight 2, Sense Emotion 3, Manipulate 4.
Biomechatronics: Machine Arm.
Equipment: Blunt instrument.

TODDY SOMERSET

- **Incidents:** Kidnapping, Censorship
- **PC Relationships:** Officer, Procurator

Toddy Somerset is Valentino Morningstar's current manager. Toddy is a short man with greasy hair (most of which left his scalp a long time ago). Toddy is completely spineless and will do anything to gain fame and status. Toddy dreams of being powerful, rich, and admired, but is severely lacking in finesse and has a knack for always getting into trouble.

Personal Goal: Taking care of number one first, and always.

Reputation: 6
Attributes: Strength 2, Agility 2, Wits 4, Empathy 5.
Skills: Move 2, Manipulate 4.
Equipment: Vibro knife.

NUTTY NADYA

- **Incidents:** Riot
- **PC Relationships:** Technician, Investigator

The hard-headed leader of the Sooty Hand, one of the most infamous gangs in the Deep.

Personal Goal: To expand her power into the Core, and she is more than willing to kill to get what she wants.

Reputation: 2
Attributes: Strength 4, Agility 5, Wits 3, Empathy 4.
Skills: Shoot 4, Fight 5, Sense Emotion 5, Manipulate 4.
Biomechatronics: Monofilament, Pain Suppressors.
Equipment: Gyrojet pistol with five rockets, hand grenade.

VALENTINO MORNINGSTAR

VALENTINO MORNINGSTAR

- **Incidents:** Kidnapping, Hostage, Censorship
- **PC Relationships:** Investigator

Valentino has never had to suffer hardship in his life. He was raised in the Crown amongst the affluent, constantly surrounded by family and relatives. His popularity amongst the social circles of the elite got him the job as the host of the Voice of Dawn show. This has done little to dampen his already inflated ego. Valentino is very confident of himself and expects everyone he meets to bow to his wishes. As the host of the program, he often personally reports on news and events in the Deep without realizing the risks he is putting himself in.

Personal Goal: To bask in everyone's smiles and applause.

Reputation: 11
Attributes: Strength 2, Agility 3, Wits 2, Empathy 5.
Skills: Sneak 2, Move 4, Manipulate 5.
Equipment: None.

VALERIA WARBURG

- **Incidents:** Censorship, Kidnapping
- **RP Relationships:** Officer

Valeria grew up in luxury and opulence and is utterly tired of being pampered. She is looking for some thrills and challenges in her life but does not really have a plan to achieve this goal. The romance with Valentino was exciting in the beginning, until she realized how self-absorbed the show host really is. Marrying him is purely a tactical maneuver. Valeria is an actress and is really good at keeping up appearances.

Personal Goal: To seek new thrills and challenges.

Reputation: 10
Attributes: Strength 2, Agility 3, Wits 2, Empathy 5.
Skills: Sneak 2, Move 3, Sense Emotion 3, Manipulate 5.
Equipment: None.

VALERIA WARBURG

11

INCIDENTS

In this chapter you'll find detailed descriptions of the eleven Incidents of the *Guardians of the Fall* campaign. An incident resembles a Special Zone Sector (if you are familiar with *Mutant: Year Zero*) but is generally more limited in time and space.

An Incident is an event your judicator character is sent to handle at a specific location. Think of an Incident as a mini-scenario, usually meant to take one gaming session to resolve. If *Mutant: Elysium* were a television series, an Incident would be one episode of the show.

The eight normal Incidents are described first, followed by the three GM-controlled special Incidents. How Incidents are used in the game is described in the previous chapter.

The House: In each Incident description, "the House" always refers to the House that staged the Incident (see page 149) unless otherwise is stated.

VICTORY CONDITIONS

Each Incident clearly states what the PCs must achieve for their handling of the Incident to be considered successful. Failure will trigger the Incident's final effects (see page 149).

INCIDENTS IN THE CORE

- Censorship
- Epidemic
- Kidnapping
- Murder
- Sabotage

INCIDENTS IN THE DEEP

- Hostage
- Riots
- Strike

CENSORSHIP

- **Section:** The Core
- **Starting Effect:** Culture -D6
- **Final Effect:** House Control +1 in the sector, Security -D6

Lately the Imperator Theater has been receiving serious threats. This evening is the premiere of "Towards the Deep," a play about Elysium's history. Someone threatened to kill the actors and the director, Preston Morningstar. Demonstrations against the play have been reported. Attend tonight's performance and investigate any potential threats. But you must be discreet, your work must in no way interfere with the performance. House Morningstar's head, Constantine, will visit the premiere himself. This play is very important to him.

THE PLAY

The play "Towards the Deep" was created by the renowned director Preston Morningstar (alternatively Kilgore, see below) and is a dramatization of Elysium's history. The action revolves around a young couple, Jasper and Eliza – he is a worker and she is a dynast – along with their faithful companion, the robot Tonka.

Against all odds, Jasper and Eliza fall in love, and after a great many hardships and tribulations, they finally find safety within Elysium I, where Jasper eventually dies from his injuries. In this tragic ending, it is revealed that Eliza is pregnant. The future of the child, and humanity, will be in the depths of the Earth.

Eliza is played by Elysium's greatest actress, Valeria Warburg, and Jasper by the blonde up and coming star Lex Fredicius.

OVERVIEW

The PCs arrive at the Imperator Theater just before the performance begins. Outside the entrance there is a small group of protesters with posters that read "the surface is free," "life is waiting up there" and "the Houses are holding us hostage underground." Some security guards are keeping an eye on things to ensure that the well-dressed theater visitors can get in undisturbed.

If the PCs talk with the protesters, who are a motley mix of workers from the Core, they say that they "have heard" that the surface world is now habitable and that the Houses keep this a secret to preserve their own power. They are visibly upset, although not violent and will do as told if the PCs interfere.

The rumor about the Earth's surface is true, which the PCs will already know if they have played the "Signal from *Genlab Alpha*" special Incident. However, revealing that information to the public would threaten the prevailing law and order in Elysium, thus constituting a serious act of misconduct for a judicator.

The mood is good inside the theater's foyer. House dynasts mingle while the drinks flow. In between whispers and chuckles can be heard comments admiring the protagonists and how Valeria Warburg and Lex Fredicius make such a beautiful couple, and that Valeria's fiancé Valentino Morningstar should be jealous. The PCs can meet a range of familiar faces, such as Valentino himself, Valeria's cousin Esmeralda Warburg, Melina, Toddy Somerset, Colonel Casimir Montague, and, last but not least, Constantine Morningstar in person.

Before the performance begins, the PCs can approach the director Preston Morningstar as well as any of the stars or actors in the play. Adelia Kruger – prompter, janitor, and security officer, must be Manipulated if the PCs want access to the dressing rooms so close to curtain time. Even if the judicators gain access, they will be disappointed to find that the ensemble has nothing to tell – they have heard about the threats but dismiss them as "nonsense."

THE SITUATION

In order to create anxiety in the sector and increase their influence, the House staging this Incident is taking advantage of common rumors everyone has heard – that the surface is habitable. This has triggered angry protests outside the theater before the premiere of the play, which praises life in the enclave.

In addition, the House's agent Gunther Glass has recruited Adelia Kruger, a former stage star at Theater Imperator, who now makes a living as a prompter. Adelia has cultivated a long and bitter resentment against the Houses in general and Preston Morningstar in particular.

On behalf of the House, Gunther Glass has convinced Adelia that the Houses are holding the inhabitants of the enclave prisoners in the deep, and that the play "Towards the Deep" is just a propaganda ploy used to keep the truth from coming out. This all happens to be true, but that's of minor consequence to the House, which is just using the rumor to further its own agenda.

Filled with hatred, Adelia believes she is about to play the role of her life. She has allowed Gunther Glass to re-program the robot Tonka, a supporting actor in the play, so that Gunther can control it remotely from his place in the audience. The premiere will not turn out as Preston had planned...

Note: If the House staging this Incident is Morningstar, let Preston be a Kilgore instead.

LOCATIONS

Described here are the most important locations in the theater:

1. ENTRANCE

A wide staircase where people often linger for a glimpse at the prominent family dynasts visiting the theater. The entrance is flanked by statues of famous historical personalities from the Houses.

2. FOYER

The foyer is decorated in dark reds and gold. There is a ticket box and several coat rooms.

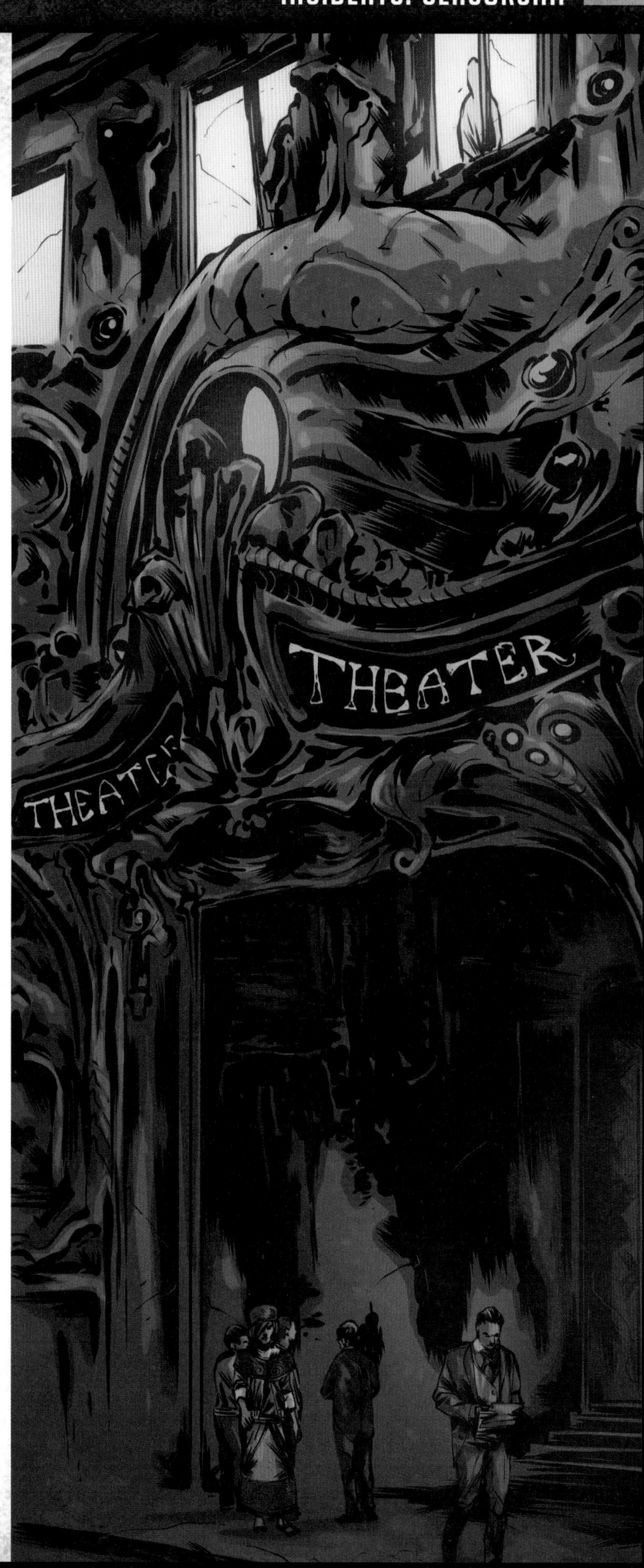

THE IMPERATOR THEATER

1. Entrance
2. Foyer
3. Actor Dressing Room
4. Stage
5. Theater Bar
6. Inner Bar
7. Balcony Seats
8. Extras Dressing Room
9. Director's Office
10. Upper Machine Room
11. Basement Storage
12. Lower Machine Room
13. Wardrobe
14. Costume Storage
15. Stagehand Area

□ 1 x 1 yard

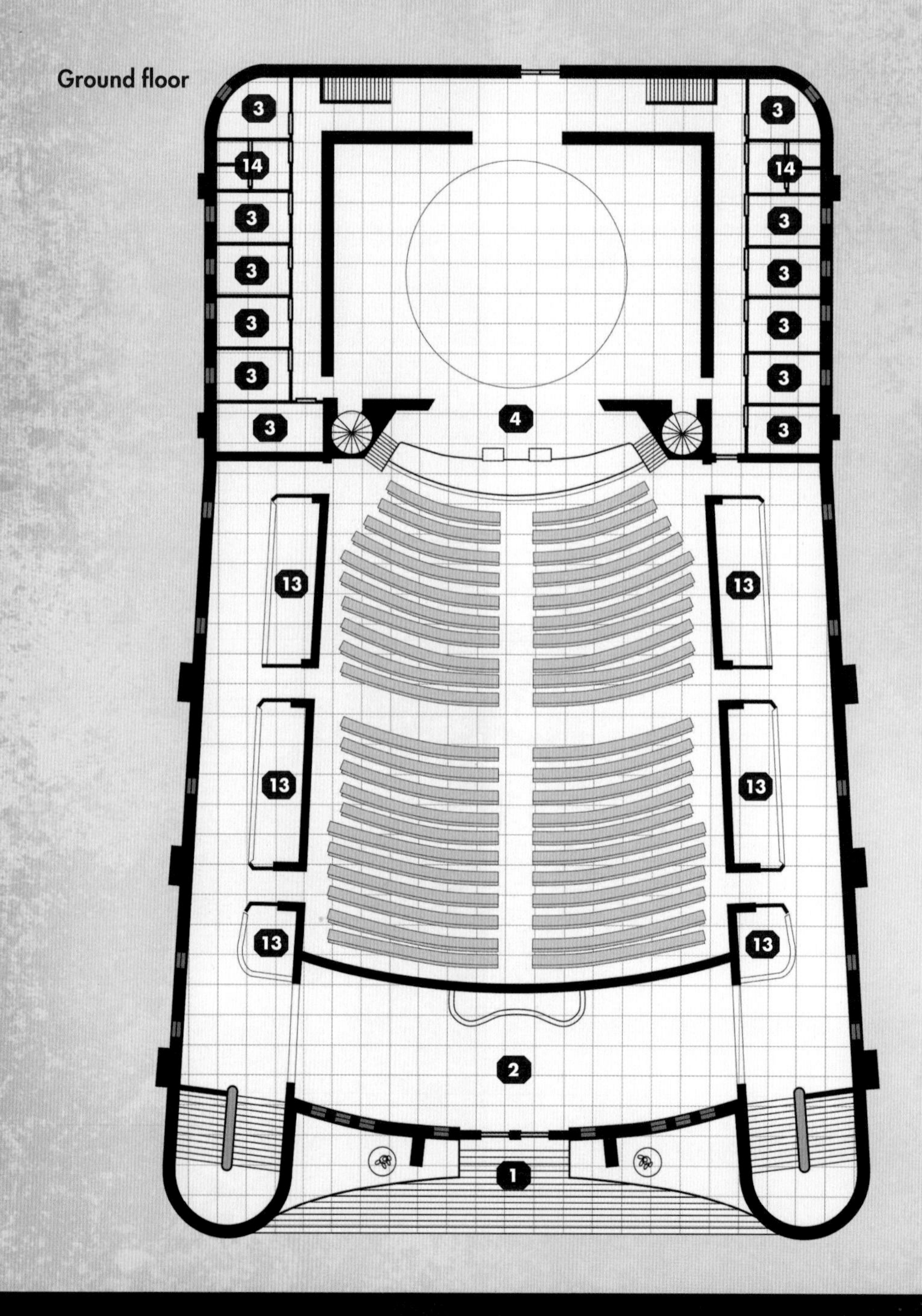

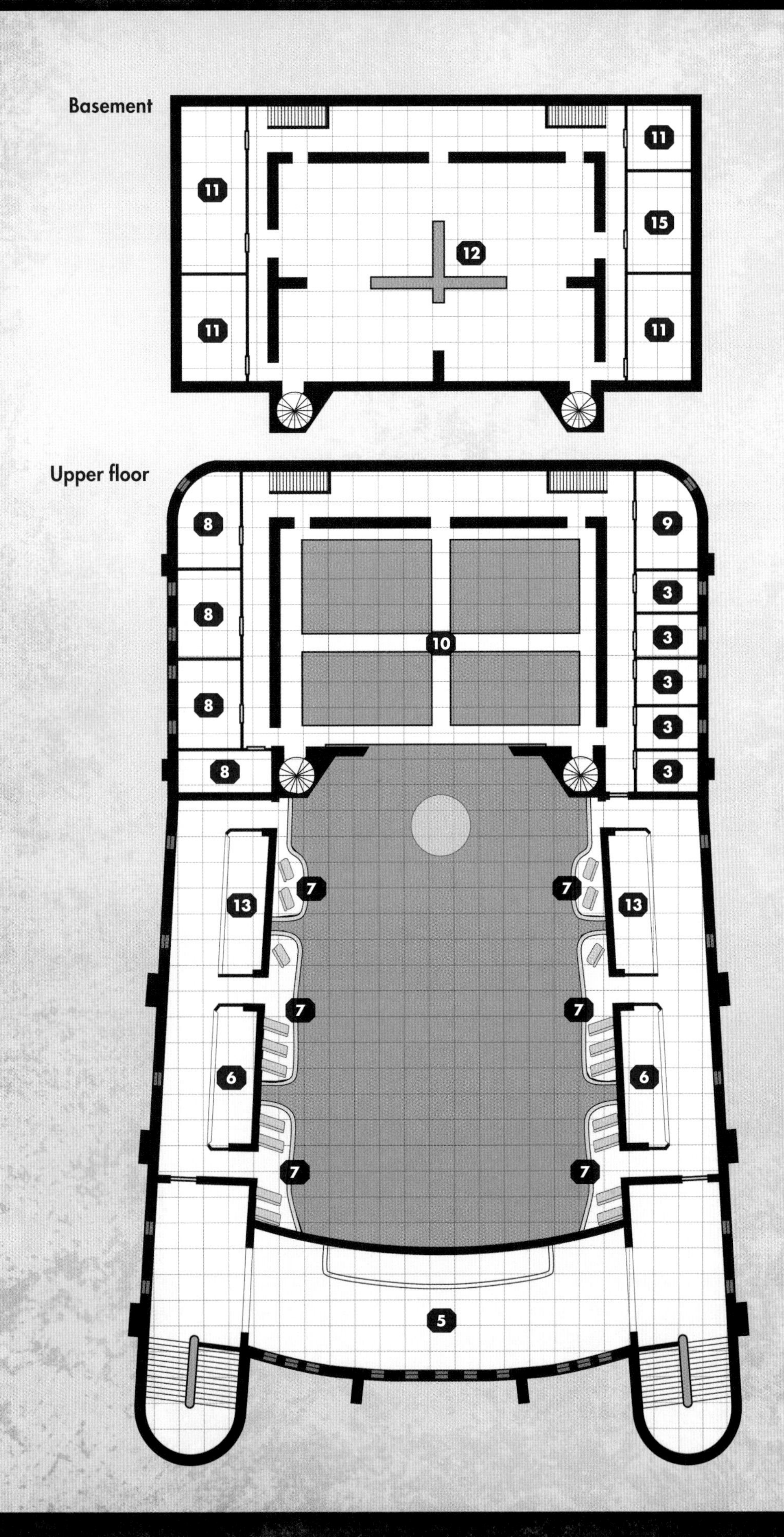

Basement
11
11
11
15
12
11
11
Upper floor
8
9
8
3
3
10
8
3
3
8
3
7
7
13
13
7
7
6
6
7
7
5

3. ACTOR DRESSING ROOMS
The more prominent the actor, the closer their dressing room is to the stage. Valeria Warburg's is the biggest one, immediately to the left of the stage.

4. STAGE
The big stage has a platform that can be raised and lowered where actors and props can be hoisted up and down. A magnificent chandelier hangs over the stalls.

A PC who goes back stage can find a small device on the floor. A Technician or another PC who makes a Comprehend roll identifies it as an electronic tool (artifact, see page 135) that is used on advanced equipment such as energy weapons and robots. This is a strange object to find in a theater. Gunther Glass dropped the tool when he used it to program Tonka.

5. THEATER BAR
Above the foyer is a bar serving drinks and light snacks. Round wooden tables are available where visitors can have a drink during the intermission.

6. INNER BAR
Doors flanked by guards lead from the public bar to a private room for the more prominent guests.

7. BALCONY SEATS
The best seats in the theater, reserved for the most important visitors from the Houses.

8. EXTRAS DRESSING ROOMS
Upstairs there are small dressing rooms for the extras. During big performances, there is usually a lot of activity in these corridors.

9. DIRECTOR'S OFFICE
A comfortable and elegant office decorated in Art Nouveau style.

10. UPPER MACHINE ROOM
Two narrow plank bridges run high above the stage. From there, stage workers hoist props up and down. The whole space is a whirlwind of ropes, pulleys and hooks.

11. BASEMENT STORAGE
In the basement there are storage areas for props, furniture, scenery, and other supplies.

12. LOWER MACHINE ROOM
Underneath the stage there is a machine room where stagehands can lift up scenery, actors, and other props through carefully designed openings.

NPCS

Of the campaign's key NPCs, Valentino Morningstar and Valeria Warburg are present during this Incident. Melina, Toddy Somerset and Casimir Montague can also be present, but do not play central roles. Other NPCs are described below.

PRESTON MORNINGSTAR

A renowned director and a socialite favorite among the rich and famous of Elysium I. He is a self-centered man with a deep appreciation of great art. He is ashamed about how he has treated Adelia Kruger but doesn't dare do anything about it. Preston is a 50-year old, white-haired man with an intricate haircut and an equally elaborate beard.

Personal Goal: To awe the enclave with his new play.

Reputation: 9
Attributes: Strength 3, Agility 2, Wits 3, Empathy 5.
Skills: Manipulate 2.

ADELIA KRUGER

Adelia is an experienced actress. However, her long career came to an abrupt end when Preston Morningstar arrived as lead director at Theater Imperator. Adelia was allowed to remain at the theater, but only as a prompter. She has platinum blonde hair and always wears black clothes and heavy makeup.

Personal Goal: To have her revenge against the Houses and Preston in particular, and to escape to the surface world.

Reputation: 6
Attributes: Strength 3, Agility 4, Wits 2, Empathy 4.
Skills: Move 2, Shoot 2, Manipulate 3.
Gear: Scrap pistol with three bullets.

GUNTHER GLASS

A pale, middle-aged man with a sullen demeanor, always wearing octagonal glasses. He comes from a worker's family and serves the House for money. He is in a romantic relationship with Adelia Kruger, but he's not ready to give his life for her.

Personal Goal: To fulfill his mission and escape alive.

Reputation: 3
Attributes: Strength 3, Agility 5, Wits 3, Empathy 2.
Skills: Fight 3, Sneak 4, Shoot 4, Sense Emotion 4, Comprehend 4.
Gear: Gauss-pistol, E-pack, comm radio.

TONKA

The mechanical actor known as Tonka started his career as a security robot with the formal designation TNK-097. It has now been reprogrammed by Gunther Glass, who has total control over it.

Personal Goal: To follow Gunther's every command.

CONSTANTINE MORNINGSTAR

Reputation: 3
Attributes: Servos 8, Stability 6, Processor 2, Network 2 (see *Mutant: Mechatron*).
Armor Rating: 10
Programs: Assault 4, Shoot 4, Scan 3, Protect 4.
Modules: Riot Control (5 EP).
Secondary Functions: Command Override, Arm Lock, Self-Destruct Mechanism, Crank Generator.
Gear: Laser pistol (mounted, Gear Bonus +2, Weapon Damage 3, Short range), stun baton.

ESMERALDA WARBURG

Esmeralda is Valeria's cousin and childhood friend. She is blonde and wears a blood red dress. She has never had to work a day in her life and expects to be the center of attention. Has always been jealous of Valeria.

Note: Esmeralda also appears in the Kidnapping Incident.

Personal Goal: To replace Valeria as the darling of the Elysium social elites.

Reputation: 6
Attributes: Strength 2, Agility 3, Wits 3, Empathy 4.
Skills: Manipulate 2.

CONSTANTINE MORNINGSTAR

Constantine has been house Morningstar's leader for several decades. He sees it as his top priority to follow what is happening with the enclave's theater scene. "Towards the Deep" is Constantine's personal pet project. It is even rumored that he wrote some of the scenes himself.

Personal Goal: To maintain his power over the people of Elysium.

Reputation: 12
Attributes: Strength 3, Agility 4, Wits 4, Empathy 5.
Skills: Fight 2, Move 2, Shoot 2, Sense Emotion 5, Manipulate 5.

ACTORS

The rest of the ensemble consists of lesser known actors of different ages.

Personal Goal: To one day land a leading role.

Reputation: 2–4
Attributes: Strength 2, Agility 3, Wits 2, Empathy 4.
Skills: Manipulate 3.

ROBOTS

The mechanics that describe how robots work are explained in detail in *Mutant: Mechatron*. If you do not have access to that book, you can handle Tonka as a human being. When doing so, simply replace the attributes and programs/ skills as per the list below. Don't roll on the critical injuries table if the robot's Servos/Strength reaches zero – if this happens the robot is simply deactivated.

- Servos = Strength
- Stability = Agility
- Processor = Wits
- Network = Empathy
- Assault = Fight
- Scan = Scout

STAGEHANDS

Workers who went after something more cultural, although the job is not much easier than it would be in any factory in the Deep.

Personal Goal: To make a living.

Reputation: 1
Attributes: Strength 3, Agility 3, Wits 2, Empathy 2.
Skills: Move 2.

VISITORS

Wealthy people from the four great Houses as well as some from minor families of renown.

Personal Goal: To socialize with like-minded people.

Reputation: 3–6
Attributes: Strength 2, Agility 2, Wits 2, Empathy 3.
Skills: Manipulate 2.

EVENTS

Below are some events that could take place during this Incident. It may be fun to have several of them happen at the same time to put pressure on the judicators.

- During the first act of the play, a PC who actively Scouts the audience or makes an Investigate roll notices a person trying to sneak away from their seat and into the unattended door to the dressing rooms. It is Esmeralda Warburg, who plans to invite Lex Fredicius to a romantic liaison – something that is unappealing to Lex because he prefers men. If surprised by the PCs instead, Esmeralda will become very upset.
- A PC who Scouts or Investigates can also spot a dark shadow moving on the beams in the upper machine room above the stage. It's just stage workers doing their job, and they get very annoyed if PCs interrupt their work – but the players might think there's is something sinister going on.
- During the intermission, Preston comes out to mingle with the guests at the bar. He is quickly surrounded by a growing crowd of admirers. Any PC can also approach and talk to him. He dismisses the threats to the theater with an exaggerated laugh. He is in fact quite worried.
- Valentino Morningstar is broadcasting live for the Voice of the Dawn and wants to interview a PC. What are the judicators doing here at the premiere? Is there a threat to the play? The public wants to know!
- Adelia Kruger approaches the PCs and says she is a prompter but also a security officer (which is correct). She proudly mentions that she used to be an actress and points at a yellowed poster on the wall that shows her in a lead roll. Adelia wonders what the PCs know about the threats to the play and says she feels safe now that judicators are present. In reality, their presence makes her very nervous, but she decides to go through with her plan anyway. A PC that successfully makes a Sense Emotion roll on Adelia will sense that she is hiding something.
- A street demonstrator manages to get into the foyer carrying a poster that reads "Elysium = Our Prison." He chants "Freedom is waiting on the surface!" and harasses Preston unless the PCs intervene.
- The PCs witness a loud and very public argument between Valeria Warburg and Valentino Morningstar. Rumors about Valeria and Lex have triggered Valentino's jealousy – or maybe he is simply jealous that she is getting more attention than him this evening. It's possible that he himself does not know which. This has nothing to do with the Incident, but the PCs can get involved anyway.
- Adelia stands by the bar and is whispering something to a man in a black suit and octagonal glasses. His hand rests on her. If any PC approaches them, the man quickly excuses himself and disappears. If a PC asks Adelia about the man, she says it was just a regular visitor. The man is in fact Gunther Glass. If a PC tries to follow him, they must make a Scout roll against Gunther's Sneak. Gunther returns to his place, which is on the right-side rear balcony of the stage.
- During the second act, a PC who actively Scouts the audience or makes an Investigate roll will spot a shadow moving on the right-hand balcony. Gunther is having some trouble with the remote control he uses to command Tonka and moves to the balcony closest to the scene. When the guest sitting there protests, Gunther kills him with his monofilament. The PCs cannot see the act from their seats in the stalls. Gunther hides the body behind the armchair. In order to find Gunther, PCs must make a Scout roll against Gunther's Sneak. In order to approach him unnoticed, they must then make a Sneak roll against his Scout.
- During the play's dramatic final scene with Jasper, Eliza and Tonka, Gunther takes control of Tonka. The robot suddenly stops, raises its weapon, and fires it at the great chandelier in the auditorium, making it fall to the floor with a huge crash. Tonka then aims

his weapon at the audience, which at this point is screaming in panic.

- Adelia climbs up on stage from her prompter hatch. She is carrying a scrap gun that she aims at Lex and Valeria. She instructs the guests to remain seated and says that Tonka will shoot anyone who tries to flee. She also states that she has several agents hidden in the audience who control the robot (in fact, there is only one). A guest tries to run and is promptly gunned down (broken) by the robot, on Gunther's command.
- Adelia says that she has a message to the enclave and demands that Valentino airs her speech on the Voice of Dawn. Valentino is terrified but at the same time sees the chance to broadcast this dramatic turn of events live to his viewers. He will do as she commands unless the PCs stop him. Adelia then reads her speech (see boxed text).
- Preston gets up on the stage, his legs shaking visibly. He tries appealing to Adelia's senses and asks her to stop. She reacts with anger and shoots the director with the scrap gun. He is broken and must be Healed or will soon die.
- The PCs can handle the situation however they think best. They can try to Manipulate Adelia, but she will resort to violence rather than backing down. They can try to find Gunther, but they must then manage to Sneak or Adelia will spot them. If the PCs finds Gunther, he tries to kill them with his monofilament. PCs can attempt to use violence to stop Adelia, but Tonka is a tough opponent and there is a high risk of loss of innocent life. Adelia will not give up unless broken.
- The protesters outside the theater have heard Adelia's speech, and a dozen of them try get inside to join her. Adelia welcomes them in. The protestors (for stats see page 127) may try to attack the PCs.
- The Houses flatly reject Adelia's demands. Instead, the Deep Watch is sent to surround the Imperator theater, to secure the area and make sure no one escapes – including the PCs, who are ordered to stay and resolve the situation inside.
- Once the hour is up – or if Adelia is cornered – she orders Gunther to activate Tonka's secondary function, a self-destruct mechanism with Blast Power 12. A verbal countdown commences. After three rounds of combat the explosion goes off, killing Adelia but also many people in the ensemble and the audience – unless the PCs succeed in disarming the bomb (by rolling Tinker), evacuate the hall, or move Tonka to a secured place (such as the orchestra pit). The self-destruct mechanism is also activated automatically if Tonka is broken/deactivated.

ADELIA'S SPEECH

"My name is Adelia Kruger. I was once an actress, but today I'm the warrior of truth. I regret that I must keep you as hostages, but it is a necessity in order to free us all. Not only those present here with me, but all residents of Elysium I. The great Houses hold us all hostage. For decades they told us that the Earth's surface is deadly, that anyone who leaves the enclave will die. This may have been the case once, but it is no longer so. The Earth has healed. We can survive up there. There are many of us who know this for a fact. The Houses keep this truth hidden from us because they know they would lose their power and control over us once we step out of the enclave and live as free people. I demand that the Houses let me leave this prison and let anyone who wants to follow me to the surface. Together, we shall breathe the fresh air and see the blue sky. If the Houses refuse my demands, none of us will leave this theater alive. I give them one hour to comply."

VICTORY CONDITIONS

In order to consider this Incident a success for the PCs, Adelia and Gunther must be stopped and serious loss of life in the audience be prevented.

EPIDEMIC

- **Section:** The Core
- **Starting Effect:** Production -D6
- **Final Effect:** Control -1 in the sector for all Houses, Production -D6, Culture -D6

Code RED. Several deaths caused by an unknown infection have been reported in the Pandora block. More infected people remain on site. Deceased victims and living patients are kept on site to avoid spreading the infection and causing a panic. Secure the area, find the source of the infection and stop it from spreading further. Your contact on site is guard officer Rupert Acton.

OVERVIEW

The PCs must stop this epidemic as quickly as possible. If they ask for protective gear against the infection for themselves, they get simple paper face masks and are told that's all that's available.

The Pandora block is located about a hundred yards from the Shaft. PCs may walk on foot or fly with their patrol hovercraft through the narrow alleys of the Core. The news of deaths has not yet spread, and a lot of people are out and about.

SCHOLAR PC

A Scholar PC who makes an Enlighten roll knows about the Red Plague – the very disease that killed the world. How it made its way into Elysium I is unknown, and very distressing. The PC is familiar with the general characteristics of the infection and that a cure for the infection can be cultivated. However, for it to work samples must be taken from "Patient Zero," the source of the current outbreak. The cure can only be cultivated in a science lab, which is only available at the Clinic (not in Pandora block). If no PC is a Scholar or if the roll fails, Oswin can instead give them this information.

Pandora is a maze of alleys and walkways on different levels between the housing structures, which have three or four floors, and reach up 30 feet, all the way to the ceiling of the sector. Many of the buildings have ornaments in Neo-Nouveau style, but these are all worn and crumbling. The lighting is bad in the alleys, where all kinds of shady deals are made. PCs can feel many eyes directed towards them as they pass in the dark.

When the PCs approach Pandora, they are met by the visibly excited medic Oswin. He leads the PCs on a short walk to the Scot Dobbling's bar and gambling den, where the local security guard commander Rupert Acton awaits. If one of the PCs knows Acton, he will speak directly to that character, otherwise he will focus on the group's leader. The bar's proprietor, Molly Finkel, is also in the smoky room when the characters arrive. Oswin stays outside to keep guard and ensure the discussion is not overheard. Acton orders that no one be allowed in or out.

In a packed cold room behind the bar there are three dead bodies, two men and one woman. In a storage room next door are two very ill people, still alive, though by the looks of them, not for long. All five are bleeding from their eyes, mouths and nose (see the next page).

Molly can attest that all five infected are regulars at the bar. She says it all began about four hours ago. One after another, the victims began to cough and complain of headaches. Shortly thereafter they collapsed. Molly first thought that they drank something inappropriate and tried to help them. When they got worse, she called for help, but by then it was too late.

The PCs might very well fear becoming infected themselves. Let them take the precautionary measures they deem appropriate. The truth, however, is that virus particles have already around the room – as soon as the PCs stepped through the door, they were exposed. Whether or not they contract the disease is up to you, the GM (see Events, below).

THE RED PLAGUE

The Red Plague is transmitted through consumption of contaminated or through body contact with an infected person. This genetically altered version of the Red Plague acts very quickly. Only hours after being infected, the victim begins to exhibit the first symptom – heavily bloodshot eyes, that soon begin to bleed. Fever, chills and severe nausea quickly follow, then hemorrhaging from all body orifices, and finally a painful death. If the PCs have access to a blood sample from Ephraim Dunkle, they can cultivate an effective antidote. Anyone who is injected with a dose of the antidote automatically recovers.

THE SITUATION

The Houses are continuously conducting secret projects involving the study of the surface world. One of these is Project Polaris, which examines viruses and bacteria from the Zone.

As part of this research, the House made a drastic decision: a genetically modified version of the Red Plague was to be released into a sector in the enclave. The purpose is twofold. Firstly, the House wants to test the properties of the infection to develop both vaccines and a biological weapon, and a well-placed epidemic outbreak may reduce the Control of the other Houses in the affected sector.

For this purpose, the agents of the House found a suitable vehicle for the contagion – the drunken worker Ephraim Dunkle, whom they randomly encountered at Scat Dobbling's. They spiked his drink with the virus and left unnoticed.

The House assumed Dunkle would keel over and die quickly, causing only a limited outbreak. However, Dunkle happened to be naturally resistant to the virus, and he has infected many people in the Pandora block without evening knowing that he's infected. In order to stop the infection from spreading throughout the enclave, the House tips off the Deep Watch, which arrives shortly after the PCs.

LOCATIONS

This incident occurs primarily in the Pandora block. Pandora may be located in any sector of the Core. Key locations in Pandora are marked on the map to the right and described below.

1. PANDORA SQUARE

A crowded square in the center of Pandora. Every available space is filled with street vendors selling all manner of scrap and food items. Four narrow alleys lead out of the square.

2. SCAT DOBBLING'S

An old and tired pub and gambling den that has seen better days yet manages to keep a steady crowd. At the bar, Molly Finkel serves both soft drinks as well as the stronger, illegal kind – and frequently shares stories from the underbelly of the enclave.

3. RISTO'S PAWNSHOP

A cramped locale filled to the brim with all kinds of scrap and trinkets. The proprietor, Risto, is a chain smoker and hard negotiator.

INVESTIGATOR PC

A PC Investigator who makes an Investigate roll at Scat Dobbling's will find a matchbox labeled "Nighthawk" on the floor near a window. The PC knows of this café, which is in the Pandora block. If Ephraim Dunkle is later mentioned by someone, the PC will remember him as someone who frequents the Nighthawk.

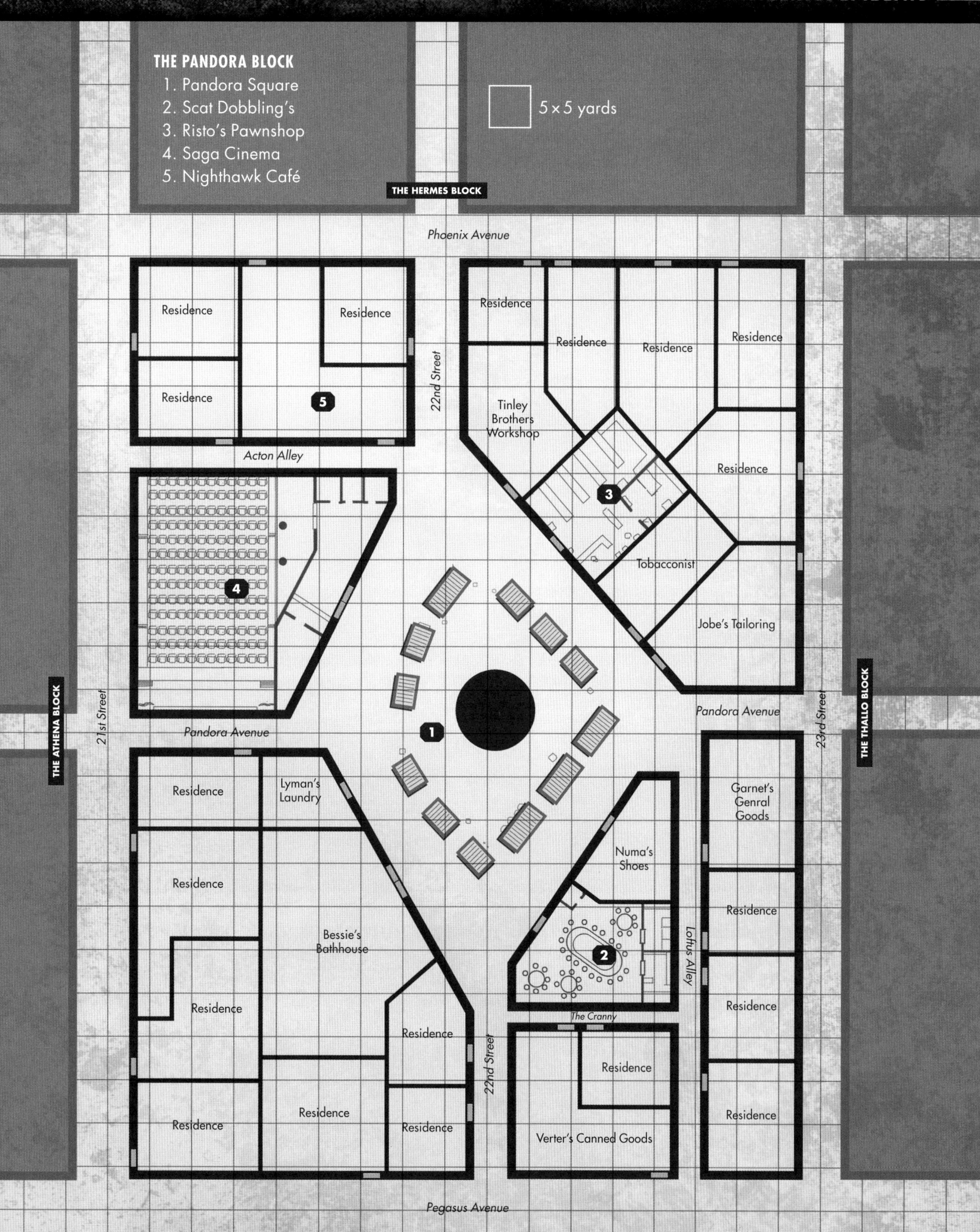
THE PANDORA BLOCK
1. Pandora Square
2. Scat Dobbling's
3. Risto's Pawnshop
4. Saga Cinema
5. Nighthawk Café
5 × 5 yards
THE HERMES BLOCK
Phoenix Avenue
Residence
Residence
Residence
22nd Street
Acton Alley
Residence
Residence
Residence
Residence
Residence
Tinley Brothers Workshop
Residence
Tobacconist
Jobe's Tailoring
Pandora Avenue
23rd Street
THE THALLO BLOCK
THE ATHENA BLOCK
21st Street
Pandora Avenue
Residence
Lyman's Laundry
Residence
Bessie's Bathhouse
Residence
Residence
Residence
Residence
Residence
Garnet's Genral Goods
Numa's Shoes
Loftus Alley
Residence
Residence
The Cranny
22nd Street
Residence
Verter's Canned Goods
Residence
Pegasus Avenue
THE CARPO BLOCK

4. SAGA CINEMA

Moving pictures have become a scarce luxury in the enclave. Yet, in dark and drab cinemas like this, people can still come to watch old classics from the ancient times. The selection is lean and heavily controlled by the Houses. The lounge at the Saga contains about 150 seats, but rarely sees more than a handful of visitors at a time.

5. NIGHTHAWK CAFÉ

A small café with large windows facing the street. It's open around the clock, mostly serving workers and others working night shifts.

NPCS

Of the campaign's key NPCs, Molly Finkel, Ephraim Dunkle, Rupert Acton, and Colonel Casimir Montague all have a role in this incident. Other NPCs are described below.

OSWIN

A nervous medic sent from the Clinic, now torn between his loyalty to Rupert Acton and his growing horror over the Red Plague. May break down or act irrationally at any time. He would much rather flee from the whole situation.

Personal Goal: Avoid personal risk and conflict at all costs.

Reputation: 2
Attributes: Strength 2, Agility 2, Wits 3, Empathy 4.
Skills: Comprehend 3, Heal 3.
Talent: Field Surgeon.
Gear: First Aid Kit.

DEEP WATCH SOLDIERS

Twenty disciplined soldiers in well-tended uniforms.

Personal Goal: To follow the orders of Colonel Montague, unless the PCs can persuade them to do otherwise.

Reputation: 2
Attributes: Strength 4, Agility 4, Wits 3, Empathy 2.
Skills: Fight 2, Shoot 3, Press On 2.
Biomechatronics: Targeting Scope.
Talent: True Grit.
Gear: Gauss rifle, E-pack. Four of the twenty soldiers (one in each squad) carry a flame-thrower instead of the gauss rifle.

EVENTS

The following events may occur during this incident:

- Molly Finkel becomes ill and starts coughing. She appeals to the PCs to take her to the Clinic. Acton refuses. Molly will try to personally appeal to any character she already knows. If the PCs refuse, she asks them to shoot her in the head rather than let her die horribly from the Red Plague.
- The medic Oswin storms in with dire news. More people have fallen ill, this time in Risto's Pawnshop, which is nearby. If the PCs go there, they'll be met by a gathering of horrified people outside. Inside the store, Risto himself is on the floor, sick with the Red Plague but still conscious.
- If the PCs asks Molly or any of the infected about who they have met recently, they will all mention Ephraim Dunkle. They will also mention others (select random names from the list on page 100), so the PCs need to talk with more than one victim to realize that Dunkle is the one they should look for.
- Rupert Acton falls ill. First, he coughs a bit, then more and more. He appeals to the PCs for help. Even he would rather be put down by one of the judicators than die of the Red Plague.
- More people in the neighborhood fall ill. About ten infected are on the floor of the Saga Cinema foyer. If asked, these individuals will attest to seeing Ephraim Dunkle there a couple of hours earlier.
- A stern voice echoes over Pandora's speaker system. Colonel Casimir Montague proclaims that the entire neighborhood has now been quarantined by the Deep Watch. Anyone who tries to leave the area will be shot on the spot. All exits are blocked by a squad of soldiers equal in number to the PCs. In total, Montague has twenty soldiers deployed to the area.
- Oswin panics and rushes towards the Deep Watch checkpoint. Unless the characters stop him, he is killed by the soldiers posted there.
- The characters should sooner or later understand that Dunkle is patient zero and a carrier of the infection. If they don't figure it out, Molly, Rupert, or Oswin can help point them in the right direction. If any of the PCs know Dunkle, they'll know that he frequents the Nighthawk Café. A PC with the Snitch contact (see page 65) can also learn this. Otherwise, the PCs can ask around Pandora.
- Dunkle can be found at the Nighthawk, trying to sober up. He will refuse to have the

judicators take a blood sample from him, as he doesn't feel ill and is also quite drunk. If the PCs have a previous relationship to Dunkle, they can Manipulate him to comply. If not, he will need to be subdued by force.

- Even if the judicators secure a blood sample from Dunkle, they'll need to get it to a lab at the Clinic very quickly. In order to do that, one of more of them need to get past the checkpoints around Pandora. They can try to fight their way out, talk their way out (any attempt to Manipulate Montague gets a -3 modification, and even if they succeed he will only give them a few hours before purging Pandora), try to Sneak out (preferably by using some form of diversion), or climb out through the narrow service tunnels (finding them requires a successful Tinker roll). Acton asks some of the PCs to stay to maintain order in the panicking neighborhood.

- In order to gain access to a suitable laboratory at the Clinic, a successful Manipulate roll is required, or an appropriate contact used. Creating the cure (preferably injected into the patient with a syringe) requires a successful Comprehend roll. If the PCs cannot do it, they may recruit the aid of Oswin or another suitable medical specialist. The process takes D6 hours and generates a large number of doses.
- The PCs start to show symptoms of the Red Plague. This can happen either inside the Pandora district, or outside of it. It can affect several different PCs at different times, all to increase the sense of stress.
- In Pandora, the infection explodes into a full-blown epidemic. People are collapsing sick everywhere and total panic breaks out. Some try to force their way past the quarantine checkpoints – with bloody results unless the PCs can keep the situation under control. Unless the PCs can gain access to a cure in some way, the whole situation will end in a bloodbath.
- PCs returning to Pandora with the cure are not allowed in, on the orders of Colonel Montague. Again, the PCs must somehow circumvent the checkpoint (see above). Infected who receive the cure make a quick recovery.
- Whether the PCs manage to produce the cure or not, Montague gets orders to completely "purge" the Pandora block. Soldiers with gas masks and flamethrowers move into the area and kill everyone in their way. The PCs must fight, flee, or succeed in persuading Montague to stop the purge (with an unmodified Manipulate roll if they have the cure, otherwise with -3).

VICTORY CONDITIONS

For the Incident to be considered successfully resolved, the PC must have both found the cure and prevented a massacre in the Pandora block.

HOSTAGE

- **Section:** The Deep
- **Starting Effect:** Security -D6
- **Final Effect:** House Control +1 in the sector, Security -D6

Emergency in the Deep. Judicator Florian has been taken hostage in the Night Hall correctional factory. The penal workers' self-appointed leader, Antonius Block, demands that they all be released, and he threatens to kill Florian if the demand is not met. The Council will not succumb to extortion. Regain control over the facility immediately and free the hostage. Use of deadly force is authorized.

OVERVIEW

When the PCs arrive at Night Hall, the security guard commander Rupert Acton is in position outside the gate, along with two other guards. Rupert does not have much to say – the gate is locked, and the prisoners have refused to negotiate before the judicators arrive.

Acton can tell the characters that Antonius Block is behind the hostage taking. If none of the PCs have met Block, Acton will explain who he is. Acton adds that the only way to communicate with Block is via the terminal at the port.

If the PCs use the terminal, Block responds quickly. He first wants to know who the judicators are and tells them to approach the camera. He then starts to speak, saying that the oppression of the Houses ends now. Night Hall is no longer a prison but a sanctuary for freed penal workers. Antonius Block also requires all penal workers in the enclave to be given a full pardon.

Unless the Council promises this in a public statement aired on Voice of Dawn within five hours, Block will begin to execute the hostages one by one. After stating this, Block promptly ends the call and does not respond to any further attempts to reach him until it suits him (see Events).

> **SECRET MISSION**
>
> In addition to ensuring the success of the judicators' efforts, the PC belonging to the House staging this Incident was given a secret mission: to contact Antonius Block and offer him 1,000 credits from the House as a "gift" for his continued cooperation. Along with the money, the character is also to give Block a comm radio to communicate with the House headquarters. This task must of course be managed with the utmost secrecy.

THE SITUATION

The unfortunate judicator Florian (if he is related to a PC they belong to the same House, otherwise he is a Warburg) was deceived by the House and convinced to go to Night Hall to question some penal workers about suspected black market trading in the Bazaar.

The true intent of the House is to enrage the workers and create an atmosphere of general discontent, while at the same time establishing a closer relationship with Antonius Block – the leader of the penal workers, and a strong supporter of the Temple.

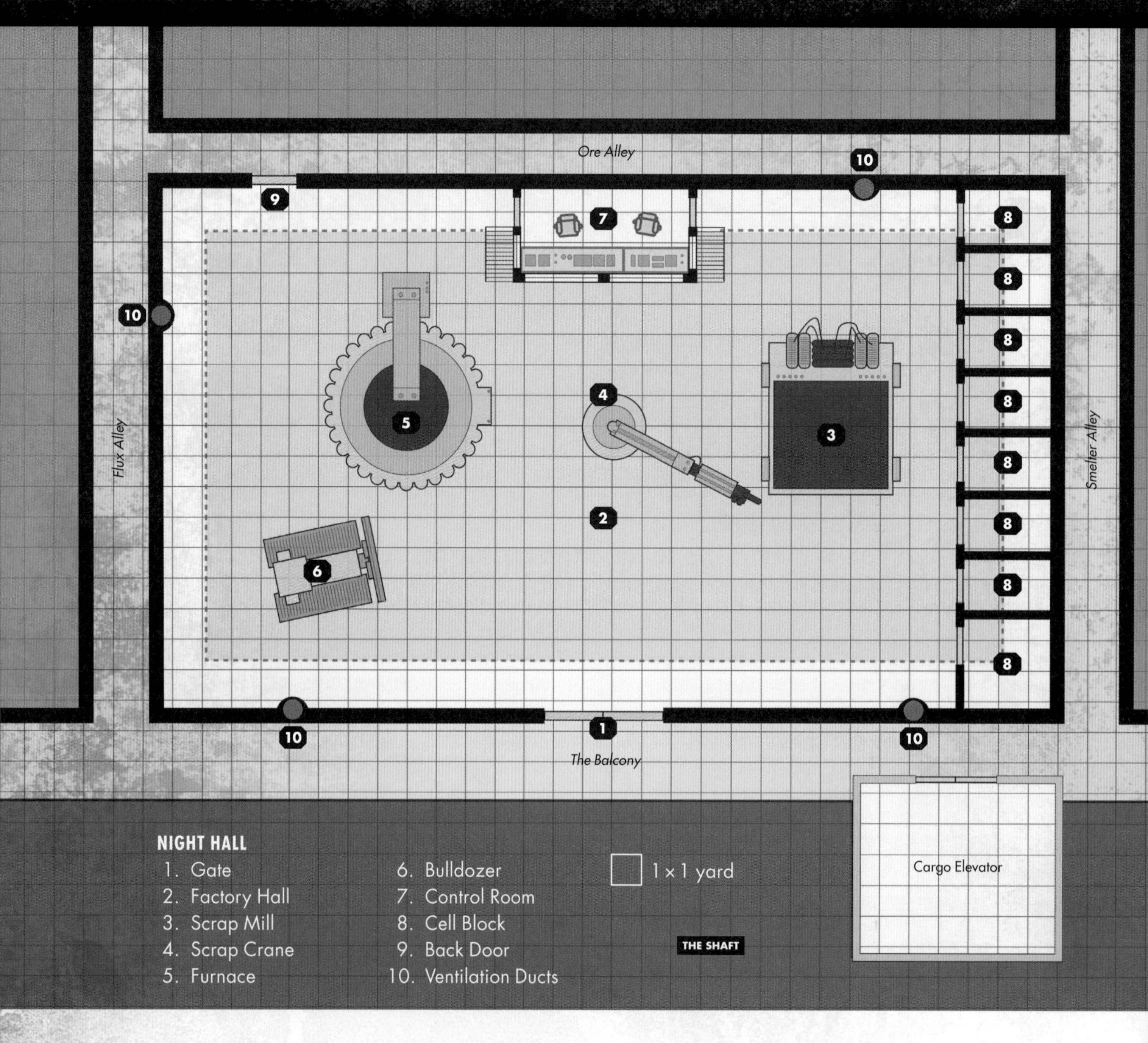

Using bribed guards at Night Hall, the House got in contact with Block and spoke about Florian's impending visit. The House then suggested that Block use the opportunity to create a hostage situation, asserting that the House would work behind the scenes to meet Block's demands.

It does not matter whether Florian himself belongs to the House staging the Incident or not – if this is the case the House decided that Florian could be sacrificed, because he had an annoying habit of putting his duties as a judicator before the interests of his House.

In the name of the Temple, Block has organized twenty of Night Hall's penal workers into a disciplined force. During Florian's visit, Block put his plan into action. Upon his signal the workers overpowered Florian, who was caught completely off guard. He was promptly locked in a cell, along with some other hostages.

So far, the House's plan is working. But Antonius Block has his own agenda and will try to exploit the situation to trigger a full-blown revolt against the Houses.

LOCATIONS

Night Hall is known as the harshest facility in all of Elysium. The plant is primarily tasked with dismantling broken machines and equipment for recycling, both heavy and dirty work. Nobody arrives at Night Hall voluntarily – workers are sentenced to its grime and grease spattered halls for committing minor infractions. More severe criminals end up in the Catacombs.

1. GATE

The main entrance to Night Hall is a massive, rusty metal set of double doors located directly next to the Shaft and a freight elevator. The only way to force the gate open is to use powerful explosives and a successful Tinker roll. Next to the gate there is a small video terminal, where visitors can call the on-duty guard inside. The guard has been taken as a hostage and Antonius Block answers any calls himself.

2. FACTORY HALL

In the heart of Night Hall lies the factory hall, with high walls, floors, and ceilings made of rusty metal. The hall is about 100 feet from wall to wall, crowded, and hot. The roof is about 30 feet high, with walkways and ramps along the walls.

3. SCRAP MILL

A powerful machine that shreds metal scrap into small bits. A person who finds himself inside when the machine is turned on must roll Move to escape. Failure means death.

4. SCRAP CRANE

A crane that lifts the finely shredded scrap from the mill and drops it into the furnace.

5. FURNACE

A lot of heat radiates from the large melting furnace, which is used to recycle metal scrap. Anyone that falls into the furnace has no chance of survival.

6. BULLDOZER

A tracked vehicle with a power shovel and flatbed. It's used to move scrap to and from the freight elevator in the Shaft. Controlling the machine requires a successful Comprehend roll.

7. CONTROL ROOM

The control room is built 15 feet above the factory floor and has a large window. This was typically where Rex Halbarad, the foreman, used to sit. It has a good view of the work area below. During the Incident, Antonius Block resides here.

8. CELL BLOCK

Twenty narrow cells on two floors. Usually the workers are locked in between their work shifts. Now the foreman Rex Halbarad, three guards, and the judicator Florian are held prisoner in the cells. Antonius Block has the keys. It takes 25 points of damage to break open a cell. A Technician can open the door from the outside by rolling Tinker.

9. BACK DOOR

This door leads to a narrow alley at the back of the factory. The door is usually locked and only Antonius Block has a key. To break it open requires dealing 30 points of damage to it.

10. VENTILATION DUCTS

The melting furnace requires good ventilation and several ducts run through the factory. A technician who successfully rolls Tinker can find the right path. Crawling through a ventilation duct requires a Force roll, and a Sneak roll if the character wants to remain unnoticed.

NPCS

From the list of key NPCs, the following can appear in this Incident: Rupert Acton, judicator Florian, worker leader Antonius Block, Cassandra, the Eminence Creon, and perhaps Valentino Morningstar. The rest of the NPCs are described below.

WORKERS IN NIGHT HALL

These hardened men and women are considered to be at the absolute bottom of society in Elysium I and have nothing to lose.

Personal Goal: To follow Antonius Block and gain freedom from the forced labor in Night Hall.

Reputation: 0
Attributes: Strength 5, Agility 3, Wits 2, Empathy 2.
Skills: Endure 3, Force 3, Fight 2.
Biomechatronics: Trash Gut and Reinforced Skull, Machine Arm, or Machine Legs.
Gear: Blunt instrument. Three of the workers will be carrying the stun guns they stole from the guards.

EVENTS

Any and all of the following can occur during this Incident:

- In order to even be allowed into the factory, PCs must be able to Manipulate Antonius Block through the radio at the gate. Even if they succeed, he will require something substantial in return, for example, that several of the characters surrender themselves as hostages in place of some of the current ones.
- It's not possible for the PCs to Manipulate Antonius Block into surrendering straight away. They must ask for small concessions first and earn his trust in the negotiations. And even when these rolls succeed, Block will require something in return.
- Block demands food and water for his workers and the prisoners. However, he does not trust the judicators and stipulates that a novice from the Temple must deliver the goods. If the PCs contact the Temple, Cassandra will appear. She is ready to help solve the situation but refuses to lie or trick. However, she can be Manipulated into following any plan the PCs might have.
- Block threatens to kill hostages if he's not allowed to speak on Voice of Dawn. The PCs may need to use their contacts and relationships to accommodate this demand. Perhaps Valentino Morningstar might come to the facility and report directly from the heart of the drama? He depicts Block as a dangerous terrorist.
- If Block gets the chance to speak on Voice of Dawn, he goes on a tirade about how the great families exploit Elysium's workers for their own gain. He also praises the Temple, which according to him, is the only organization standing up for the poor and weak in the enclave. Valentino interrupts him after about a minute.
- If the PCs don't wish to, or are unsuccessful at, talking their way into Night Hall, they can shoot or blow their way in through the main gate or back door, or sneak in by climbing through the ventilation ducts. In either case, the PCs will quickly be confronted by Block and his underlings. Solving the situation with violence is difficult, but not impossible. If Antonius Block is arrested or killed, the other workers will give up.
- In his cell, Florian has begun to realize that he was betrayed by the House and is boiling with anger. In the midst of the negotiations, Florian overpowers a worker entering his cell to deliver food. Florian threatens to break the man's neck if he is not released. Block will not bend to threats. The situation will end in bloodshed unless the PCs intervene.
- In an attempt at a show of force, Block kills a hostage. It may be a guard or the foreman Rex Halbarad. PCs may be forced to use violence to stop Block.
- Suddenly, when tensions are at their highest, Creon shows up accompanied by several novices. Creon claims to be able to solve the situation without any bloodshed. Let the players react to this as they wish. If Creon is allowed to talk with Block, he offers him a deal – the hostages are to be released under the condition that Block is allowed to leave with Creon, under the protection of the Temple. The other workers are to be released unharmed. Block accepts, and Creon presents the deal to the PCs, who may accept or reject it. The PCs have the choice of betraying the deal after the hostages are released, which will make Creon hostile to them later (see special Incident 2 and 3). If Block leaves with Creon, he will be brought to Cryolab Delta and might appear in special Incident 3.

- Florian – if he is still alive and in the area – tries to kill Block, seize Creon, or both at the same time, because he now believes they are working together. Creon and his novices will stop Florian. If the PCs don't intervene, Florian will likely get himself killed.

VICTORY CONDITIONS

For the PCs to be considered successful in this Incident, they must secure Florian's safe release.

KIDNAPPING

- **Section:** The Core
- **Starting Effect:** Culture -D6
- **Final Effect:** Control -1 in the sector for all Houses except the one staging the Incident, Culture -D6

We have an urgent case that threatens the enclave's morale and cohesion. Valentino Morningstar, show host on Voice of Dawn, and his fiancée, Valeria Warburg, have just been abducted by unknown assailants. Head immediately to the crime scene, Casino Nancy.

OVERVIEW

Casino Nancy, popular among the enclave's rich and famous, is located in one of the finer neighborhoods in the sector. The alleyway outside is wide and well lit, the facades along the street are tastefully ornamented in Neo-Nouveau style and maintained with the most technologically advanced amenities available.

The PCs arrive to a whirlwind of chaos. A security guard is lying dead in the street outside the casino. The body is covered in a white tablecloth, but a large puddle of blood has formed, much of it soaking through the thin fabric. A growing crowd has gathered around the victim and four other guards are trying to maintain order and keep the curious gawkers from stepping all over the crime scene.

A PC who takes a look at the victim immediately sees he has been shot. A successful Investigate roll reveals that the guard was shot with a gyrojet weapon, a deadly but also rare and expensive technological device. A successful Scout or Investigate roll allows the PC to find a fresh trail of blood that leads away from the site.

The guards on the street wave the PCs inside the casino. The muffled and velvet-clad interior is empty, apart from the guard officer Captain Rupert Acton and three other people. These three, one woman and two men, are all dressed in fine suits of the latest cut. They belonged to the same group as Valentino and Valeria, and they are now all very upset, both about what happened and because Acton will not let them leave. Acton wanted to give the judicators an opportunity to question them.

The three guests are: Toddy Somerset (a socialite and Valentino's manager), Esmeralda Warburg (Valeria's cousin), and Gabriel Morningstar, best man at Valentino and Valeria's upcoming wedding.

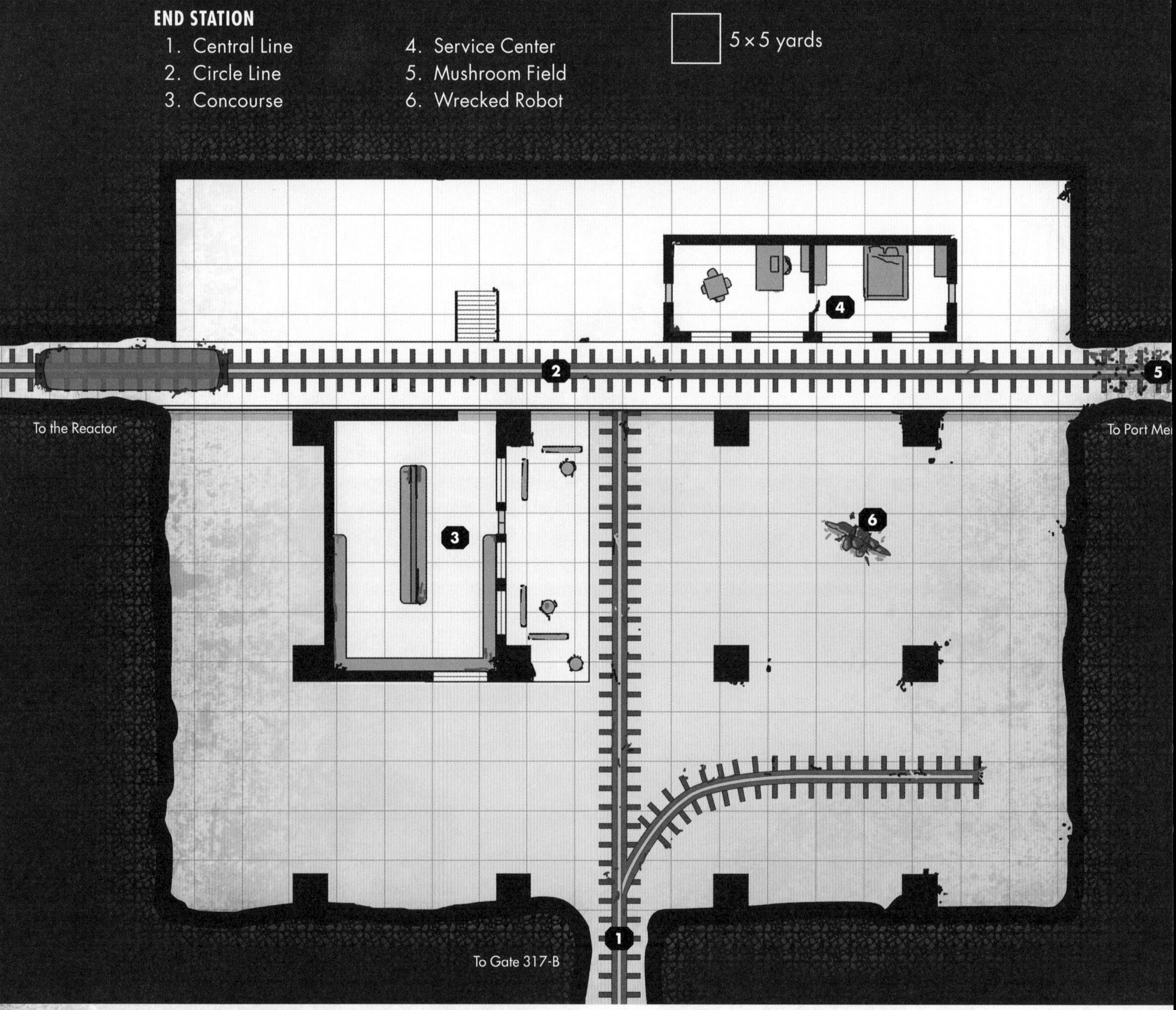

END STATION

1. Central Line
2. Circle Line
3. Concourse
4. Service Center
5. Mushroom Field
6. Wrecked Robot

5 x 5 yards

To the Reactor

To Port Me

To Gate 317-B

THE SITUATION

A complicated web of intrigue has led to the kidnapping. The House behind it all wants to stop the marriage between Valentino and Valeria, as it would strengthen the ties between the Warburg and Morningstar families. It is quite possible that the House is one of these two families – internal rivalry within Houses is common.

The House has contacts in the Catacombs and hired the brutal gang "The Cravats" to kidnap the couple. The House bribed Valentino's agent, Toddy Somerset, who revealed when the couple would be at Casino Nancy. The House then proceeded to smuggle the three criminals out of the Catacombs and into the enclave. They also provided them with gyrojet weapons so that they could easily get past the guards at the casino.

The kidnappers dragged Valentino and Valeria through the crowded streets in Old Koly and escaped through a series of hidden service tunnels into the gang's hideout in the Catacombs, where the couple is now being held hostage. The House intends to send the judicators on a rescue mission that will end with the tragic death of the couple.

The House has missed one key element of the plan however – the Eminences had already enlisted the Cravats to their cause, and the Gray didn't take kindly to the House outbidding them for the gang's brutal services. As a result, the PCs might get help from an unexpected party.

LOCATIONS

The most important place in this incident is not Casino Nancy, but a place called End Station in the Catacombs. You can find an overview map of the Catacombs on page 190 and a map of End Station to the left. End Station (Terminal B on the overview map) is an old station for the monorail train that previously connected Elysium I with its external facilities.

1. CENTRAL LINE

This monorail track leads to the core of the enclave. This will be the PCs' entry route. A staircase leads from the platform up to the Circle Line.

2. CIRCLE LINE

The Circle Line track runs above the Central Line. Signs on the platform read "REACTOR" to the north and "PORT MENDEL, CRYOLAB DELTA" to the south. The raised platform is used for the Scrap King's speeches to his henchmen. A broken and abandoned monorail train stands on the rail a few meters north of the station. The train has been there for decades, but a Technician who makes a Tinker roll can make it run for D6 minutes for each rolled. However, PCs won't be able to ride very far along the Circle Line during this Incident – the Cravats or Creon will stop them if they try. Later, it might be possible to go further (see page 229).

3. CONCOURSE

An area with benches along the Central Line platform has been transformed into the Cravats' meeting and party area. They have placed several burning barrels here for lighting and heat

4.SERVICE CENTER

A simple cabin at the top level that now serves as the Scrap King's personal quarters. A Combat Armor (artifact) can be found inside.

5. MUSHROOM FIELD

In the tunnel leading north, the Cravats are growing mushrooms, which serve as their main food source. The mushrooms are also distilled into a smelly sparkling drink, which is enjoyed by the gang members.

6. WRECKED ROBOT

The wreck of an old battle robot has been left behind here. The humanoid robot, over 12 feet tall and standing with arms extended, has become a kind of mascot for the Cravats. The gang has hung chains and other scrap around its neck. Valentino and Valeria are presently also hanging from its arms. The two hostages are tied up and looking a little worse for wear, but still alive (current score of 1 in all attributes).

NPCS

Of the campaign's key NPCs, Valentino Morningstar, Valeria Warburg, Melina, Toddy Somerset, Colonel Casimir Montague, the Scrap King, and the Eminence Creon all participate in this event. Other NPCs are described below.

ESMERALDA WARBURG

Esmeralda is Valeria's cousin and childhood friend. She is blonde and wears a blood red dress. She has never had to work a day in her life and expects to be the center of attention. Has always been jealous of Valeria.

Note: Esmeralda also appears in the Censorship Incident.

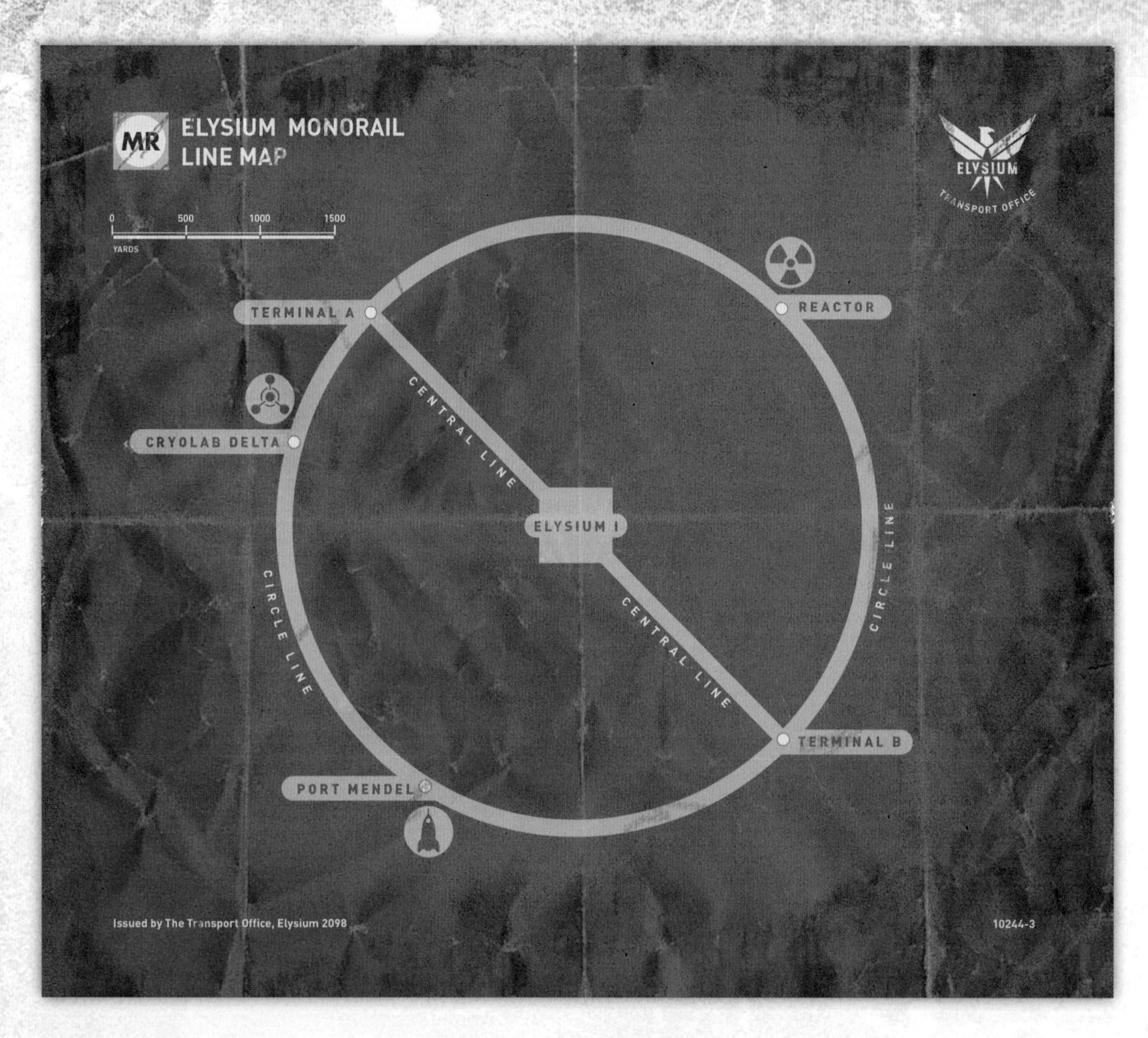

Personal Goal: To replace Valeria as the darling of the Elysium social elites.

Reputation: 6
Attributes: Strength 2, Agility 3, Wits 3, Empathy 4.
Skills: Manipulate 2.

GABRIEL MORNINGSTAR

A bearded man in a tuxedo. He parts his hair to the side and has a crooked face. He is most upset over the interruption of his roulette game at Casino Nancy.

Personal Goal: To gamble, eat and drink.

Reputation: 5
Attributes: Strength 3, Agility 2, Wits 2, Empathy 3.
Skills: Move 2.

LEIDA

A young exiled worker who found comfort in the Temple. Very loyal to Creon, whom she only knows as “the Master.” Leida is a young and pale woman with spiked black hair. She dresses in simple, leather worker’s garb.

Personal Goal: To help the PCs and thus prove herself to Creon.

Reputation: 0
Attributes: Strength 3, Agility 4, Wits 3, Empathy 2.
Skills: Sneak 4, Move 3, Shoot 2.
Talent: Rot Resistant.
Mutation: Human Magnet (if you have access to *Mutant: Year Zero).*
Gear: Scrap gun, three bullets.

CANNIBALS

These exiles have lived in the Catacombs for decades and are completely insane. They are pale and hairless and are clothed in rags.

Personal Goal: To consume fresh human flesh.

Reputation: 0
Attributes: Strength 4, Agility 2, Wits 2, Empathy 1.
Skills: Fight 2.
Gear: Scrap knife.
Special: These cannibals are so insane that they cannot be Manipulated.

THE EXILED

The exiles at the final station are all convicted criminals from the enclave. The great majority are former workers, but there are a few highborn members here as well. The exiles are lean and pale, eager and grateful for the slightest crumble of food.

Personal Goal: To survive, one day at a time.

Reputation: 0–2
Attributes: Strength 3, Agility 3, Wits 3, Empathy 3.
Skills: Fight 2, Move 2.
Gear: Blunt instrument.

THE CRAVATS

This is one of the dominant gangs in the Catacombs. Their hideout is End Station, where their rule is absolute. Their signature look is a piece of cloth worn around their necks, like their namesake, by men and women gang members alike. In total, the gang consists of about 30 individuals, roughly 20 of which can be found at End Station at any given time.

Personal Goal: To drink, fight, and make the Scrap King proud.

Reputation: 1
Attributes: Strength 4, Agility 3, Wits 2, Empathy 2.
Skills: Fight 2, Shoot 2.
Gear: Scrap pistol, D6 bullets, a club. Two of the gang members are armed with gyrojet pistols with D6 rockets. The Scrap King himself has another gyrojet pistol.

EVENTS

This Incident is a little different, as it takes place primarily in two locations instead of one. The first part takes place at Casino Nancy, from where the PCs will be commanded to head down to the Catacombs.

- If the PCs want to question Toddy Somerset, Esmeralda Warburg, and Gabriel Morningstar at Casino Nancy, they treat the judicators with contempt. All three want to leave the place immediately, and the PCs must Manipulate them for them to say anything other than "we've already told Acton everything." Only Melina is more accommodating to the PCs.
- All four describe the same chain of events - three armed individuals stormed into the Casino with firearms and dragged Valentino and Valeria away. They asked for the couple and didn't seem to recognize them, which is strange considering their celebrity status. One witness mentions that the perpetrators wore a piece of cloth knotted around their necks. A PC with the Snitch contact can get a tip about the gang "the Cravats," which is said to be based in the Catacombs.
- If the PCs pressure Toddy Somerset, he admits he was bribed into revealing that Valentino and Valeria would be at Casino Nancy this evening. Toddy, however, does not know who is behind it - some unknown "thugs" contacted him and bribed him.

11

- If the PCs ask around the street looking for witnesses, have them roll Manipulate or Prosecute – success means that a witness tells them he heard the culprits say they were heading "to the gate" before disappearing in the direction of Hindenburg. If the PCs try to follow the blood trail mentioned earlier using Scout or Investigate, it can lead them all the way to the rusty Gate 317-B and into the infamous Catacombs. Blood traces can be found on the gate, and witnesses can confirm that a group of thugs opened the gate and disappeared inside about an hour earlier. This is suspicious because Security Class V is required to open the door, and it happens very rarely.
- If the PCs inform their shift commander Astride Fortescue that the hostages have likely been transferred to the Catacombs, she asks them to hold and calls back a few minutes later. "We have new information about your case. The hostages are indeed being held in the Catacombs, by an exile group called the Cravats. Your mission is to rescue the hostages. Head to Gate 317-B and wait for further instructions." If the PCs had not figured out that the hostages were being kept in the Catacombs, Astride will point them in the right direction.
- Once at gate 317-B, Casimir Montague appears, accompanied by a patrol from the Deep Watch. He hands a gyrojet rifle with a mounted flashlight to each of the PCs. "You may need these," says Montague, who then opens the gate for the judicators. His task is to make sure that nothing escapes out of the gate. If the PCs asks Montague or their headquarters why a larger unit is not being deployed, they are told that a larger force would endanger the hostages' lives. A small unit moving in secret is more likely to succeed. Montague has no further information for the PCs – time is short and the PCs need to leave.
- It's dark and cold on the other side of the gate. A wide service tunnel cuts through the bedrock. Take the time to set the mood. A monorail track runs down the tunnel and on it stands a rusty tram, out of service for decades. Occasionally, wild screams echo out of the darkness. The glare from fires can be seen from afar. Smaller tunnels lead off to the sides. If the PCs leave the main tunnel, they soon run into cannibals (as many as the number of characters, although the prospect of a fresh meal will quickly attract more).
- Leida, the Temple's agent in this part of the Catacombs, soon spots the PCs and begins to Sneak after them by climbing above them on the ceiling. If the PCs discover her, she stretches her hands in the air and gives a wide smile. She says that the PCs seem to be newcomers in the Catacombs and offers to show them the way. If the PCs attack, she tries to escape (Move roll) but will continue to stalk them whenever she deems it safe.
- About half a mile into the tunnel, the PCs approach some large fires. A number of cannibals (about 20) have set up their camp here. The PCs must decide if they want to try to talk their way past the cannibals (not possible) or shoot their way through (very hard) or try to get past this obstacle through narrow service tunnels. If the PCs have not met Leida, she will reveal herself here and offer a way through the side tunnel. The PCs must decide if they want to trust her or not.
- If the judicators follow Leida she will lead them through the service tunnel. The passage is narrow and partially collapsed, and this area is a Rot hotspot (1 Rot point per minute). To get through, the PCs need to make a Force roll. Failure means that the characters must stop and rest, forcing on them another Rot point. The service tunnel leads back to the main tunnel, about 100 feet behind the cannibal camp. The PCs must still Sneak if they wish to avoid detection.
- The Scrap King is prepared for the PCs' arrival – his mission from the House is to kill the hostages with judicators as witnesses, and then chase them away. The Scrap King is loyal only to himself however and is open to negotiations with the PCs – but the judicators

will have to make him a really good offer in order for him to release the hostages. The PCs will have to handle the situation as best they can. They can use violence to try and free the hostages, but it is unlikely to end well. They can also try to create a diversion, or Sneak in when the gang's guard is down. Reward creative and bold players. The Cravats will Heal a broken PC, but the PC will be added to the hostages and hanged on the robot with the rest.

- When everything seems to be over, the Eminence Creon suddenly appears, accompanied by four novices from the Temple. The PCs are likely to be shocked to see them here in the Catacombs, but the Scrap King and the Cravats don't seem to be surprised. They treat Creon with respect. Leida stands at Creon's side while he praises her efforts to help the PCs. If any of the characters has been taken hostage, the Scrap King is ordered to release them, and he reluctantly does as he is told. Creon sends his novices to accompany the PCs and the hostages back to the enclave. Even the cannibals stay away from the Temple's novices. The novices leave the PCs and the hostages just before they arrive back at Gate 317-B.
- If a PC asks Creon about his appearance in the Catacomb, without elaborating he answers: "The Temple is open to all souls in Elysium, even the exiles out here. My task here is just to contribute to a peaceful solution to this dangerous incident."

VICTORY CONDITIONS

For the PCs to be considered successful in resolving this Incident, they must return both Valentino and Valeria alive to the enclave.

MURDER

- **Sector:** The Core
- **Starting Effect:** Science -D6
- **Final Effect:** Control +1 in the sector for the House, Science -D6

We have received reports from the Academy about a death, the nature of which is exceedingly suspicious. Head there immediately and contact the chief researcher in the Department of Biomechatronics. Find out the crime's true cause, identify any perpetrators, and dispense the appropriate punishment.

OVERVIEW

The Academy consists of twenty floors that run through three levels, surrounded by elevated walkways, bridges and small decayed parks. The ornamented facade of the building was once the pride of the sector but is now dirty and unkempt. Read more about the Academy on page 97.

The PCs arrive and will probably head directly to the entrance. They are met there by the chief researcher Melina and her assistant Oswald Battenburg. Melina (who belongs to the same House as the one staging this Incident) is noticeably shaken, but not as badly as Oswald, a young man in a white lab coat. He is pale and has tears in his eyes.

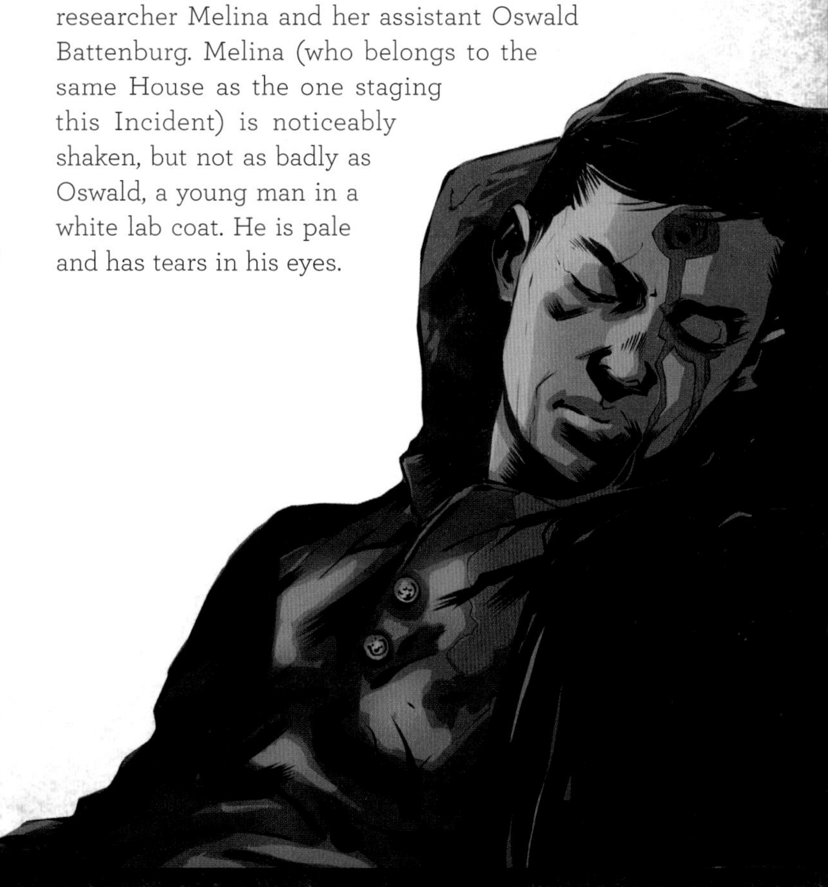

Melina says that "Oswald was the one who found her." She quickly leads the PCs through dark corridors, an elevator, and a locked glass door that controls access to the Department of Biomechatronics. In a dim room with Neo-Nouveau décor sits a dark-haired woman. She has a gunshot wound to her forehead and blood all over her face. It is evident that she is dead.

This may be a shock to one or more of the PCs – the dead woman is Theodora, which may be a former student or even a sister to a PC. If none of the PCs is related to Theodora, she is a Kilgore. If the PCs don't know who Theodora is, Melina will explain. She says that Oswald found her here just over a half an hour ago.

SITUATION

Theodora was researching a top-secret project on the interaction between biomechatronics and psionic powers, so-called psychotronics. Theodora had made significant progress in her research, more than she had reported to Melina.

Theodora was also a strong supporter of the Temple, and she shared her results with the novice Cassandra. Melina's assistant Oswald Battenburg was secretly in love with Theodora but is also in the House's pocket. When he found Theodora's secret communication with the Temple, he passed the information to the House, who informed Melina and ordered her to stop the leak of information.

When Melina confronted Theodora, a violent argument broke out. Theodora mocked Melina who, in anger, shot Theodora in the head. Shortly thereafter, Oswald found Theodora's dead body. He drew the correct conclusion – that she was killed as a result of him revealing her secret to the House – and is therefore devastated by sadness and guilt. He has not realized that it was Melina who pulled the trigger.

LOCATIONS

The Department of Biomechatronics is located on a floor high up in the labyrinthine Academy. The institution is located directly adjacent to the Shaft.

1.ENTRANCE

A heavy metal door with an electronic lock leads to the front desk, which is usually unmanned. Pass cards are required to get in and out. The reception

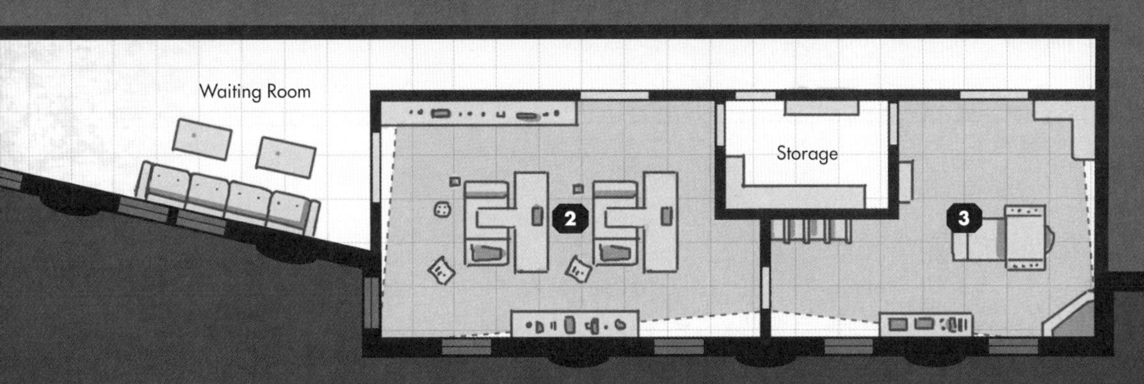

THE DEPARTMENT OF BIOMECHATRONICS

1. Entrance
2. Biomechatronics Lab
3. Recovery Room
4. Psionics Lab
5. Melina's Office
6. Theodora's Office
7. Oswald's Office
8. Other Offices
9. Lounge

1 x 1 yard

Monitored Area

area is monitored by a video camera. Only Melina and the robot Pix have access to the video files, which are stored for 24 hours and then erased.

2.BIOMECHATRONICS LAB

A cluttered lab with lots of advanced technological equipment. It contains hospital beds and operating equipment for the surgical implantation of biomechatronics.

3.RECOVERY ROOM

A resting room for subjects who have undergone biomechatronic surgery. It is currently empty.

4. PSIONICS LAB

A cramped laboratory full of a chaotic array of equipment. A large helmet-like object is attached to a machine. Anyone who wears the helmet and activates the machine becomes unconscious for D6 minutes and wakes up with a random psionic mutation (see *Mutant: Year Zero*) and D6 Mutation Points. The process is painful and gives as many points of fatigue as it does MP. The mutation will only work for D6 hours, or until all MP are consumed.

5. MELINA'S OFFICE

A relatively spacious office with a desk made of dark artificial wood. On the desk stands a data terminal. A stained-glass door leads to a small balcony overlooking the Shaft.

6. THEODORA'S OFFICE

The office next to Melina's. It is almost as large, but without a balcony. Beautifully decorated in Neo-Nouveau style.

7. OSWALD'S OFFICE

A small, dimly lit office with a desk free of clutter. Hidden under the desk is a data tablet with Oswald's diary (see Events).

8. OTHER OFFICES

Five other offices, just as small and dark as Oswald's. There is nothing of interest here.

9. LOUNGE

A room with an oval table that seats up to eight people. Neo-Nouveau interior. It has a kitchenette and a toilet.

NPCS

Of this campaign's important NPCs, Melina and the novice Cassandra will participate in this incident. Note that Melina belongs to the House staging this Incident. Other NPCs are described below.

OSWALD BATTENBURG

This young researcher is a diligent worker, but his brilliance pales in comparison to that of Melina or Theodora. He was hopelessly in love with Theodora, but revealed her conversations with the Temple to the House and is now devoured by feelings of guilt and despair.

Personal Goal: To take his own life, for he cannot live with the guilt of knowing he caused Theodora's death.

Reputation: 2
Attributes: Strength 2, Agility 2, Wits 4, Empathy 2.
Skills: Comprehend 4, Enlighten 2.
Gear: Data tablet.

RESEARCH ASSISTANTS

Egerton, Brenda, Gordon, Idina and Claiborne are all relatively anonymous and bland individuals in their 30s. Brenda and Gordon have a secret and unlicensed romance that they do not want anyone to find out about.

Personal Goal: To avoid getting involved in the investigation.

Reputation: 1
Attributes: Strength 2, Agility 2, Wits 4, Empathy 3.
Skills: Comprehend 3.
Gear: Data tablet.

PIX-339, LAB ROBOT

A mechanical aid, referred to as simply Pix, that helps with practical tasks in the Academy.

Personal Goal: To do what the humans say.

Reputation: 0
Attributes: Servos 3, Stability 3, Processor 6, Network 1 (See *Mutant: Mechatron*)
Armor Rating: 3
Programs: Analyze 4, Scan 5, Question 3, Assault 3.
Secondary Functions: Analysis Unit.
Gear: Scalpel hand (Weapon Damage 2), arm-injector (Weapon Damage 1).

EVENTS

This Incident is a whodunnit, where the PCs' job is to uncover the truth about Theodora's murder. Events therefore depend much on the players themselves. The following may occur:

- Theodora's body is still warm when the PCs arrive and rigor mortis has not set in yet. A PC who makes an Investigate roll can determine that death occurred no more than two hours ago. The cause of death is a shot to the head by a gauss weapon. The shot was fired at very close range, went straight through the head and into the wall behind Theodora. There is no indication that she was moved after her death. There are no traces of theft, and no signs of a forced entry.
- There are security cameras at the entrance and inside the two laboratories, but not in the rest of the facility. Melina or Pix can play the recorded footage from the time of the murder upon request, but nothing suspicious can be seen.
- There are currently only seven people in the facility; Melina, Oswald, and the five research assistants. All of them say they saw and heard nothing, which is not surprising considering that gauss weapons are silent and leave no traceable component like gunpowder residue on the shooter's hands. No one in the Academy admits to owning any weapon, and nobody knows about anyone who does. PCs will not be able to find any weapons on the premises, no matter how thorough they

are. After committing the murder Melina threw her weapon down the Shaft from her balcony.

- The last person to have seen Theodora alive seems to be the same person who found her dead: Oswald Battenburg. He met with her in the lounge about two hours prior to the murder. He says he noticed nothing unusual about her behavior. Understanding Oswald is difficult because of his state of shock. After a while, he asks to go and rest in his office (see below).
- In Theodora's office there is a computer terminal. Her notes in the terminal are encrypted and accessing them requires a successful Tinker roll. If there is no Technician in the group, the robot Pix can unlock the files. The notes are complicated and are about psychotronics – the interaction between biomechatronics and psionic abilities. A PC who makes a Comprehend roll will realize that Theodora's reports to Melina were incomplete, deliberately giving the impression that her work progressed less than it actually had. In a different folder labeled "to C" there are much more detailed reports. In a digital calendar there are several entries labeled "meeting C." Visits to the Temple are also mentioned several times. See Handout #1.
- Others in the lab can confirm that Theodora often visited the Temple and was amicable towards the Eminences. However, no one knows the identity of "C" (it is the novice Cassandra).
- If the PCs review the surveillance recordings from the entire day, they can conclude that three of the five research assistants – Egerton, Idina, and Claiborne – have solid alibis for the time of the murder. They were all in one of the camera-monitored labs when it occurred. Brenda, Gordon, Oswald, and Melina herself all lack an alibi. They all claim to have been in their offices during the time of the murder. If the PCs put pressure on Brenda and Gordon (roll Manipulate), the pair breaks down and confesses that they were together in the lounge – they have an unauthorized and unlicensed romantic relationship. The robot Pix happened to be in the lounge at the time and can confirm this.
- When the PCs have been investigating the crime for a while, a scream is heard from the biomechatronics lab. When the PCs arrive, they find Oswald lifeless on the floor. One of the other research assistants has just found him. Oswald has no heartbeat and is beyond medical care. Next to him on the floor is an empty syringe. If the PCs analyze the content of the syringe (requires a successful Comprehend roll in a lab), they will learn that it contains residue of sodium cyanide – a powerful poison. The laboratory camera is functioning properly and recording. If the PCs ask to see the recording, they'll see Oswald, as if in a trance, slowly mixing the components of the poison and injecting himself. The players may believe that psionics were used to force him into committing suicide – but in fact, Oswald took his life in despair for causing Theodora's death.
- If the PCs investigate Oswald's office, they find a data tablet hidden under his desk. It contains a diary, and almost every post is about Oswald's unrequited love for Theodora.

SPOTTING LIARS

It is possible the PCs try to use the Sense Emotion skill on each of the suspects to determine who is the murderer. This is fine, but keep in mind that the skill does not allow mind reading. A successful roll can let a PC know that an NPC lies – but not about what, or why. Several NPCs lie or omit information during the investigation, but that does not mean they are the killer. Oswald lies about his feelings for Theodora, and the research assistants Gordon and Brenda are doing their best to hide their relationship. On the other hand, the PCs can use Sense Emotion to exclude suspects who are not lying – Egerton, Idina and Claiborne.

HANDOUT #1: THEODORA'S CALENDAR

The posts meander between platonic love, desire, anger over her rejection, and deep despair for having failed her. One entry is of particular interest – see Handout #2. If asked, Melina mentions that Oswald has been very moody lately – she is trying to lead the PCs to think he was the murderer.

- A woman arrives at the facility and demands to meet with Theodora. She introduces herself as Ashley and says that she is an old friend. If she finds out what happened she gets very upset and demands to see the body. She also says she wants to gather Theodora's personal belongings – a ruse to search her office. "Ashley" is in fact Cassandra from the Temple, and Theodora's secret contact. The two also had a budding romantic relationship. Cassandra is not currently wearing her novice robes, but she is wearing the Temple symbol as a pendant on her necklace. In addition, a PC may have already met her in a previous Incident and might recognize her. If a PC points out that she belongs to the Temple, she won't deny it. If Cassandra gets access to Theodora's office, she will use this opportunity to search for the information about psychotronics and delete it.
- If Cassandra is allowed to get past the entrance, Melina becomes very upset and demands that she be thrown out. She mocks the "superstitious fools" from the Temple, saying that they used to follow Theodora and tried to ensnare her in their cult. Cassandra responds angrily and the PCs might need to intervene. Cassandra will leave rather than risk being arrested.

HANDOUT #2: OSWALD'S DIARY

- Sooner or later, the PCs will likely start to suspect Melina. The list of potential suspects is not long, and the research assistants all have an alibi or appear on the surveillance cameras in another place. Another possible method is to develop temporary telepathy in the psionics lab (above) and read Melina's mind. Melina will try to avoid suspicion for as long as she can, but if the PCs confront her, she eventually breaks. In anger, she accuses Theodora of selling out the Academy's secrets to the Temple. The gun was only meant to threaten her. It was never her intention to kill the other researcher. If Melina is in her office when she confesses, she will take her own life rather than live in disgrace. She throws herself from the balcony and falls to her death at the bottom of the Shaft.

PSYCHOTRONICS

The PCs might wonder why the Temple is interested in advanced research on psychotronics. It's a good question that will be answered later in the campaign. They will not be able to find out during this Incident – Cassandra herself does not know the answer. It is exclusively Creon's secret at this point.

VICTORY CONDITIONS

For the PCs to be considered successful in resolving the Incident, they must a perpetrator to pin Theodora's murder on.

RIOTS

- **Section:** The Deep
- **Starting Effect:** Security -D6
- **Final Effect:** Control -1 in the sector for all Houses, Security -D6, Production -D6

Property damage and civil unrest has been reported in the Cantina down in the Deep. Security guards have retreated from the sector. Proceed there immediately and restore order.

OVERVIEW

The PCs can smell smoke on their way down the Shaft. They can tell the fire originates within the Deep. Several fires are burning on the level of the enclave where the Cantina is located. Which level this is depends on which sector the Incident is taking place in – choose any level in the sector (see the map on the inside covers of this book).

The PCs can land their hovercraft anywhere they please on the level, which, aside from the Cantina, consists of factories, workers' quarters, and small service facilities. Show the players the map of the level (to the right) and briefly describe the most important locations.

The PCs find themselves in the middle of a war zone. Gang members and angry armed mobs are on the move, attacking security forces and anyone else displaying open loyalty to the Houses. Most authority figures have fled the sector entirely or have gone into hiding. The characters are on their own.

SITUATION

The reason for the riots is that a rumor has been spreading in the sector that the surface world is habitable and that the Houses know it but have chosen to keep it secret to maintain control over the population.

The rumors sparked angry protests among the workers. The security guards in the sector responded with stun batons. The Sooty Hands intervened, leading to further aggression from the guards. The clashes escalated, until the guards had to flee the area. The gang, supported by the workers, has now all but taken control of the sector.

The rumor that triggered the riots was spread by the House to destabilize the sector and shift the balance of power in their favor. The rumor is true, but the House is not concerned by this, as the gangs in the Deep are not seen as a serious threat to the rule of the Houses.

The House wants the judicators to fail and has therefore made sure that no reinforcements are available. The House is willing to sacrifice their own member of the judicator patrol. The PCs are about to find themselves in a world of hurt.

LOCATIONS

This incident takes place on an entire level of the enclave surrounding the Shaft. See the map to the right. Below are the most important locations.

THE CANTINA

A columned hall with low ceilings serves as the enclave's large dining hall for workers and anyone with limited funds. During this Incident, the interior of the Cantina is vandalized. A number of security guards and a few workers still loyal to the Houses, including Ephraim Dunkle, have managed to keep

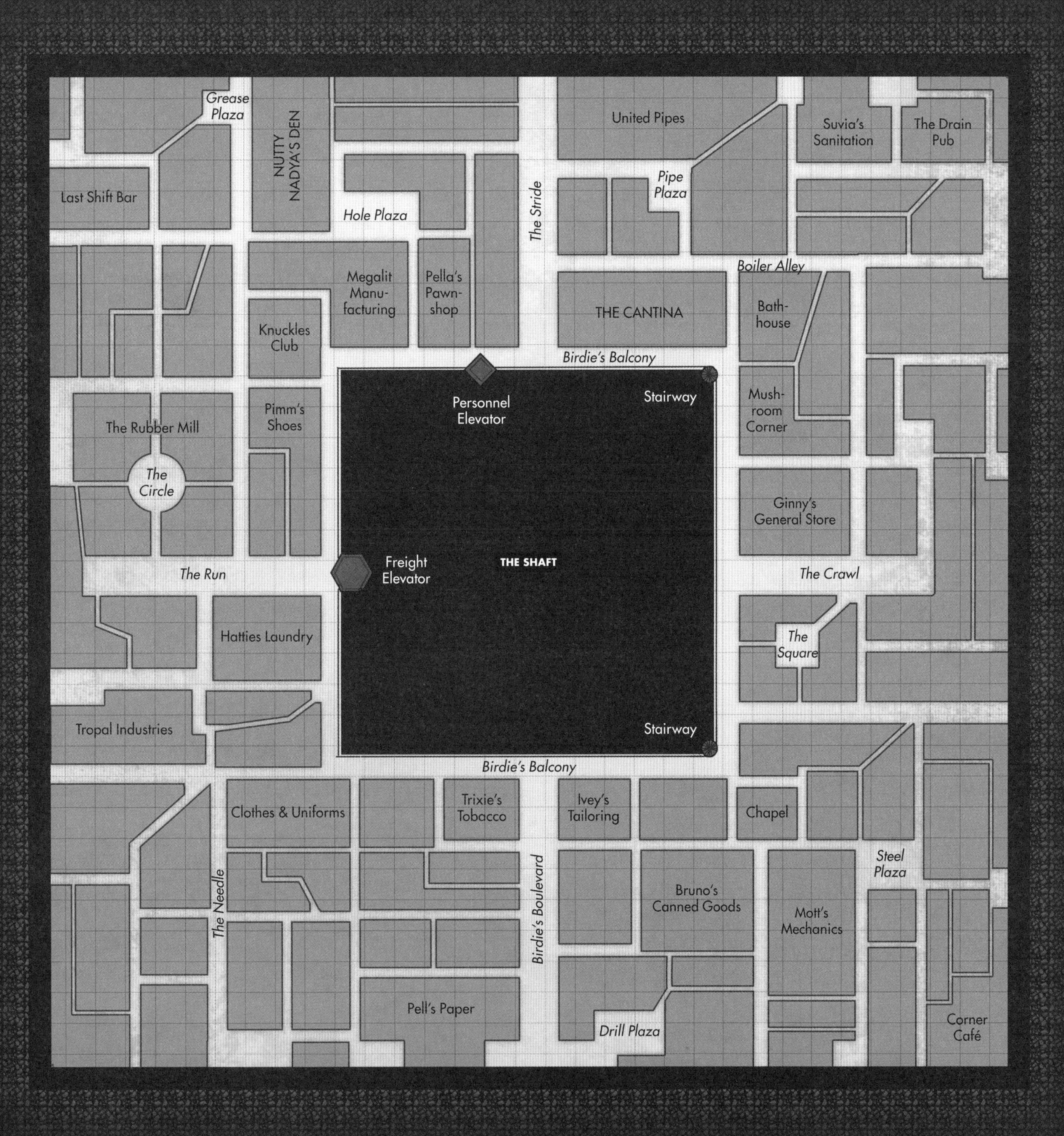
10 × 10 yards
Grease Plaza
NUTTY NADYA'S DEN
United Pipes
Suvia's Sanitation
The Drain Pub
Pipe Plaza
Last Shift Bar
Hole Plaza
The Stride
Boiler Alley
Megalit Manu-facturing
Pella's Pawn-shop
THE CANTINA
Bath-house
Knuckles Club
Birdie's Balcony
Personnel Elevator
Stairway
Mush-room Corner
The Rubber Mill
Pimm's Shoes
The Circle
Ginny's General Store
The Run
Freight Elevator
THE SHAFT
The Crawl
Hatties Laundry
The Square
Tropal Industries
Stairway
Birdie's Balcony
Clothes & Uniforms
Trixie's Tobacco
Ivey's Tailoring
Chapel
Steel Plaza
The Needle
Birdie's Boulevard
Bruno's Canned Goods
Mott's Mechanics
Pell's Paper
Drill Plaza
Corner Café

the Sooty Hand out, and barricaded the door with upturned tables. Several angry gang members are outside throwing fire bombs every now and then. Read more about the Cantina on page 99.

INDUSTRIES

There are several small industrial workshops on this level of the enclave. Some of them have closed long ago, others are still running but are suffering from chronic shortages of raw materials while the workers constantly patch things up to keep the shops functional. During this Incident all work has stopped. The workers either participate in the riots or hide in their housing modules.

NUTTY NADYA'S DEN

The Sooty Hand's lair is found in a large, abandoned industrial site. Several fires light up the dirty hall. Currently, a number of moaning, injured people fill the space after Nutty Nadya ordered the hideout be used as an impromptu infirmary for citizens injured in the riots.

STAIRS AND ELEVATORS

Spiral staircases and cargo elevator lifts are the only way to exit this level without access to hovercraft. During this Incident, all stairs and elevators are barricaded and guarded by groups of gang members and workers, as many as the PCs at each point.

NPCS

Of the campaign's important NPCs, Nutty Nadya, Ephraim Dunkle, and possibly Colonel Casimir Montague participate in this incident. The other NPCs are described below.

GANG MEMBERS

The Sooty Hand's followers are rebellious youngsters who refuse to succumb to the worker's harsh life, instead surviving on the wrong side of the law. Despite this, the gang is well respected in the area, and its members spend a great deal of time in the community, helping where they can. Although judicators sometimes raid the gang's turf, they usually let them be as long as they don't cause too much trouble. This Incident is a prime example of "too much trouble." In total, the Sooty Hand has about 30 members, and everyone is present on this level of the enclave during this Incident. All members have their right hands painted black.

Personal Goal: To ensure the well-being of the citizens they consider to be under their care.

Reputation: 1–2

Attributes: Strength 4, Agility 3, Wits 2, Empathy 2.

Skills: Fight 3, Shoot 2.

Biomechatronics: Reinforced Skull, Machine Arm, or Pain Inhibitors.

Gear: Scrap pistol (five bullets) and a blunt instrument. The gang also has access to one scrap thrower (see page 75).

WORKERS

Ragged men and women who lead hard lives in the Deep. For many, the charity of the Sooty Hand is all that makes their lives bearable. During this Incident, almost all the workers have given their support to the Sooty Hand gang. Even those who aren't actively participating in the riots will lend aid to any gang members in need.

Personal Goal: To take control of their lives and their sector.

Reputation: 1

Attributes: Strength 4, Agility 3, Wits 2, Empathy 2.

Skills: Endure 3, Force 3, Fight 2.

Biomechatronics: Reinforced Skull, Machine Arm, or Machine Legs.

Gear: Blunt instrument.

DEEP WATCH SOLDIERS

Colonel Montague leads this platoon of twenty soldiers. They arrive at the sector in an armored combat hovercraft and a transport hovercraft.

Personal Goal: To follow Montague's every order.

Reputation: 2
Attributes: Strength 4, Agility 4, Wits 2, Empathy 2.
Skills: Fight 2, Shoot 3, Press On 2.
Talent: True Grit.
Gear: Gauss carbine, E-pack, combat armor, frag grenade.

EVENTS

This is an action-oriented Incident. The players should feel that they can't get a moment of rest, always vulnerable and left to defend themselves.

- Wherever the PCs land, they will quickly be surrounded by citizens with bad teeth and crude biomechatronic implants. Some of them have their right hand painted black. A Scholar can make an Enlighten roll to know that the those with painted hands belong to the Sooty Hand gang, led by the infamous Nutty Nadya. After a tense pause, one of the gang members will demand that the PCs leave immediately. The mob refuses to let the PCs pass, but will not attack unless the PCs make an aggressive move first. If a worker or gang member is broken the mob will quickly disperse. If the PCs are defeated, the gang members will take them to Nutty Nadya's den.
- If the PCs head to the Cantina, they see gang members outside (twice as many as the number of PCs) trying to get in. Inside the venue are several security guards and a few workers, including Ephraim Dunkle, who were unable to escape the sector after the riots broke out. The gang members will flee when half of

them are broken. If the PCs drive them off, the guards inside will be grateful. They will inform the judicators where Nutty Nadya's den is located.

- If the PCs interrogate gang members or workers about the cause of the riots, they are told about the rumors that the surface world is habitable. The Houses are said to know this but have chosen to keep it secret in order to preserve their control over the enclave. The rumor sparked angry protests, and when the security forces responded with violence events quickly degenerated into rioting and looting.
- If the PCs don't post a guard by their hovercraft, it will be vandalized. Several fire bombs will be thrown on the vehicle, which is quickly destroyed in the flames. If this happens, the characters are stuck on this level of the enclave, as all stairs and cargo elevators are guarded by the gang. If the PCs manage to raise an alarm through their comm radios and request backup, they will be surprised to hear that their request is denied – all other patrols are occupied elsewhere. The PCs will have to handle the situation by themselves.
- At some point, Nutty Nadya tries to communicate with the PCs, either personally or through a messenger. She tells them that so long as they stay out of the way and don't harm any workers or gang members, the PCs will be left alone, but if they use violence, the gang will react in kind.
- A group of gang members (as many in number as there are PCs) drag a security guard by the hair from an industrial building and start kicking him. What the PCs don't know is that this is the guard who started the riots by violently attacking a worker.
- A major fire breaks out. Large flames engulf a residential block. Several workers are stuck inside a building and are crying for help. Getting in requires a successful Force roll, and merely being inside the building is treated as exposure to an explosion with Blast Power 6 every round. The sprinkler system is operational, but insufficient to stop the fire. There is a fire station nearby, but the hose must be deployed to stop the fire. Setting it up will require an Endure roll. If the fire is not contained it will spread across the sector. Several members of the Sooty Hand will attempt to help those stuck inside, and may even work with the PCs.
- When the PCs are close to the Shaft, if they have initiated any acts of violence while in the sector, the Sooty Hand opens fire on them from the other side of the Shaft with a scrap thrower. Treat this as an ambush. At the same time, workers (as many as there are PCs) attack from the sides in an attempt to surround the PCs. If the PCs flee, the Sooty Hand will give chase.
- Sooner or later, the PCs will meet Nutty Nadya herself. This can happen if they defeat a large number of gang members – then Nadya will handle the threat personally and will lead her people from the front lines. Contrary to her nickname, Nadya isn't stupid. She doesn't take any needless risks and will back off if hurt or if the local citizens are threatened. If she gets broken, other gang members will try to Heal her. If Nadya estimates that the battle cannot be won, she will try to negotiate with the PCs, even offering herself up in exchange for clemency for the rest of her gang.
- If the PCs are captured or broken, they will be taken to Nutty Nadya's den. The gang will Heal any broken PCs. Nadya's goal is to use the PCs and any captured security guards as leverage in exchange for better working conditions in the sector and more control over how things are run. The Council does not intend to negotiate any such trade. Give the PCs the chance to flee or negotiate with Nadya, and reward creative ideas.
- Ephraim Dunkle and a few security guards have had enough and decide to make a stand against the Sooty Hand. If the PCs have been taken hostage, this group will attempt to free them.
- After several hours, if the PCs have been unsuccessful in taking down or capturing

Nutty Nadya and the Sooty Hand, the Deep Watch will attack in full force. A heavy attack hovercraft with a platoon of soldiers under the command of Colonel Montague is sent to the level. The attack hovercraft will shoot at everything that moves with its mounted gauss cannon and drop twenty heavily armed soldiers to clear the level. The Sooty Hand is thoroughly defeated, but both workers and PCs are at risk of getting caught up in the deadly crossfire. Nutty Nadya disappears in the ensuing chaos.

VICTORY CONDITIONS

For the PCs to be considered successful in resolving the Incident, they must kill or capture Nutty Nadya before the Deep Watch arrives.

SABOTAGE

- **Section:** The Core
- **Starting Effect:** Science -D6
- **Final Effect:** Control -1 in the sector for all Houses except the one staging the Incident, Production -D6, Science -D6

We have a serious situation. A powerful explosion has taken place in hydroponic farm Julita-57. No personal injuries were reported, but the irrigation and heating systems were destroyed. Julita-57 accounts for 37 percent of the enclave's production of vegetables. Judicator Florian is already on location. Go there and help him assess the damage, investigate the situation, and punish the guilty party.

Note that Florian may be related to a PC. If that is the case, he belongs to the same House as the PC. If not, he's a Warburg.

OVERVIEW

As the PCs pass through the airlock and into the huge hall that houses Julita-57, they hear outraged voices. Amidst the rows of hydroponic tubes, judicator Florian is arguing with a group of workers. They are led by a woman named Sonya Carp (the PCs can recognize her if they played the Strike Incident).

The floor in the whole hall is flooded knee-deep with water. It is also quite cold in the hall, only about ten degrees Celsius – too cold to grow vegetables. At the far end of the hall, the PCs see the cause of both the flooding and the cold – the large water pump facility is a twisted and charred wreck, clearly destroyed by an explosion.

Florian tries to arrest the entire team of workers in the plant, as he believes they have caused the explosion by negligence. The workers protest violently as Sonya Carp tries to mediate. In the background, the foreman of the farm, Mortimer Loftus, is looking sad. When Florian spots the PCs, he asks for their help in apprehending the workers. If they refuse, he gets very upset.

THE SITUATION

The House caused the explosion to hike the price of vegetables, favoring another hydroponic plant which the House owns. In fact, the perpetrator is not one of the workers but the foreman himself, Mortimer Loftus.

JULITA-57 HYDROPONICS FARM

1. Hydroponic Drums
2. Seed Bank
3. Production Plant
4. Warehouse
5. Office
6. Workers' Barracks
7. Pumping Plant
8. Freight Elevator
9. Composts

□ 1 x 1 yard

⬚ Monitored Area

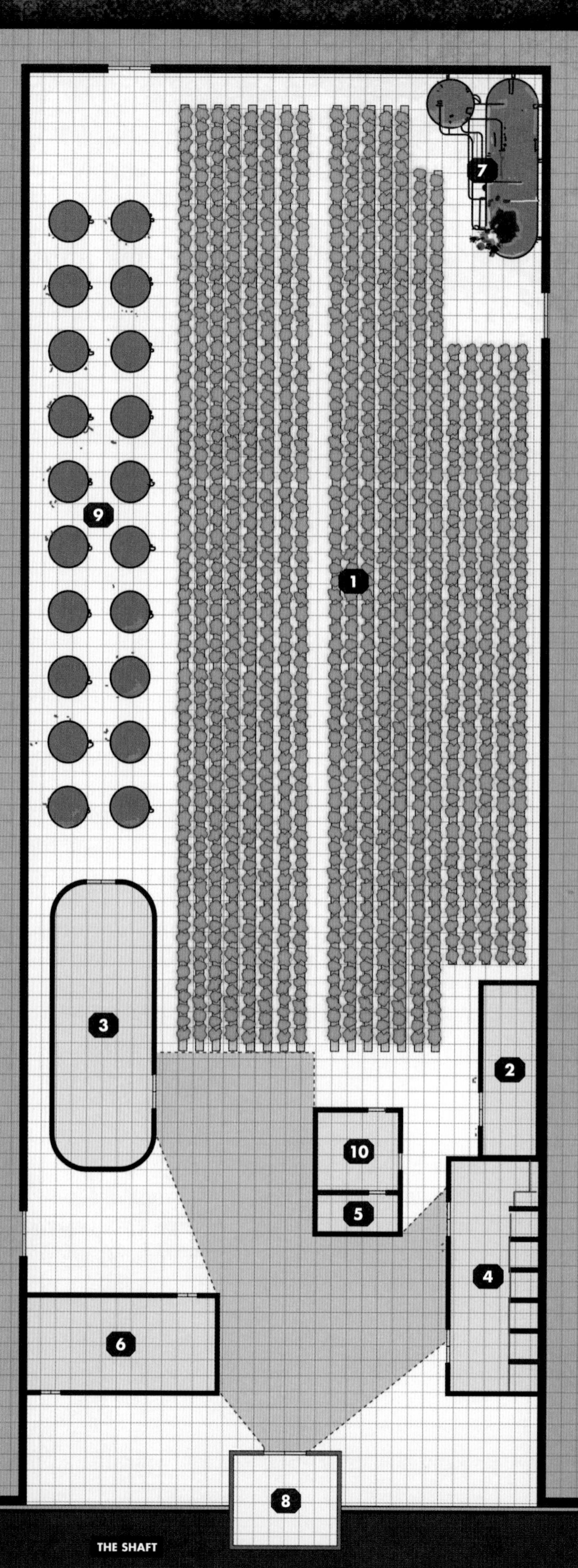

Loftus is having a secret affair with Esmeralda Warburg, famous socialite and sister of the star Valeria Warburg. (Esmeralda appears in the Censorship and Kidnapping Incidents). Mortimer has been desperate to get a better job to impress Esmeralda.

The House promised Mortimer a prestigious position in a theater if he sabotaged his own farm. The offer was exactly the opportunity that Loftus was waiting for. In order to pull off the plan without interruption, he allowed all workers at Julita-57 to go home early before placing the explosive with a timer. Only one worker, Quitman Weld, remained in the plant during the night to monitor the compost. Everyone else spent the night in their homes.

The explosive charge detonated shortly after the workers arrived for the morning shift. Luckily no one was killed during the explosion, but Quitman Weld was wounded, and is now resting on his bunk in the barracks.

LOCATIONS

Julita-57 is one of the largest hydroponic farms in Elysium I. It is essential for the production of vegetables in the enclave.

1. HYDROPONIC DRUMS

The plants grow in long rows of hydroponic drums (only using water, no soil). The ceiling has strong lamps that simulate sunlight. Usually it's hot and humid in here, but it is currently quite cold. The vegetables are wilting rapidly. The water in the room is knee-deep.

2. SEED BANK

This freezer stores thousands of small vacuumed-sealed bags with seeds of agricultural plants from the Old Age. The seeds are to be preserved here until the day when humanity can return to the surface. But now the cooling system is out of order and the seeds are thawing, which will destroy them.

3. PRODUCTION PLANT

A greenhouse with an ornamented metal roof and large windows. This is where the hydroponic drums are prepared. Nutrients, seeds, and sprouts are all handled here.

4. WAREHOUSE

Space where tools, machinery, and farming materials are stored. Under a loose piece of the metal floor grating the PCs can find three explosive devices of the same type used in the enclave mines. There is a blood stain on the floor. A PC who successfully Investigates here will learn that the stain is only a few hours old. There is also blood on a sharp edge of the grating itself – someone seems to have cut themselves.

Quitman Weld and other workers on the farm all have minor cuts from their hard work, but nothing that would have reasonably caused the blood stain. The one who cut himself on the grate is Mortimer Loftus.

5. OFFICE

A small and crowded space where Mortimer Loftus works. Among the terminals and books, there is a cupboard where Mortimer keeps a bottle of liquor.

A PC who Investigates the office can, in a terminal, find desperate job applications for the Imperator Theater, a cultural committee, and the Saga Cinema. In a drawer, mounted in a brass frame, is the photograph of a beautiful blond woman. The name Esmeralda Warburg is engraved in the frame. The PCs may have met Esmeralda in an earlier Incident.

In the office there is also a video monitor connected to the camera by the elevator.

6. WORKERS' BARRACKS

A simple barracks building with a dozen bunks and small lockers for clothes and personal items. Wrapped in a blanket under Quitman Weld's bunk is a bag of special fertilizer that he has "borrowed" from the farm. A PC who Investigates the area or actively searches the bunks will find the bag. A Technician or Scholar will know that manure can be used to produce explosives. The truth, however, is that Quitman wants to use the fertilizer for his illegal onion farm that he keeps at his old grandmother's home.

7. PUMPING PLANT

A massive water pumping plant and machine room. After the explosion, the water pumps and pipes are cracked and covered in burned soot.

A PC who actively examines the plant or successfully rolls Investigate will find a beautiful but dirty lady's glove among the scrap on the floor. The glove is labeled with the initials "E.W." Mortimer dropped it when he was placing the bomb. The glove belongs to Esmeralda Warburg. She gave it to him as a token of affection.

8. FREIGHT ELEVATOR

A freight elevator in the Shaft stops outside the ID card-controlled gates to the farm. The climate inside the farm itself is carefully controlled. There are large, ornamental glass windows that separate the room from the outside of the Shaft.

9. COMPOSTS

Twenty vertical metal cylinders where the compost is maintained. The area stinks. The compost is managed and guarded by at least one worker. Without constant attention there is a risk that the compost can spontaneously combust.

NPCS

Of the campaign's key NPCs, only Sonya Carp and the judicator Florian (who is a Warburg if no PC is related to him) are involved in this incident. Other NPCs are described below.

MORTIMER LOFTUS

The foreman at Julita-57 is in love - and not just with Esmeralda Warburg, but perhaps even more so with the idea of himself in the beautiful salons as a socialite. And he is prepared to do whatever is necessary to make it happen. Growing old and dying as a foreman of a tiny farm is a fate that he can't accept. Mortimer is a slender man with a waxed mustache and clothes that are a little too nice for his workplace.

Mortimer has a deep cut in his right hand from when he cut himself hiding the explosives in the warehouse. He hides the cut by wearing gloves at all times. If the cut is exposed, he'll lie and claim he cut himself at home.

Personal Goal: To leave Julita-57 at all costs, and to be able show his love for Esmeralda Warburg openly.

REPUTATION: 3

ATTRIBUTES: Strength 3, Agility 4, Wits 4, Empathy 3.

SKILLS: Shoot 2, Comprehend 3, Manipulate 3, Tinker 4.

GEAR: Gauss pistol, E-pack, two-time bombs (Blast Power 12). The explosives are hidden in the office.

QUITMAN WELD

This heavy set, middle aged worker has big and dirty hands and is usually in a good mood. He lives alone and rarely leaves Julita-57. He volunteered to oversee the compost at night. What few know about Quitman is that he is a member of the Temple and is very devoted. During the limited free time he has available he managed to become a Temple novice.

Personal Goal: To serve the Temple, and do what's best for the enclave.

REPUTATION: 1

ATTRIBUTES: Strength 5, Agility 3, Wits 2, Empathy 3.

SKILLS: Endure 4, Fight 3.

EQUIPMENT: Spade (blunt instrument), necklace with the Temple's Sun and Moon symbol.

WORKERS

20 workers labor in Julita-57. Most of them are from the Deep but many sleep in the barracks at night. Farm work is harsh, but it fosters close friendships among the workers.

Personal Goal: To provide for their families.

REPUTATION: 1

ATTRIBUTES: Strength 4, Agility 3, Wits 2, Empathy 2.

SKILLS: Endure 3, Fight 1.

EQUIPMENT: Various tools (blunt instruments).

EVENTS

How this Incident plays out depends largely on what the PCs do to handle the situation. Here are some suggested events:

- Florian behaves as if he is in charge and proceeds to order the PCs around. He will get very upset if the PCs go against his wishes. They may need to roll Manipulate or Prosecute to get him to calm down.
- Sonya Carp, who was sent to Julita-57, although she is not normally stationed there, refuses to let Florian or the PCs arrest the workers.
- PCs who examine the site of the explosion and make an Investigate or Tinker roll will know the explosive charge was both powerful and well-positioned. The saboteur knew exactly where it should be placed for maximum effect.
- The PCs can question both the workers and the foreman Mortimer Loftus. Several workers will attest that the water plant was in good condition on the afternoon one day prior to the explosion, at least until the workers left for the evening. The workers were released earlier than usual, which they will confirm if asked.
- Mortimer Loftus says he stayed working late in the office and went home around midnight. This is also confirmed by the security camera at the freight elevator. A PC who successfully uses Sense Emotion on Mortimer will sense that he's not telling the whole story.
- It soon becomes apparent that only Quitman Weld was in the farm at night to watch the compost. If the PCs can't figure this out on their own, Mortimer Loftus will point it out to them.
- Quitman denies any wrongdoing. He claims he sat watching the compost all night. He says he neither heard nor saw anything suspicious. He admits, however, that he may have dozed off once or twice during his shift. The only other person he saw after the rest of the workers were sent home was Mortimer Loftus.
- If the PCs ask for access to the security system, Mortimer tells them that there is only one camera at the entrance of the freight elevator. This camera shows that nothing out of the ordinary occurred in the last 24 hours.
- A PC who makes a Tinker roll can temporarily fix the pump system. This makes the workers happy, but Mortimer Loftus sees it as his plan falling apart and will consider taking drastic measures. Whenever he gets the chance, he will attempt to Sneak into the pumping plant to place another explosive device there. This new detonation will wound a worker, or perhaps even a PC.
- Quitman Weld or another worker runs up to the PCs. He tells them that the refrigeration unit in the seed bank was damaged by the explosion. The priceless collection of seeds from the Old Age are about to thaw and will be destroyed! A Technician PC can Tinker for a temporary fix, otherwise they need to call for help.
- If the PCs question Mortimer, he will try to direct all suspicion towards Quitman Weld. He will take drastic action to save the situation at all costs. He places another bomb at a strategic location (preferably in the seed bank or at the compost) and will try to arrange for the PCs to die in this explosion.
- Unexpectedly, the compost catches fire. Thick black smoke rises from the fermented mass. This may happen when the PCs are busy with something else. To stop the fire, the PCs must repair the pumping plant (if they have not done so already). If the fire is not contained, the hall will soon be full of smoke. The fire and smoke will spread throughout the rest of the enclave and will soon become a serious problem.

VICTORY CONDITIONS

For the PCs to be considered successful in resolving this Incident, they must identify a cause for the explosion and prevent the harvest in Julita-57 from being lost.

STRIKE

- **Section:** The Deep
- **Starting Effect:** Production -D6
- **Final Effect:** Control +1 for the House in the sector, Production -D6

An unauthorized strike is under way at the Garpenberg-15 mining plant. Workers led by worker leader Sonya Carp have ceased all production. This is a dire situation for the enclave. Judicators need to stop the strike and ensure continued production. Your contact at the site is mining director Reginald.

Note that Reginald can be the father of a PC, see NPCs below.

OVERVIEW

Even before the PCs arrive at the mining facility, they can hear the workers chanting. About 50 of them have gathered outside the mining office (see below). Due to the scarcity of paper and paint, they have used their own clothes and even bodies as banners, scrawling anti-House slogans with bits of coal from the mine. Some nervous security guards are still manning the entrance. The workers, many swinging their shirts over their heads, yell and taunt the PCs when they arrive, but they will not resort to violence. PCs can enter the mining office without incident and meet with Reginald. If they'd rather address the workers directly, they will soon get in contact with Sonya Carp.

Reginald is terrified and very relieved to see the PCs. He demands that they act quickly and harshly, and force the workers back to their stations. He has no knowledge or understanding of the workers' demands. He claims that wages have been lowered because the mined iron ore has been of poorer quality than usual, but this is a lie. Inside the office is also the mining technician Beldon – Reginald's son – who remains silent in Reginald's company but will try to talk with the PCs whenever he is alone with them.

Sonya Carp treats the PCs bluntly but with respect. She explains that the workers are on strike because the mining director has slashed their salary in half without a valid explanation, other than simply stating that "these are hard times." The workers refuse to return to work if they do not get their salary back. Carp also requires that the mining director be replaced.

THE SITUATION

The mining director Reginald is being blackmailed by the House. They found out that he was selling gold from the mine on the black market of the Bazaar. Through its agent Symon Spander, who is under cover as one of the workers in the mine, the House told Reginald to lower the wages – otherwise they would expose his crimes.

Reginald is prepared to go very far to protect his secret, even staging a massacre of the workers, if he can blame it on someone else.

The House's goal is to increase their influence in the area by spreading fear and disorder, and then replacing both Reginald and Sonya Carp with individuals under their control.

The wild card in this explosive game is Reginald's son Beldon, who correctly suspects that something is not right and hopes that the PCs will solve the situation.

LOCATIONS

The Garpenberg-15 mining facility is located in the Deep and occupies a whole level with the Shaft in the middle. Ceiling height is about 30 feet. The rock walls are rough and moist. Narrow mine tunnels lead horizontally into the mountain. It's an uncomfortably hot and dirty place.

1. THE DIRECTOR'S OFFICE

A simple building of rusty metal built next to the rock wall. Inside there is an office and a weapon rack with four stun batons and two gauss carbines. Outside, two guards stand watch.

2. WORKERS' QUARTERS

In this simple building made of corrugated metal, miners rest and eat between their shifts. This is also where they store their equipment. The workers' quarters have become the headquarters for the ongoing strike.

3. MINE TUNNELS

These tunnels lead from the main platform deep into the rock walls. When the mine is in use, four small but powerful tracked bulldozers go out into the mines. Now they are still.

4. ORE RESERVES

Huge piles of ore from the mine tunnels. The ore is mainly iron, but smaller amounts of precious metals are also mined.

REGINALD AND THE HOUSES

If it happens that Reginald himself belongs to the House staging the incident, his background needs to be adjusted slightly. In this case, the House simply ordered Reginald to reduce production, something he was very reluctant to do because he knew the reaction this would trigger. In order to pressure Reginald into compliance, the House threatened to reveal his secret and hired Symon Spander.

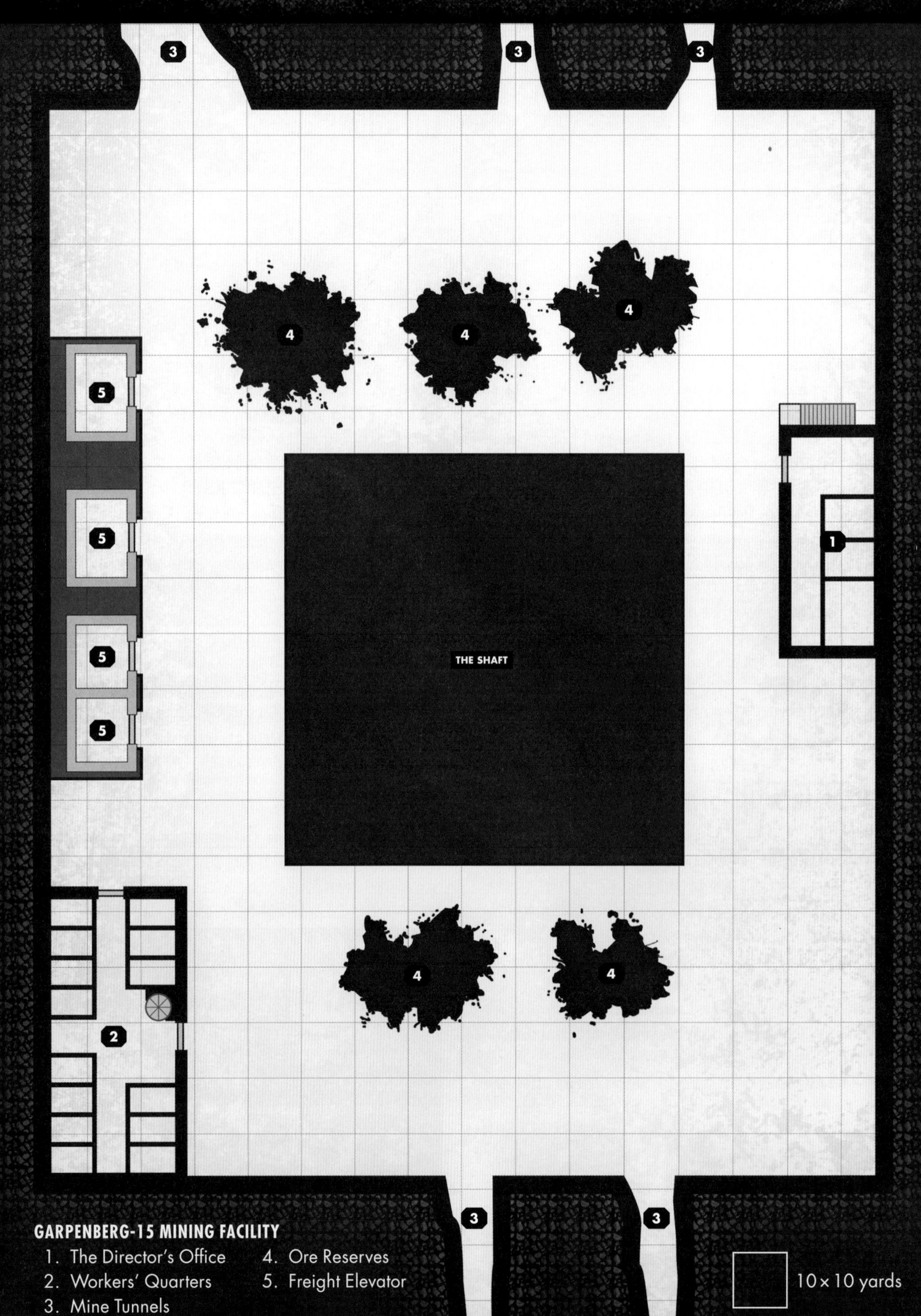

GARPENBERG-15 MINING FACILITY

1. The Director's Office
2. Workers' Quarters
3. Mine Tunnels
4. Ore Reserves
5. Freight Elevator

5. FREIGHT ELEVATORS

These elevators lead from the mines to the industrial sectors located on higher levels of the enclave. The large elevators haul ore and the smaller ones carry the workers.

NPCS

Of the campaign's key NPCs, both Sonya Carp and Casimir Montague participate in this incident. Other NPCs are described below.

Note that a Technician PC might have defined Reginald as his father and/or Beldon as his brother. If this is the case, Reginald and Beldon belong to the same House as this PC. If not, they are Warburgs.

REGINALD

The mining director is a man on the verge of collapse. He has had his back against the wall for a while and has no idea how to get out of his predicament. He is ready to take drastic, even violent, action to protect his secret. If exposed he is likely to break down.

Personal Goal: To maintain his secret at all costs.

Reputation: 3

Attributes: Strength 3, Agility 2, Wits 4, Empathy 3.

Skills: Shoot 2, Comprehend 3, Manipulate 3, Tinker 4.

Gear: Gauss pistol, E-pack.

BELDON

Beldon is the son of the mining director, which is how he got his job here at Garpenberg-15, a job he is none too fond of. Beldon has lived under his father's shadow all his life. Lately however, he has noticed that something is not right with Reginald.

Personal Goal: To find out what it is tormenting his father.

Reputation: 3

Attributes: Strength 3, Agility 3, Wits 4, Empathy 3.

Skills: Fight 2, Comprehend 2, Tinker 4.

Gear: Stun baton, E-pack, electronic tools.

SYMON SPANDER

The House's agent in Garpenberg-15 is a worker who grew tired of the eternal grind in the mines. The House didn't have to pay much for his services. Symon is a lean man with a mustache and an intense look. He is constantly smoking Ritz cigarettes.

Personal Goal: To complete the mission he has been paid for. Nothing else matters.

Reputation: 1

Attributes: Strength 3, Agility 5, Wits 3, Empathy 4.

Skills: Fight 2, Sneak 4, Shoot 3, Sense Emotion 3, Manipulate 4, Scout 4.

Biomechatronics: Shock Grip.

Gear: Gyrojet pistol (7 rockets), one dose of Bellicin.

MINERS

It is crucial for many industries in Elysium I that Garpenberg-15 remain operational. About 50 men and women work here, and they know their worth. They have taken steps to protest openly, and they will not back down without getting something in return. They trust Sonya Carp, but they do not follow her blindly.

Personal Goal: To improve their lot in life.

INVESTIGATING THE ORE

A Technician or Scholar PC who investigates the iron ore in the ore layer and makes a successful Tinker or Enlighten roll notes that the ore is not of low quality, quite the opposite. Reginald is clearly lying.

Reputation: 1
Attributes: Strength 5, Agility 3, Wits 2, Empathy 2.
Skills: Endure 3, Force 2, Fight 1.
BIOMECHATRONICS: Reinforced Skull, Machine Arm, or Machine Legs.
Gear: Overalls (Armor Rating 2). Some workers have jury-rigged fire bombs (Blast Power 6) and scrap pistols (with D6 bullets each).

EVENTS

PCs must handle the situation with great caution – the risk of violence is high.

- The mining technician Beldon approaches one of the PCs (preferably his brother if he is a PC, or another Technician) and will speak candidly. This may require some finesse – Reginald and his guards keep a watchful eye on the PCs. If the PCs earn Beldon's trust, he says he suspects something is wrong here. He adds that Reginald has been behaving strangely lately, and has refused to answer Beldon's questions.
- If the PCs press Beldon for answers, he will also tell them that a few weeks ago he saw Reginald holding a secret meeting with a worker – Symon Spander.
- Sonya Carp will try to speak with the PCs. She says she wants to resolve the situation peacefully. She demands that the mine director Reginald be fired and the workers' wages be returned to their previous rate – only then will the workers resume their work. Carp suspects foul play. She thinks an external force is behind the situation and that the workers themselves have been infiltrated. She doesn't know the identity of the double agent.
- Symon Spander climbs up on one of the bulldozers and gives a fiery speech. He condemns "the tyrannical Houses" and "their lackey" Reginald. He urges workers to storm the director's office and take over the mine through violence. He threatens the PCs and condemns Sonya Carp as a "coward." If the PCs don't intervene, Symon's provocation will succeed, and rioters will storm Reginald's office.
- Reginald reaches his breaking point. He reveals his secret and asks the PCs for help. He identifies Symon Spander as the extortionist. Reginald suspects Spander acts on orders from someone highly placed but does not know who. He asks the PCs to apprehend Spander.
- If the situation goes unresolved for too long, a Deep Watch (see page 106) platoon arrives under the command of Colonel Casimir Montague. His mission is to pacify the workers by use of force. The platoon lands in an attack hovercraft shortly after the PCs receive a message warning them to get to safety. The players can choose to have their characters stay in order to act as human shields and negotiate with Montague. The miners will refuse to back down and it will be up to the PCs to avoid a bloodbath.

VICTORY CONDITIONS

For PCs to be considered successful in resolving the Incident they must restore production in the mine and avoid the massacre that will occur if Montague storms the mine.

SPECIAL INCIDENTS

This section describes the three Special Incidents in the *Guardians of the Fall* campaign. They must be played in the presented order. We recommend that you introduce the first of the three special incidents, "Signal from Genlab Alpha," when approximately half of the campaign has been played (after three to five normal Incidents). The last two special incidents, "A Day to Remember" and "Assault on Cryolab Delta" constitute the campaign finale. These should not be played until all eight normal incidents have been resolved (or as many as you intend to play).

Special Incidents don't affect the Development Levels of the enclave.

PLAYING SPECIAL INCIDENTS

Special Incidents are extraordinary events beyond the normal power struggle between the Houses. When it's time to play a new strategic round, simply announce that the PCs have instead been called to a very important special assignment. The strategic round is cancelled, and the Special Incident is played instead.

SIGNAL FROM GENLAB ALPHA

This incident begins with a regular pre-shift brief at the Capitolium before the characters go out on their patrol. Shift commander Astride Fortescue asks the PCs to stay behind to talk to her after the brief. She will then present the mission to the characters.

THE MISSION

Listen very carefully. Your patrol has been chosen by the Council for an important mission. It seems you are considered particularly suitable for this mission, don't ask me why.

The situation is as follows: Our scouts have captured a signal from another enclave: Elysium IV. If you remember your history, you'll recall that it's been 137 years since we last had contact with Elysium IV. This must be investigated immediately. The signal did not come from the enclave itself, but instead from an external xenogenetics research center called Genlab Alpha.

Ladies and gentlemen, it's time for you to experience the surface world. Your mission is to travel to Genlab Alpha and discover who, or what, sent the signal. More importantly, if anything sentient remains alive, you are to use any means at your disposal to bring back living specimens for study. Elysium I would benefit greatly from any knowledge surviving surface dwellers might possess, as well as the information our scientists could extract from them.

Accompanying you will be a patrol from the Deep Watch, who is set to take care of the latter task. Two hovercraft are standing by at the Breach. Oh, one more thing! As you know, the outer world is fatal to humans. You will be assigned hermetically sealed protective suits. Whatever you do, don't take them off.

What are you waiting for? Move out!

THE JOURNEY

After Astride Fortescue's brief, the PCs are expected to immediately head to the Breach, just a short walk away through the Winter Garden. At the rusty old battle robots, two humming hovercraft are waiting: a gunship and personnel carrier.

The commander of the Deep Watch, Colonel Casimir Montague, greets the PCs with a crisp salute. Montague is probably already known to the PCs from previous Incidents, and they might not be on the best of terms.

Montague leads the PCs into the smaller of the two hovercraft. Inside are four hardened Deep Watch soldiers, all wearing fully sealed combat armor (see page 221). Similar suits are provided for the PCs, and Montague urges them to put them on. He reiterates that the outer world is lethal to humans and that the special gear must be worn throughout the mission. Each PC is also given a gyrojet carbine and five rockets.

Montague points out that all equipment must be returned in good condition, otherwise they will have to answer for it.

UP AND AWAY

As soon as the PCs take their seats, the hovercraft takes off and flies into the Breach above. The PCs cannot see where they are headed because the gunship hold lacks windows. Above the Crown's dome there is a deserted cargo terminal that has been haphazardly repaired. The two hovercraft pass through a large airlock and the gates rumble open. The PCs are now on the surface!

The PCs are likely curious, but they are trapped in their hovercraft and thus cannot see what the terrain outside the enclave looks like. If they ask Montague about this, he simply says that it is classified and that the PCs are not cleared.

The journey to Genlab Alpha takes about an hour. You can fast-forward to the arrival or play the trip as a short scene. PCs can talk to Montague or any of the soldiers. They're gung-ho and boastful and seem to be under the impression that their mission is to "shoot surface critters." They joke that the smallest damage to their protective gear would mean certain death, because the surface world is infested by the Red Plague.

THE HOVERCRAFT

The two hovercraft are equipped with enough air, food and water to last the core crew a week. If the personnel carrier is fully loaded with living beings, the air supply will only last a few hours (enough for the return trip to Elysium I but not much more).

DEJA VU

This Incident depicts a scene from the end of the Escape from Paradise campaign of *Mutant: Genlab Alpha*, but this time from the other side. Instead of playing the animals in Paradise Valley, the players take the role of the people from Elysium I coming to inspect the facility.

If you have previously played this scene in *Genlab Alpha*, you may need to adjust the events a bit, so that the sequence of events matches what happened in your campaign.

If you have access to the *Genlab Alpha* book, you can let the PCs explore the facility in more detail. It is mostly destroyed, but maybe the PCs can find a way in and make some interesting discoveries?

OVERVIEW

When the two hovercraft arrive in Paradise Valley, Montague walks up to the cockpit and motions the PCs to follow him. Through the windshield the PCs bask in a vision more powerful than anything they have seen before. A magnificent mountain landscape, with tall white peaks and deep green valleys stretches into the distance. A glowing twilight fills a sky that never seems to end. For the PCs, who have never seen the sky before, the experience can be overwhelming. All PCs must roll for Wits (only the basic attribute). Those who fail suffer one point of Confusion.

The pilot lands the hovercraft on a low concrete bunker at the foot of a mountain. Montague steps out and instructs the PCs to follow him. He reminds them to make sure their protective suits are sealed. Communication is via comm radio. If the PCs move out, they will take their first steps on the surface world – but there won't be much time to take in this monumental experience.

THE SITUATION

The mutant animals from Genlab Alpha have just managed to defeat the robots that kept them imprisoned in Paradise Valley. The underground genetics laboratory has been destroyed, and the electric fencing around the valley is now deactivated. When the PCs arrive, the animals have gathered for a meeting in order to determine their future.

The animals in Paradise Valley have never seen living humans before. For them, it is like meeting living gods. How the animals react depends largely on the PCs' actions.

What the PCs don't know is that Colonel Montague has secret orders. Once all has been done to save any human survivors from Genlab Alpha, his instructions are to round up as many of the "test subjects" (the mutant animals) as will fit into the personnel carrier and abandon the rest. The Council is not interested in providing aid or even maintaining communications with whatever survivors are to be found at Genlab Alpha.

During this mission, PCs can make a shattering discovery: The outer world is no longer lethal to humans. The surface of the Earth is again habitable. The PCs will likely wonder if the leaders of the Houses knew this, and if so, why they kept it secret.

LOCATIONS

This Incident occurs at two sites connected to Genlab Alpha: "Restricted Area 1," where an entrance to the underground lab is located, and "Bear Park," the main outpost in the mutant bears' habitat in Paradise Valley. The PCs originally land in Restricted Area 1 and can later visit Bear Park (see Events).

RESTRICTED AREA 1

This area is found on the slopes of a mountain. It is about 500 yards across and surrounded by a high fence. The terrain outside consists of low trees and bushes. Inside the fence, all vegetation has been removed. The area is barren and crisscrossed by vehicle tracks.

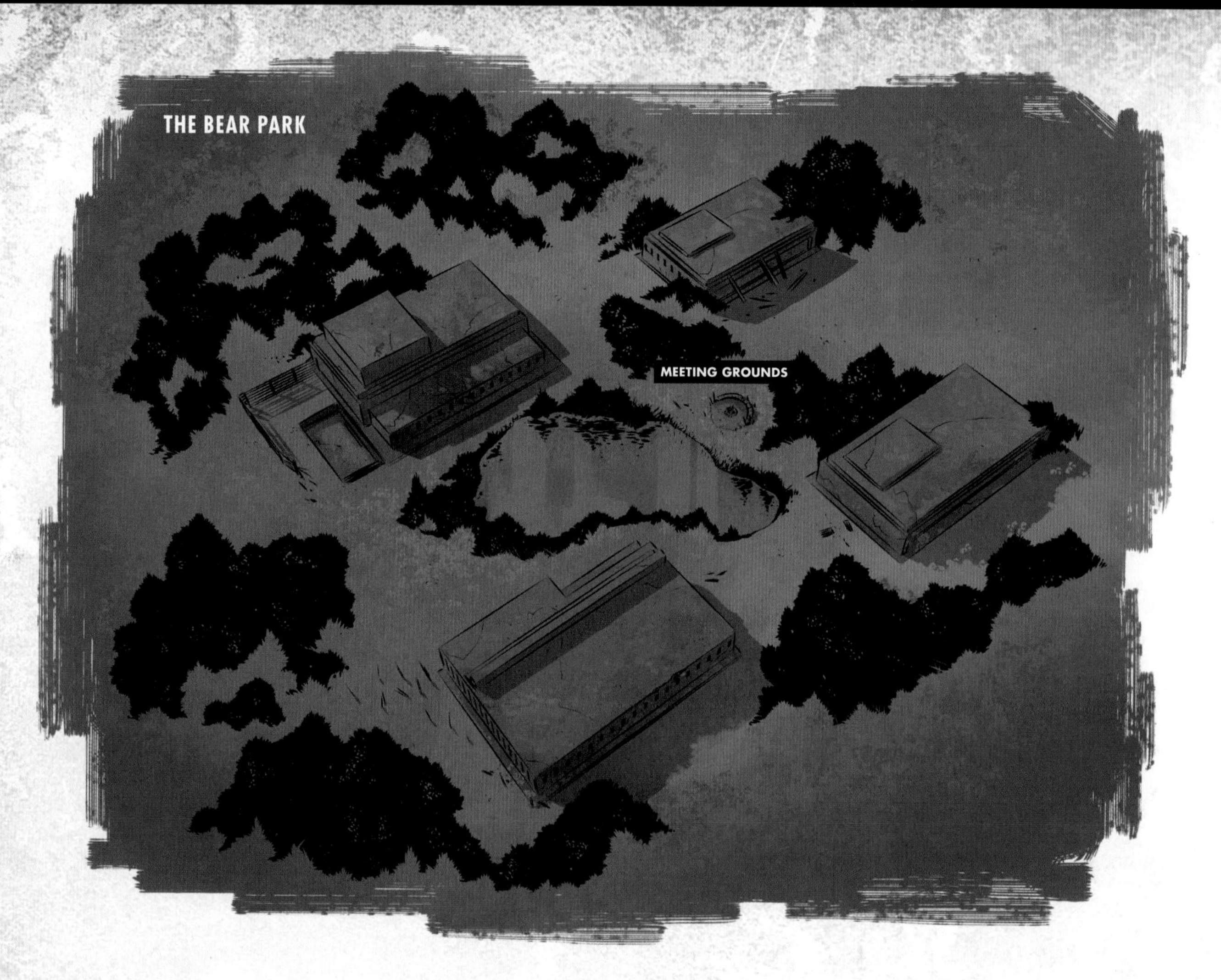

THE BUNKER

In the middle of Restricted Area 1 there is a low concrete bunker. It is evident that something dramatic has happened here. The bunker's double doors, decorated by the Elysium eagle emblem and the text "GENLAB ALPHA," lie on the ground, charred and blown out. There are no traces of any living creatures here.

A PC who makes a successful Investigate roll, or anyone who asks the GM detailed questions, will realize that a powerful explosion has blown out the gates from the inside. The soot and burn marks reveal that the explosion took place recently, perhaps no more than a few days ago.

THE TUNNEL

Inside the gate, a 10-foot wide and equally high tunnel leads straight into the mountain. The walls are covered in soot. About 100 feet into the tunnel, the way is blocked by rubble that is impossible to clear. The Rot Level by the rubble is 3 – the PCs suffer 1 Rot Point per minute. By searching the rubble, the PCs can find a random artifact.

THE BEAR PARK

Four low, decayed and overgrown concrete buildings can be found in a forested area on the eastern side of Paradise Valley. Rusty bars cover the few windows. The area is completely overgrown, and the buildings are partially hidden by trees and shrubbery.

The buildings have served as the main outpost of the Bear Clan in Paradise Valley. There is nothing of value in the buildings.

MEETING GROUNDS

Near the buildings there is a small lake, and on its shore there is an open area with a large fireplace. A blazing bonfire burns here when the PCs arrive – several hundred mutant animals of different species and sizes have gathered to discuss recent events.

NPCS

Of the campaign's key NPCs, only Casimir Montague participates in this Incident. The rest are described below.

DEEP WATCH SOLDIERS

Montague has eight soldiers under his command during this Incident. Four of them travel in the PCs' gunship and four in the personnel carrier.

Personal Goal: To follow Montague's orders and "shoot surface critters."

Reputation: 2
Attributes: Strength 4, Agility 4, Wits 2, Empathy 2.
Skills: Fight 2, Shoot 3, Press On 2.
Talent: True Grit.
Gear: Gauss rifle, E-pack, combat armor, frag grenade.

MUTANT ANIMALS

There are several hundred mutated animals in the Bear Park – all survivors from Genlab Alpha. If you have access to *Mutant: Genlab Alpha*, you can use game data from that book, including animal powers. Otherwise, use the following.

Personal Goal: To live in freedom.

MONKEYS:

Attributes: Strength 2, Agility 4, Wits 3, Empathy 3.
Skills: Fight 2, Manipulate 2.
Gear: Club (Gear Bonus +1, Weapon Damage 1).

BEARS:

Attributes: Strength 5, Agility 3, Wits 2, Empathy 2.
Skills: Fight 3.
Gear: Teeth and claws (no Gear Bonus, Weapon Damage 2).

DOGS

Attributes: Strength 3, Agility 4, Wits 2, Empathy 4.
Skills: Fight 2, Shoot 2.
Gear: Teeth (no Gear Bonus, Weapon Damage 2), bow (Gear Bonus +1, Weapon Damage 1, Long range).

11

EVENTS

The visit to Genlab Alpha can become a very dramatic scene. The PCs first arrive at Restricted Area 1. These are some of the potential events:

- After the PCs have spent some time searching the bunker, Colonel Montague shrugs his shoulders and gets ready for departure. Genlab Alpha seems to be completely destroyed. The gunship pilot then receives a message via comm radio – the other hovercraft has spotted a large gathering of individuals at another location in the valley, nine miles to the east. Montague gives the order to immediately proceed there.
- On their approach, the PCs can see the glare from a big bonfire in the distance. As the hovercraft comes closer, the PCs see hundreds of creatures gathered around the fire. They stand upright on two legs, but some are small like children while others are bigger than adult humans. Before long the characters will realize that the creatures are not human at all, but animals walking upright. Dogs, cats, bears, rats, and other species, wearing clothes and carrying weapons. Montague orders the pilot to land. He lets the PCs take the lead in communicating with the animals and follows with his soldiers in tow.
- The animals' reactions will depend on the PCs' actions. Some fall on their knees. Others seem skeptical, while others hiss and growl, showing their teeth. This is a volatile situation. If the PCs are looking for a leader to address, a large female bear comes forward. She speaks with a deep voice and introduces herself. Her name is Wildpaw. If the PCs can convince her that they come in peace (with a Manipulate roll), she will tell them about the animals' battle against the machines (see *Mutant: Genlab Alpha*) and that she now wants to leave this place to go out into the world. Wildpaw asks the PCs where they come from and what they are doing. Let the players think about how they want to resolve the situation. The animals will not come willingly with the PCs.
- An angry rabbit wearing blue war paint threatens the PCs. This is General Rotus. He calls the characters "nasty meat-eaters" (as the stories say that humans eat meat) and urges them to leave if they want to live. The PCs can try to calm him down by rolling Manipulate.
- Colonel Montague raises his weapon and speaks. "Test Area B35, codename Paradise Valley, will be vacated on the orders of the Council of Elysium I. All animals indicated will be quarantined for examination and further research. Line up and prepare for transport. Now!" All soldiers raise their weapons and take aim at the animals. If the PCs protest, Montague explains that the PCs did not seem to be making progress and that he now takes charge of the operation.
- The animals don't trust the humans and are not willing to give up their newly won freedom. The PCs can follow orders, try to stop Montague, or attempt to mediate. Any attempt to Manipulate Wildpaw into sending some animals with the PCs (to sacrifice themselves for the greater good of the clans) suffer a –2 modification, as does any attempt to Manipulate Montague into leaving the animals alone here in the valley. Whatever the PCs do, some angry mutant animals will sooner or later attack the PCs or the soldiers, and pandemonium breaks out.
- A PC (or one of the soldiers) gets hit and his protective armor is torn open. Montague orders that the individual be left behind because he is now "contaminated." The general perception in Elysium I is that the air on the surface is deadly. The individual himself will not feel anything – to the contrary, the fresh air in Paradise Valley smells wonderful. Montague knows that the air is harmless but refuses to let the "contaminated" person enter the hovercraft and leave as it would reveal the secret. Any attempt to Manipulate Montague into changing his mind gets a –2 modification.
- The conflict with the animals risks ending in a violence. Despite their high-tech weapons and armor, the soldiers cannot defeat

hundreds of mutant animals. When a few of the soldiers have fallen, Montague orders a retreat back to the hovercraft. He will not go out of his way to ensure the characters make it into the vehicles – on the contrary, the PCs may be forced to roll Move in order to board before takeoff.

- If any of the PCs are left behind in Paradise Valley, or choose to stay behind, they now leave the *Guardians of the Fall* campaign – at least temporarily. The players of these PCs should make new judicators to join the patrol. However, stranded PCs can survive on the surface and perhaps join the animals, or even try to make their way back to Elysium I (using the rules for Zone travel in *Mutant: Year Zero*).

THE SECRET OF THE SURFACE

During their visit to Genlab Alpha, PCs will likely realize that something they have been told for all their lives is a lie: the air on the surface is breathable. Humanity can return to the surface world. On the way back to the enclave, Colonel Montague admits that he knew this. He urges the PCs to keep the secret:

"Consider what would happen if the workers were told that it is possible to return to the surface. There would be chaos. We would lose everything we have. To reveal it would be a betrayal against the Council, against the Houses. You know what happens to traitors? They end up in the Catacombs."

The PCs are left to decide how to deal with the secret. If they reveal the truth, the Development Level in Science increases by 2D6, while Security decreases by 2D6. However, any PC who is caught speaking about what they saw on the surface will be punished for misconduct (see page 24) and reprimanded for "spreading disinformation." Some in the enclave will believe the PCs, but they will be discredited on Voice of Dawn and have their claim dismissed as a lie.

A DAY TO REMEMBER

Just like "Signal from Genlab Alpha," this Special Incident begins with Chief Inspector Astride Fortescue assigning the PCs to a special mission.

ASSIGNMENT

As you know, the annual Memorial Day celebration is coming up. As usual, the heads of the Houses will speak here outside the Capitolium to commemorate the history of Elysium and our fallen soldiers. As tradition dictates, a hundred workers from the Core and the Deep will be permitted into the Crown to attend the festivities. We are not expecting any problems, Memorial Day always goes smoothly, but we still want a patrol of judicators on site to manage security. This year the job is yours.

OVERVIEW

Memorial Day is the main festival in Elysium I. According to tradition, the Council always meets on this day to make the decisions that shape the future of the enclave. Thereafter, the leaders of the four Houses gather on a stage outside the Capitolium to speak to a crowd of highborn and one hundred randomly selected inhabitants from the lower levels of the enclave.

The stage where the ceremony will be held is already in place (see the map to the right). The festivities will be broadcast via Voice of Dawn to the entire enclave, with Valentino Morningstar as host and commentator. A large video screen is mounted over the stage in the Winter Garden, so that everyone can see and hear what is said. A total of about a thousand spectators are expected.

PCs are free to make whatever plans they want for the event. However, they will not have access to the heads of the Houses before the ceremony itself. Neither will they have the authority to make any changes to the program (see the boxed text to the right), nor decide which guests can participate. The Deep Watch and Honor Guard have parades in the Winter Garden during Memorial Day, but they don't participate as part of the security detail.

THE PROGRAM

Memorial Day has been celebrated for decades and is usually a boring and long-winded affair that few enclave denizens care about. This year's program doesn't differ significantly from that of previous years:

- **09.00 AM:** People start arriving at the Capitolium and the broadcast on Voice of Dawn starts.
- **10.00 AM:** The one hundred randomly selected visitors from the Deep and the Core are welcomed into the Crown.
- **11.00 AM:** The ceremony begins with two different parades in the Winter Garden, one put on by the Deep Watch, and the other by the Honor Guard.
- **11.30 AM:** A military orchestra starts playing on the stage. Several lower dignitaries speak on stage.
- **12.00 PM:** The heads of the four Houses climb on stage and give their speeches. The order of the speakers is determined by current total Control. Break any ties randomly.
- **1.00 PM:** The ceremony ends with a minute of silence for the fallen and a salute from the Deep Watch.

THE SITUATION

Memorial Day this year will truly be a day to remember. The Eminence Creon has chosen this day to launch the final phase of the plan to overthrow the Houses and seize control of the enclave (see page 144). The plan has several parts that are set to begin simultaneously.

Four Machine Guards – powerful biomechatronic soldiers – have infiltrated the crowd of workers invited to the ceremony in the Winter Garden. The four Machine Guards are disguised as ordinary members of the Temple and are dressed as novices in robes. Their mission is to interrupt the ceremony and kill the four leaders of the Houses. It is hoped that this will spread panic and disrupt the leadership of the enclave.

At the same time as the attacks are launched in the Winter Garden, the Temple springs into action throughout the rest of the Elysium I. The operation is carefully planned, coordinated, and will happen very fast. Using novices, recruited street gangs like the Cravats, and machine guards, the Temple quickly takes control of all key elevators and stairs. Soon, all of the Deep and the Core will be under the de facto control of the Temple. Most security guards surrender without putting up much of a fight and any judicators who get in the way are either killed or captured.

The PCs are about to have a very bad day at work.

LOCATIONS

This Incident takes place in the Winter Garden, around a large stage built outside the Capitolium. Show the map below to the players so that they can plan their security measures on Memorial Day.

1. WINTER GARDEN

A park honoring fallen soldiers. The park is old and unkempt. Instead of green plants, there are now long lines of dead trees and war memorials. Close to the Breach, some rusty old wrecks of enemy battle robots still stand.

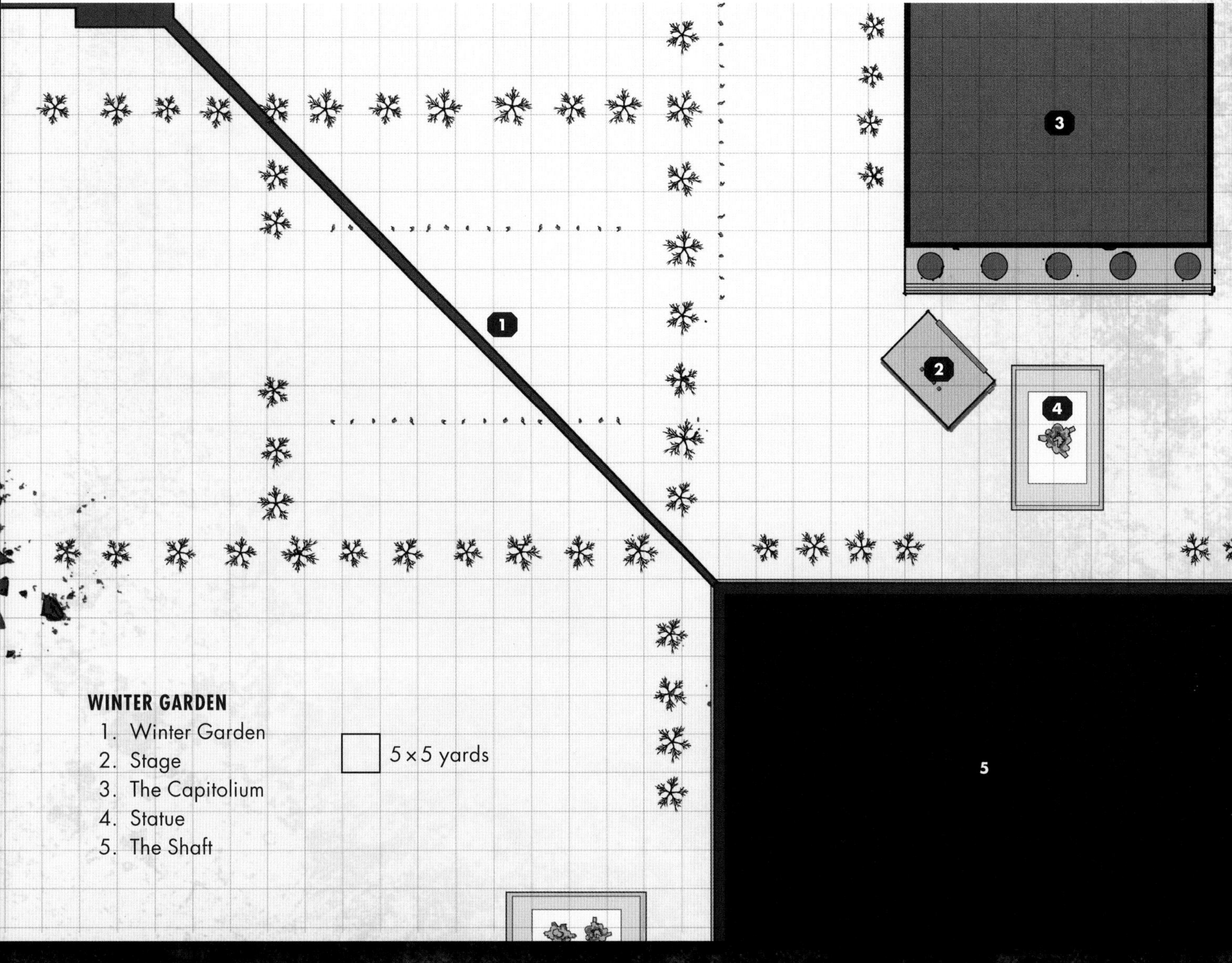

2. STAGE

The stage is 30 feet wide, 20 feet deep, and about 3 feet high. It has four podiums, each with a lectern marked with the emblem of one of the four Houses. Here, the heads of the great Houses will address the crowd. The stage is also equipped with an old speaker system and a large video display.

3. THE CAPITOLIUM

A decayed, multi-story palace of rust-brown composite tile that houses the Council meeting chambers. The building wears the scars of ancient battles. Its copper roof has a deep patina, and on the columns by the entrance the names of the enclave's fallen soldiers are engraved. The judicator headquarters is also found in the Capitolium, but the entrance is on the opposite side from the stage.

4. STATUE

The stage is flanked by a large statue depicting an Elysium soldier. He wields a sword in one hand and carries a child on his other arm.

5. THE SHAFT

In the middle of the Winter Garden there is an opening to the Shaft. The stairs and elevators that are located here lead all the way down to the Deep.

NPCS

Of the campaign's key NPCs, Valentino Morningstar participates in this incident along with Casimir Montague. Other NPCs are described below.

MACHINE GUARDS

These biomechatronic super-soldiers have been produced by the Eminences in Cryolab Delta for several years now. Their original personalities are almost erased, and they are remotely controlled by the sleeping Eminences via implanted communicators.

Personal Goal: To obey the orders of the Eminences.

Reputation: 1 (See below).

Attributes: Strength 5, Agility 5, Wits 3, Empathy 1.

Skills: Force 4, Fight 5, Shoot 4.

Biomechatronics: Reinforced Skull, Interface, Heat Vision, Communicator, Machine Arm, Machine Legs, Targeting Scope, Pain Inhibitors, Weapon Mount (gyrojet carbine), Overdrive.

Gear: Gyrojet carbine (six rockets).

Special: The Machine Guards are remotely controlled by the Eminences in Cryolab Delta and therefore cannot be Manipulated or Prosecuted, and they cannot suffer Doubt.

HONOR GUARD

The honor guard of each of the four ruling Houses holds a military parade during the ceremonies on Memorial Day. They do not participate in the security effort and are not prepared for battle, but they defend themselves if attacked and can assist at the PCs' request.

Personal Goal: To show off shinier boots and straighter lines than the honor guard of the other families.

Reputation: 5

Attributes: Strength 3, Agility 4, Wits 2, Empathy 2.

Skills: Fight 3, Shoot 2, Press On 1.

Talent: Saber dueling.

Gear: Gauss rifle, E-pack, saber.

GERTRUD WARBURG

The head of House Warburg, responsible for everything produced in the enclave. If Gertrud is killed or incapacitated, her cousin Manfred will replace her.

Personal Goal: To live a life of luxury, and to eliminate any and all threats to her lifestyle.

Reputation: 12
Attributes: Strength 4, Agility 3, Wits 5, Empathy 5.
Skills: Fight 3, Sense Emotion 4, Manipulate 5.

VALERIA FORTESCUE

The leader of House Fortescue and head of the Central Data Agency (CDA). If Valeria is killed, her cousin Margot Fortescue, General of the Deep Watch, will take over as leader of the House.

Personal Goal: To neutralize all threats to the current order in Elysium I by any means necessary.

Reputation: 12
Attributes: Strength 3, Agility 5, Wits 4, Empathy 4.
Skills: Fight 3, Move 4, Shoot 4, Sense Emotion 5, Manipulate 3.

CONSTANTINE MORNINGSTAR

Constantine has been the head of House Morningstar for decades now. His role as Chief Historian makes him responsible for the enclave's historical archives, but Constantine is more interested in the current theater scene than he is in history. If Constantine is killed or incapacitated, his daughter Octavia will replace him.

Personal Goal: To write himself into history as a great leader and savior of the enclave.

Reputation: 12
Attributes: Strength 3, Agility 4, Wits 4, Empathy 5.
Skills: Fight 2, Move 2, Shoot 2, Sense Emotion 5, Manipulate 5.

ANTONIA KILGORE

Antonia is the head of House Kilgore. She controls the Academy and has her hand in almost all major research projects. If Antonia is killed or incapacitated, her son Aston will become the next head of the House.

Personal Goal: To seek knowledge of the outside world and the potential for life out there.

Reputation: 12
Attributes: Strength 2, Agility 5, Wits 5, Empathy 4.
Skills: Shoot 2, Comprehend 5, Sense Emotion 4, Manipulate 3, Enlighten 5.

EVENTS

The preparations for Memorial Day are entirely in the hands of the players. When the ceremony starts, many things will happen. How these events play out will be affected by the PCs' preparations. Adjust the descriptions as needed.

- The ceremony starts as planned. Valentino Morningstar gets on stage and the Voice of Dawn broadcast begins. Valentino might want to interview the PCs. Depending on how past Incidents ended, they may be received warmly or given the cold shoulder.
- The selected workers from the Core and the Deep arrive on a freight elevator in the Shaft. They are one hundred people in total, a motley mix of workers from the Deep, service personnel from the Core, and novices from the Temple. They stare in awe at everything around them – few have ever set foot in the Crown before. Some are overwhelmed by the great open space and need to sit for a second to recover their bearings.
- Among the dozen Temple novices in the group, four Machine Guards are hidden. They keep a low profile. That they have heavy biomechatronic implants is noticeable to keen eyes, but there are many other reconstructed workers in the crowd, so it's nothing remarkable. The Machine Guards' weapons

are hidden in their weapon mounts and require careful scrutiny to spot. If any of the Machine Guards are confronted by a PC, they will play innocent as far as they can. Even if a Machine Guard is prevented from joining the ceremony, the rest will continue to lay low and carry out the attack. They avoid attention as much as possible and will not act until the appointed moment.

- The leaders of the Houses come out of their palaces one after another and walk to the stage amidst a mixture of jubilation and disdain. They parade past the crowd and wave. At least one of the House leaders, perhaps Constantine Morningstar, wants to stop by the crowd of selected workers and bask in their expected admiration. Instead, a worker throws an empty bottle at him and shouts "tyrant." The bottle hits its target and draws blood. It is up to the PCs to handle the situation. Whatever they do, they will be reprimanded.
- The four House leaders speak on stage. Each speech pays tribute to Elysium's glorious past and boasts of that particular House's accomplishments over the past year. Of course, none of the shady activities (like the Incidents staged by the Houses themselves) are mentioned.
- Some workers start to shout during one of the speeches, calling the House leaders "parasites" and "tyrants." The speaker tries to proceed as if nothing is happening but is clearly disturbed. The PCs will have to manage the situation.
- The PCs hear radio chatter in their communicators about unrest in the Deep. There are reports of riots breaking out in several sectors. However, the PCs are ordered to stay and complete their task in the Winter Garden. Other judicators are sent to the Deep.
- On a given signal from the Eminences, the Machine Guards attack. They draw their hidden gyrojet carbines and fire them at the House leaders. The distance is about 25 yards (Short range). Handle this as a sneak attack. Roll one Sneak roll for the Machine Guards and let each PC roll Scout. Then roll initiative for the Machine Guards and the PCs that can react in time – the other PCs miss the first round of combat. Make a collective initiative roll for the Machine Guards (do not forget that they have Overdrive and Weapon Mount). Roll openly for the attacks on the House leaders. Those that are not broken by the first shot will dive for cover. The Machine Guards will try to pursue them to finish the job. Machine Guards ignore the PCs at first but will attack anyone that gets in their way. Soldiers from the Deep Watch and the Honor Guard are nearby, but it takes a few rounds before they realize what's

going on. The Eminences do not expect the Machine Guards to survive. If they do make it, they retreat to the Shaft.

- When the battle is over, it's time for the next surprise. The big video screen above the stage that has been showing the Voice of Dawn broadcast – which now has broadcast the bloodbath in the Winter Garden to the entire enclave – crackles and Valentino's face is replaced by another: The Eminence Creon. In the background, somewhere in the enclave, there is an angry mob. A fire is burning. Creon starts to speak and his voice echoes over the Winter Garden. Everybody looks up and listens. See the boxed text below.
- After Creon's speech, the PCs hear reports confirming what Creon said – the Core and the Deep are in the hands of the Eminences. The leaders of the Houses – if any of them survived – blame each other for what is happening and retreat into their respective headquarters. The Deep Watch is ordered into the Winter Garden under the command of Colonel Montague and the entire area is secured. A tense calm settles while each House considers what to do next. The PCs – and all other judicators not taken hostage – are called to their base in the Capitolium to await new orders.

CREON'S SPEECH

"Attention, great Houses of Elysium! I am Creon, one of the ten Eminences chosen by Elysium's founders to watch over you. Every tenth year we have woken from our deep sleep to spend one year among you.

You are the heirs of the doom, on your shoulders the future of humanity rests. But you have failed. Instead of striving for the greater good of the enclave, you are plotting against each other, House against House. Instead of preparing the return to the surface, you dig deeper into the earth. Instead of building the new world, you fight each other over the scraps from the old one.

Today, Elysium changes its course. The Eminences have woken up, the Sleeping Council no longer sleeps. We have concluded that the four House can no longer be allowed to rule Elysium. What has happened here in the Winter Garden today is proof of our commitment. And while your attention has been directed here, our forces have taken control of the Core and the Deep.

Do not be afraid – our goal is not to kill you, it is to lead you back onto the righteous path. We want to negotiate, and establish a new rule for Elysium I. You have 48 hours to respond. After that we will consider you as our enemies, and we will end you.

I advise you not to attempt to retake the enclave with force. You are significantly outnumbered, and we know the alleys of the Core and the Deep better than you. Consider your next move carefully."

A CONQUERED ENCLAVE

After the attacks in the Winter Garden, the leaders of the Houses realize that the Core and Deep truly are under the control of the Eminences. Frantic Council deliberations begin, with incapacitated and deceased House leaders replaced by new members. Some advocate sending the Deep Watch to launch a large-scale attack against the Eminences, while others consider this too risky and instead advocate for a diplomatic solution.

A day of nervous waiting follows for the PCs, before the final Incident of the campaign starts. You can fast forward directly to "Attack on Cryolab Delta" but if you want to extend the campaign a little, this downtime is a good opportunity. For example, the PCs' contacts or other NPCs that are important to them may be at risk in the Core or the Deep, which may lead to personal rescue missions.

Such actions will in no way be sanctioned by judicator command, but this doesn't need to stop determined PCs who want to save their loved ones.

ATTACK ON CRYOLAB DELTA

Just over a day after the Memorial Day attack, Chief Inspector Astride Fortescue calls the PCs over their communicators. Perhaps they have rested, perhaps they have been to the Core or even the Deep, risking life and limb trying to rescue loved ones taken hostage during the uprising. Whichever the case, they are expected to report immediately – to the Council of Elysium itself. It is an honor that very few judicators ever experience.

The Council's assembly hall is located in the Capitolium as well, several floors above the judicator headquarters. Outside the door, Honor Guard soldiers stand watch. They allow the characters in without a word. Show the players the picture on page 10. The PCs are not offered to sit, they are expected to stand while being addressed by the leaders of the Houses. The PCs will notice that some of the House leaders have been newly appointed, replacements for those injured or killed.

The leader whose House has the highest current total Control addresses the PCs. Read or play out the following scene. Allow the players to ask questions. House leaders don't appreciate being interrupted however.

THE ASSIGNMENT

Judicators, you are about to be given a chance to repair your mistakes yesterday on Memorial Day. An attack on the Houses, against the Crown, against the very soul of Elysium – unthinkable! For too long the enclave has been blind to the threat that has festered in the shadows. The Gray Eminences were meant to serve us, now they are our worst enemies. They say they want to negotiate, but how can we ever trust such traitors?

We must act, and act decisively. Unfortunately, we cannot send our forces to retake the Core and the Deep. Our assault hovercraft cannot maneuver in the alleys and we do not know how many Machine Guards the Gray have.

But that is not the only reason. Have you heard of Emergency Protocol Omega? I suppose not, as it requires a higher security clearance than yours. It was created during the Enclave Wars to be activated only when the enclave is lost, a self-destruct mechanism to prevent the enclave from falling into enemy hands. The Omega Protocol means the total destruction of the enclave and death for most if not all of its inhabitants.

According to our intelligence reports, the Gray have taken control of the Omega Protocol. We don't know if they are insane enough to activate it, but we cannot take the chance. Therefore, we must act in secret, and strike directly against their headquarters. Our scholars believe that the Gray remote control their Machine Guards from there as well – a well targeted surgical strike could break the Gray's control of the Omega Protocol, and at the same time cripple their Machine Guards. Then, we will then be able to reclaim the enclave.

The Gray's base is Cryolab Delta, in the Catacombs [the House leader shows the PCs an overview of the enclave on a large screen, see map on page 190]. *There, the Sleeping Council has been in cryosleep for generations. Now all ten Eminences are awake, and this is their seat of power.*

Of course, we can't reach the cryolab through the Core or the Circle Line, the way down is too heavily guarded. But there is another way in, and we believe the Gray are not aware of it. Port Mendel is the old space port and transport terminal of the enclave. It was destroyed during the Enclave Wars long ago and has been abandoned ever since. But it is still possible to gain entry there, from the surface world.

Our plan is to send a small commando team through the Breach, across the surface, into Port Mendel, and through the monorail tunnel towards Cryolab Delta, to cut off the head of the snake. We have decided to grant you the great honor of performing this mission for us. You have previous experience on the surface, and you have, on occasion, proven yourselves capable. The Deep Watch must stay here to defend the Crown. Colonel Montague will give you the equipment you need. Move out!

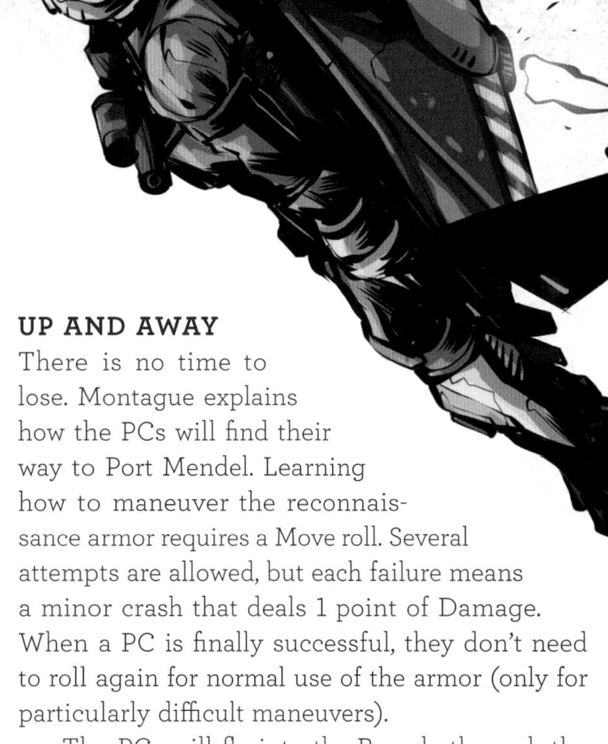

THE JOURNEY

The PCs don't get a choice on whether they accept the mission – it's an order. If the PCs refuse, they will be punished for misconduct. However, PCs can probably get away with delaying the departure for a short time if they want to discuss the plan or even catch up with something else before heading out.

RECONNAISSANCE ARMOR

Whenever the PCs are ready to leave, Colonel Casimir Montague will approach them and supply them with equipment. They will each receive a suit of reconnaissance armor (see page 137). Montague explains that the PCs will not use hovercraft this time, because the risk of discovery is too high. Instead, the PCs will fly to Port Mendel individually. He quickly explains how the suits are controlled. Unfortunately, they are in bad condition (half have Gear Bonus +2, half +1). Also, they only have enough fuel for about ten minutes of flight – enough to fly to Port Mendel and back, but not much more.

In addition, each PC is given a gyrojet carbine with four rockets. More cannot be spared according to the Colonel. One PC (a Technician if the patrol has one) also gets a laser welder (see boxed text below, also available as an Artifact Card in the *Mutant: Mechatron* custom card deck). This laser welder is needed to breach the gates of Port Mendel, which have been sealed since the Enclave Wars. The PCs are also given four rations of food and water each, and one E-pack. Montague points out that all equipment must be returned in good condition.

◘ LASER WELDER

A small tube-like item with a thin metal rod at one end. A bright red light glows at the end of the rod when the item is activated.

Effect: Gear Bonus +3 to Tinker and Jury-Rig. Gear Bonus +2 to Fight, Weapon Damage 2. Light electronic item. Energy weapon.

DEV Requirement: Technology 70

DEV Bonus: Technology +D6

UP AND AWAY

There is no time to lose. Montague explains how the PCs will find their way to Port Mendel. Learning how to maneuver the reconnaissance armor requires a Move roll. Several attempts are allowed, but each failure means a minor crash that deals 1 point of Damage. When a PC is finally successful, they don't need to roll again for normal use of the armor (only for particularly difficult maneuvers).

The PCs will fly into the Breach, through the desolate terminal above the dome of the Crown, and out through a large airlock to the surface world. For the first time, the PCs will see how the environment just outside Elysium looks. Exactly what's there depends on where in the world you have placed your game. The landscape is marked by craters from explosions, and wrecks of battle robots and rusty vehicles litter the area. If you want to describe the terrain in more detail, you can use the tables in Chapter 11 of the *Mutant: Year Zero* core book.

OVERVIEW

Port Mendel is only a mile and a half from the Breach and the PCs can easily find their way there. Keep in mind that they don't have much fuel – if they choose to fly elsewhere, they'll have a long walk back.

PORT MENDEL

The terminal consists of three deep silos used to launch rockets into space and hovercraft traveling between the Elysium enclaves. The facility was destroyed long ago, and the three silos now lay open and empty. The PCs can fly straight into one

DESERTING PCS

It's possible that the players are reluctant to continue to work for the Council. They might choose to leave the enclave for good during their trip to the surface, or even switch sides and try to join Creon. Both options are allowed, don't try to stop your players if they go this route.

If the PCs leave Elysium I for good and seek out a new life in the Zone the campaign ends early. Without the PCs' interference, the Omega Protocol will be activated, and Elysium I will be destroyed. The PCs might later meet survivors who can tell them what has happened. For further play out in the Zone, see Chapter 12 and the *Mutant: Year Zero* core book.

If the PCs try to leave the Crown to join forces with the Temple in the Core, they will first need to Sneak past the Deep Watch guard posts by the Shaft or take them out with force. Down in the Core, people will be very hostile to judicators and the PCs risk being killed or captured. At some point they will meet Cassandra (or another novice), who is distraught as she now has realized the extent of Creon's plans. Cassandra supports the revolt against the Houses but has concluded that the Eminences intend to seize control of the enclave for themselves. The only way to secure a just rule over the enclave is to stop the Eminences for good. Cassandra suggests that the PCs should strike against Cryolab Delta, and she can help sneak them into the Central Line. She can be Manipulated into accompanying them.

It's also possible that the players are divided on how to proceed, possibly even splitting the group. Allow this if it happens – this is the endgame of the campaign and you should let the players shape it the way they want.

of them and land at the bottom. Behind a pile of debris, they'll find a rusty metal gate.

Using the laser welder and a successful Tinker or Comprehend roll lets the PCs breach the gate. Port Mendel is a charred labyrinth of empty hangars and tunnels, roughly 200 meters wide. Rusty iron reinforcement rods jut out from crumbling concrete walls. Debris and the rusted wrecks of hovercraft and spacecraft are everywhere.

THE BEAST

There are more ways from the outer world into Port Mendel than the one the PCs found. A hungry devourer has found its way inside and has turned the area into its hunting ground, preying on convicts from the enclave exiled to the Catacombs.

The beast is always on the prowl and will try to make a meal out of one of the PCs by sneaking up on him. Build the mood of the scene as the PCs sneak around in an abandoned spaceport.

Scattered here and there the PCs can find human bones. Most look very old, although some are worryingly fresh. A PC who Investigates successfully finds fresh blood stains, no more than a few hours old.

A few random artifacts and a lot of scrap (use the scrap table on page 262 of the *Mutant: Year Zero* core book) can be found amid the rubble. Try to lure the PCs to split up searching for artifacts or scrap. When the time is right, the devourer attacks one of the PCs, or they see it attack members of the Sooty Hand.

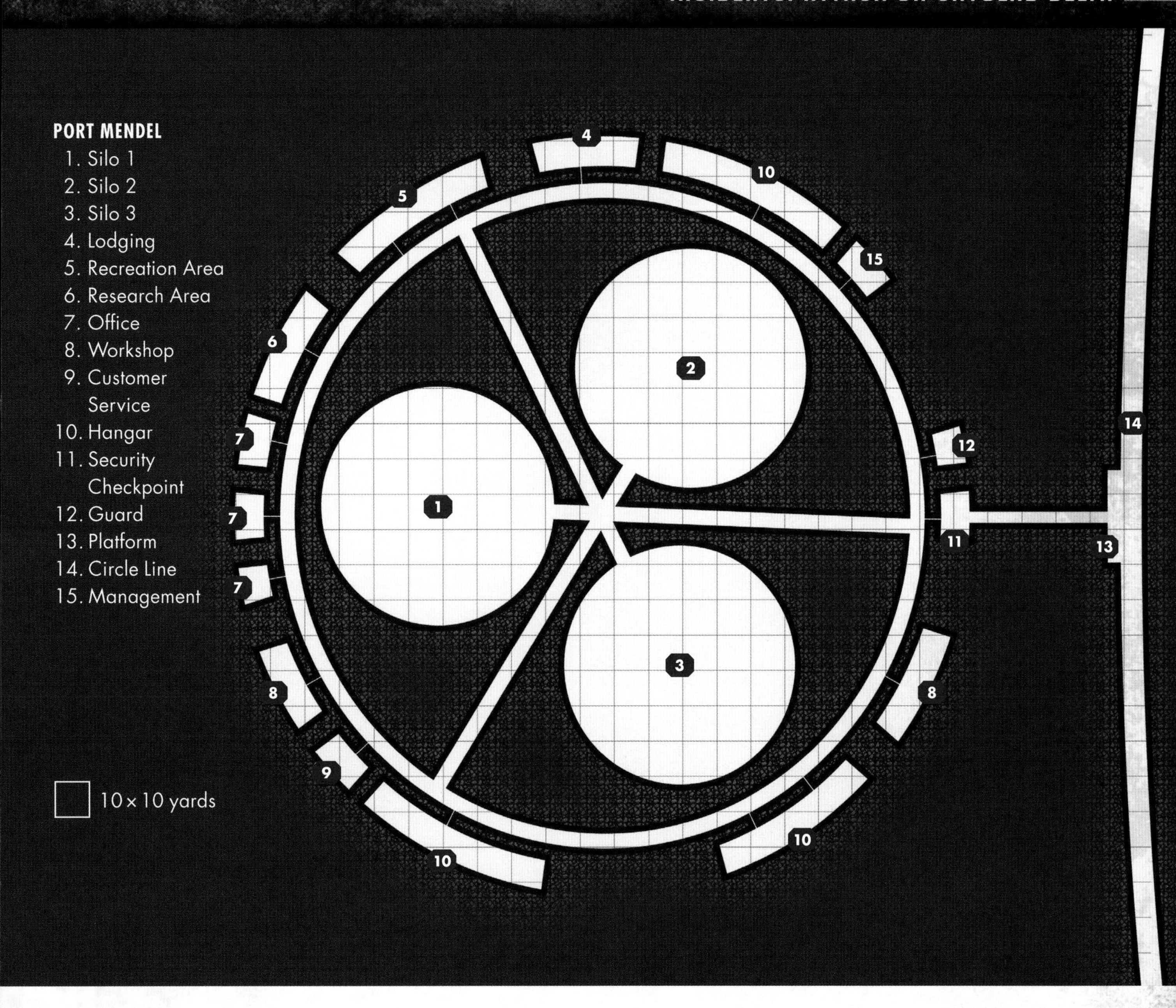

DEVOURER

A Devourer is a large and savage predator, taller than a human when it stands on its hind legs. It has dirty gray fur and resembles a scrawny bear. The beast has a huge maw, an insatiable hunger for flesh, and moves very silently. It sneaks up on its prey, who often find themselves half-way down the gullet of the beast before they realize what's going on. It can dislocate its jaws to fit the whole upper body of an adult human into its mouth. Corrosive saliva quickly kills its victim, which won't be released until it is dead or the beast is forced to flee.

Attributes: Strength 6, Agility 5.

Skills: Force 2, Fight 3, Sneak 4.

Armor Rating: 2

Weapons: Claws (Weapon Damage 1), Bite (Weapon Damage 3, but can only be used if the victim is unaware of the attack or immobilized). If the bite attack succeeds, the victim is caught in the creature's maw and takes 1 point of Damage every round. To break free, the victim must win an opposed Force roll against the beast. Each roll counts as an action for the victim.

THE SOOTY HAND

Not everyone in the Deep is on the Eminences' side. The Sooty Hand gang and its leader Nutty Nadya, whom the PCs may have already met in the Riots Incident, refuses to abide by the Temple's new rule. Nadya left the Deep with five others and took refuge in the Catacombs.

They eventually ended up in Port Mendel, where they set up a small camp. They did not anticipate the presence of the Devourer, and one of them has already succumbed to its appetite. Those still alive are scared and trying to figure out their next move. Going back to the enclave is not an option, but Cryolab Delta and its Machine Guards don't seem attractive either.

The PCs' encounter with the Sooty Hand in Port Mendel can take several different forms. The PCs can simply run into the gang and trigger a fight – the gang is on edge and has itchy trigger fingers. The PCs can also witness the beast attacking a gang member, and they'll need to decide whether to help or not. Finally, Nadya and her crew could show up and save the day if the PCs are attacked by the Devourer.

If the PCs play their cards right (or win a Manipulate roll against Nutty Nadya) they can recruit the gang's help in the attack against Cryolab Delta.

THROUGH THE TUNNELS

To get to Cryolab Delta, the PCs must walk about three miles along the Circle Line. The tunnel's illumination works here and there, as the Eminences have managed to repair certain stretches of the monorail.

You can fast forward the walk to the cryolab or add some exciting encounters along the way. Cannibals are common in the tunnels (see page 187 in the Kidnapping Incident). More Zone monster may have settled in the tunnels (such as Ruin Spiders and Zone Leeches, see *Mutant: Year Zero*), or a monorail train with Cravat members onboard may come along. If the PCs are spotted, they may need to silence the Cravats so that the Eminences are not alerted.

As the PCs approach Cryolab Delta, they see a flickering light from the monorail platform. Read more under Locations below.

THE SITUATION

The PCs are pawns in an elaborate game of intrigue. The Council is still in shock after the attack on Memorial Day and is prepared to take extreme action to destroy the Eminences and retain its power.

For this reason, the Council has not told the whole truth to the PCs. They expect the PCs to fail their mission. The purpose of sending them to Cryolab Delta is only to distract the Eminences' attention away from the real plan: to activate the Omega Protocol.

In fact, it's the Council and not the Eminences that controls the self-destruct mechanism, which entails filling the enclave with nerve gas (see page 244). The gas is denser than air, which means that it will fill the enclave from the bottom up, starting

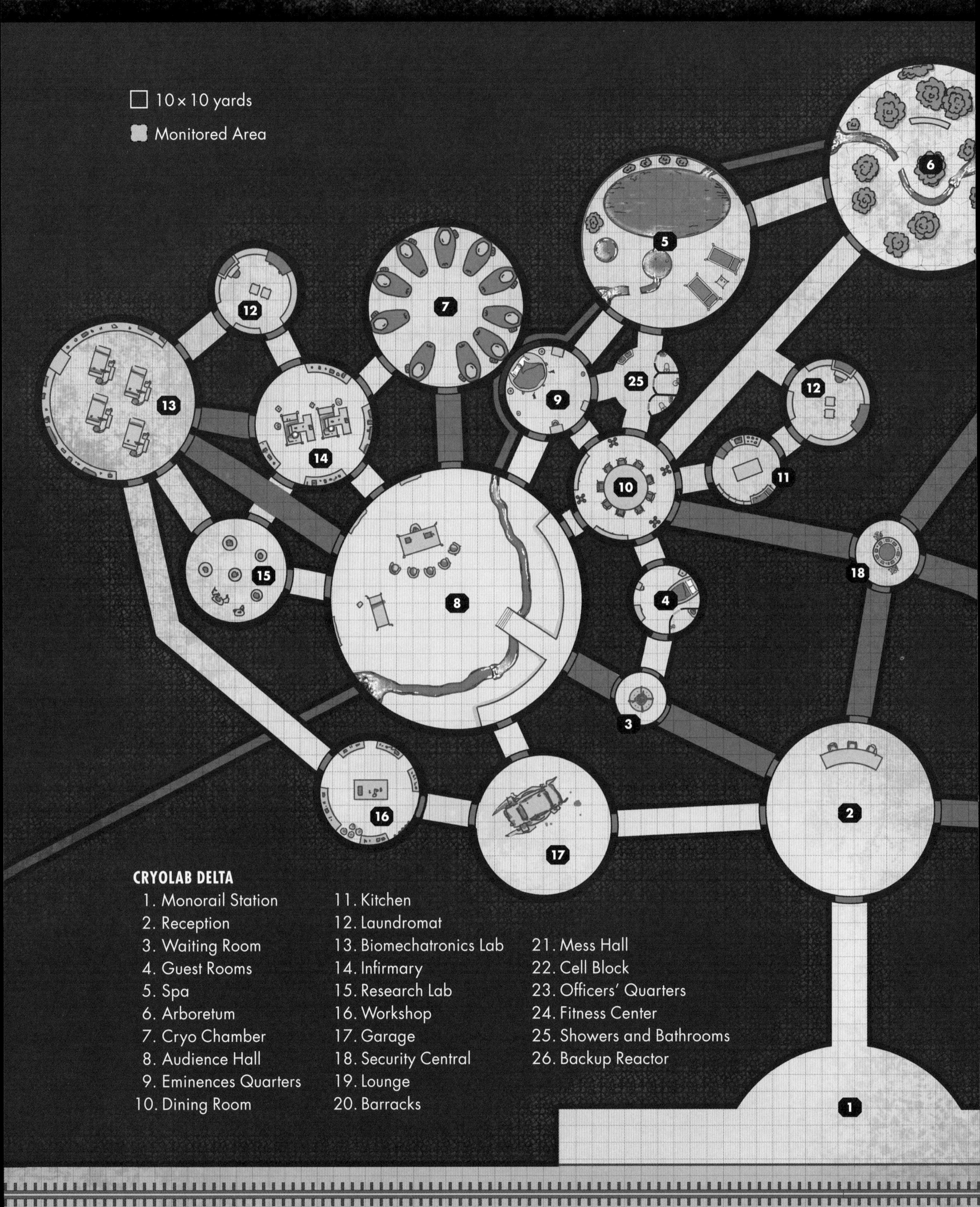
10 x 10 yards
Monitored Area
CRYOLAB DELTA
1. Monorail Station
2. Reception
3. Waiting Room
4. Guest Rooms
5. Spa
6. Arboretum
7. Cryo Chamber
8. Audience Hall
9. Eminences Quarters
10. Dining Room
11. Kitchen
12. Laundromat
13. Biomechatronics Lab
14. Infirmary
15. Research Lab
16. Workshop
17. Garage
18. Security Central
19. Lounge
20. Barracks
21. Mess Hall
22. Cell Block
23. Officers' Quarters
24. Fitness Center
25. Showers and Bathrooms
26. Backup Reactor

in the Deep. The Council's plan is to force the Eminences and those loyal to them up to the Crown, where the Deep Watch will be waiting.

The Council has made a miscalculation, however. Once the Omega Protocol is initiated it can't be stopped. The Council is aware of the risk, but is prepared to act regardless, as they see the enclave as lost anyway if the Eminences take power. The Houses must retain their power, everything else is secondary to them.

When and how the PCs will find out about this depends on how they act during the assault on Cryolab Delta. If they are not discovered by Cravats on their way in, they will be able to surprise the Gray. There are seven Eminences in the lab. They are protected by six novices including Cassandra (if the PCs haven't already met her in the Core, see the boxed text on page 230), the Scrap King and eight Cravats, and the Machine Guard Hector. Creon himself will not be here when the PCs arrive, but he will appear during their incursion.

LOCATIONS

Cryolab Delta has been the headquarters of the Gray Eminences since the enclave was founded. They have laid dormant here in cryosleep for nine years at a time, to then spend a year-long shift among the residents of Elysium I before again returning to their deep sleep.

The facility was not damaged directly during the Enclave Wars. However, the monorail system was crippled, leaving the lab isolated from the rest of the enclave. The Council knew, of course, that the Eminences remained in Cryolab Delta, but didn't give the matter much thought. The Gray were left to fend for themselves.

Cryolab Delta is not a lavish facility, but some areas offer a level of comfort otherwise only found in the Crown. However, everything is quite old and worn due to the many decades of use. The facility is illuminated with power from the backup reactor, and some areas have no operational lighting.

Doors. All doors in the lab are metal and open with the press of a button mounted on a nearby wall. The doors can be locked shut with an ID card of security class III or higher. The exceptions are the doors

to security central and the reactor, which require security class V cards. Such ID cards are carried by all Eminences.

Doors can also be locked and unlocked from security central and by an Eminence directly through their psychotronic link. If the alarm goes off, the required security class to lock and unlock all doors automatically increases to V.

A locked door can be opened without an ID card with a successful Tinker roll, or by inflicting 20 points of damage followed by a successful Force roll.

Security Cameras. There are security cameras throughout the cryolab. The map shows their locations and which areas they cover. The cameras can be monitored from security central. However, if it is manned by Cravats, there is always a 50% chance that no one is paying attention to the screens.

The Eminences can connect directly to security central via their psychotronic implants. There is also an alarm and speaker system that can be controlled from security central or directly by an individual Eminence.

1. MONORAIL STATION

A rusty sign above the platform reads "Cryolab Delta." Two Cravats usually sit here as guards, but they are often drinking and not very vigilant (current Wits of 1).

2. RECEPTION

A large round hall with the reception desk at the far end. This is where visitors signed in during their visit to the Cryolab. Nowadays it is used as the meeting place for the Temple's inner circle. Creon usually stands on the reception desk and talks to his followers. When speaking to larger groups Creon is usually out on the monorail platform.

3. WAITING ROOM

In the center of this small circular room is a round sofa with potted plants in the middle. Hidden speakers play soothing background music.

4. GUEST ROOM

There is an elliptical waterbed against one of the walls. A bathroom with a private shower occupies a small side space. On the wall opposite the bed is a beautiful fresco that depicts the Winter Garden. Another wall has an ornate wood panel. The others are decorated in gold and burgundy patterned wallpaper. A voice terminal on the night table connects to security central and the kitchen.

5. SPA

A spa facility with a small swimming pool, a whirlpool, and sun loungers. It was once very luxurious, but the tiles are now worn and cracked. One wall, however, looks like a portal to another world. It displays a beautiful sandy beach – even the sound of waves and the wind are noticeable.

The image is a hologram that can be controlled from a terminal in a small table by the sun loungers. The terminal also controls a powerful lamp on the ceiling that simulates sunlight. The terminal can be used to communicate with the kitchen or security central. A small canal of water passes through the room.

The Scrap King will be here when the PCs arrive, sitting on one of the sun loungers. A bored Cravats member sits next to him.

6. ARBORETUM

An unkempt plantation of trees, shrubs, and flowers from the Old Age. A small stream flows into the hall, forming a pond. Recorded bird chirps and the humming of bees emanates from hidden speakers. This plantation was created to preserve plant species from the ancient world and remind the Eminences of what once was. It is now overgrown and resembles a wild jungle. Nightmare Flowers also grow here (see *Mutant: Year Zero*), brought in by a careless Eminence from an expedition to the surface world.

7. CRYO CHAMBER

A dark and sterile hall that contains ten coffins, each with a glass lid and controls on the side. These coffins are where the Gray Eminences have rested. Now that all are awake the room is empty.

8. AUDIENCE HALL

A large hall divided into two parts by a six-foot-wide canal. Over the canal runs a narrow bridge without rails. On the far side is a large, ornamented desk

CENTRAL DATA AGENCY

SECURITY LEVEL: HIGH

630715 ■ PROJECT TITAN

ENTRY 630715, EMINENCE MOROS ■

Research into the Academy archives has uncovered interesting findings. Notes from 2129-2132 mention "Project Titan," carried out in Elysium IV by Chief Scientist Kaiser Kilgore. ■

Purpose: The creation of a xenogenetic organism with the ability to assimilate the memories, intellectual capacity, and psionic abilities of other organisms. Eight prototypes were created, results unclear. The project was interrupted when Elysium IV was targeted by an orbital attack. Kaiser Kilgore's fate is unknown. His daughter Beatrice Kilgore apparently survived the attack. Further investigation is recommended. ■

TERMINAL AUDIENCE HALL

CRYOLAB DELTA

HANDOUT #3: PROJECT TITAN

with a computer terminal. Around the desk there are armchairs and a sofa. On the ceiling hangs a large crystal chandelier.

This is the Eminences' auditorium. Here they gather to discuss their plans and receive important guests. The bridge over the canal can be folded back with the press of a button located under the desk. Anyone standing on the bridge when this happens must make a Move roll or fall into the canal.

In the canal there is a hungry Rotfish (see the next page) that the Eminences took from the surface world when it was just a spawn.

In the terminal, the PCs can find interesting information about the Eminences and their activities. They can read a report about two Eminences, Proteus and Rhea, who were recently sent to the surface world to contact Eminences from other Elysium enclaves. They can also read reports about research station Aros and Project Titan conducted in Elysium IV. See handouts #3–5.

When the PCs arrive, Eminences Selene and Zephyros are in the auditorium along with two Temple Novices and Cassandra (if she's not in the lab). Hector can also be found here.

THE HANDOUTS

Try to make sure that the players see the information in the audience hall, i.e. the three handouts. They give new insight into the Eminences' activities and hints that there are more Eminences out there, in other enclaves – maybe they will be back in future *Mutant* games...

CENTRAL DATA AGENCY

SECURITY LEVEL: HIGH

661213 ■ RESEARCH STATION AROS

ENTRY 661213 EMINENCE THALIA ■

The Academy archives mention the "Aros" facility, originally established by Elysium IV for the purpose of monitoring the surface environment, along with the deployment of xenogenetic creatures. Personnel in cryogenic sleep on site. Control of Uriel III ("eye in the sky") possible. Low contamination in the area makes it a good location for farming and fishing. ■

Conclusion: Optimal location for establishment of major surface settlement, for the recolonization of the outer world. Geographical position of Aros is currently unknown. Further exploration is a priority. ■

TERMINAL AUDIENCE HALL

CRYOLAB DELTA

HANDOUT #4: RESEARCH STATION AROS

THE ROTFISH

This monster resembling a huge wolffish grabs its victims and drowns them by holding them under the water.

Attributes: Strength 10, Agility 5.

Skills: Fight 3, Move 4 (underwater).

Armor Rating: 5

Weapon: Bite (Weapon Damage 2).

Drowning: If the Rotfish makes a successful attack it will pull its victim underwater to drown it. The victim can break free with a successful Move roll.

9. EMINENCES' QUARTERS

A bedroom with a large waterbed. Two porcelain panthers stand at the foot of the bed. Behind the bed is a large aquarium. Two candelabras sit on a night table, and on the wall are several paintings of nature motifs. Several sets of gray robes hang in a wardrobe with mirrored doors.

This luxurious bedroom is intended for the Eminence who is awake when the rest are in cryosleep. By the bed is a comm unit that can be used to reach the kitchen and security central. Behind one of the paintings is a hidden safe containing 200 credits, a gyrojet pistol with three rockets, and a dose of REGEN (see *Mutant: Year Zero*). Opening the safe requires a successful Tinker roll or 50 points of Damage.

The Eminence Moros is sleeping comfortably here when the PCs arrive.

HANDOUT #5: INCIDENT REPORT 690417

10. DINING ROOM

In this hall there is a round table with nine armchairs. Four large candelabras stand on the floor. There are two cupboards with plates, cutlery and glasses. Along the walls run dark and ornate wood paneling. Via a comm unit on the wall, the guests can communicate with the kitchen and security central.

The Eminences Hestia, Larissa, and Nestor are having a meal here when the PCs arrive. A Temple Novice is serving them.

11. KITCHEN

A simple yet functional kitchen with an advanced "autochef" unit that can automatically cook a selection of pies, stews, and soups. The food supply is limited, but the dishes are quite good – the Eminences have managed to acquire the best ingredients the enclave has to offer. A comm radio on the wall can communicate with the dining room, the Eminences' quarters, the spa, and security central.

12. LAUNDROMAT

A room with a large washing machine. The walls are lined with cupboards full of detergents and linens for the beds and tables. There is usually a Temple Novice here, handling the laundry.

13. BIOMECHATRONICS LAB

A large room with four operating tables. It is a very advanced and partially automated laboratory. This is where the Eminences created their Machine Guards and Temple Novices. The lab robot DZR-091, with a humanoid upper body mounted on rails, oversees the laboratory. It's a helpful machine, but it is unimaginative and not very talkative.

Adventurous PCs can get any biomechatronic implant (see Chapter 9) here – they just need to program DZR-091 correctly and lay down on the operating table. This requires a successful Comprehend roll, as DZR-091 needs very precise instructions. If the roll fails, the PC will end up with a randomly chosen implant instead. A PC who undergoes surgery is considered broken, but DZR-091 will Heal the patient (it has a Heal skill level of 5).

The Eminence Thalia and two Temple Novices are in the laboratory when the PCs arrive. Thalia is currently improving the interface on a Temple Novice while another novice assists her.

14. INFIRMARY

A room with advanced medical equipment and two hospital beds. Here, the Eminences are awoken from their cryogenic sleep.

Along the walls there are cabinets with medical equipment. There is one dose each here of REGEN, painkillers, and stimulants (see *Mutant: Year Zero*). The infirmary as a whole gives a +3 Gear Bonus to Heal but requires a Comprehend roll to be used.

15. RESEARCH LAB

A small room with dim lighting. Fetuses of mutant creatures from the surface world are preserved in glass containers and displayed throughout the room. There are monsters like the Devourer and Rotfish, along with several bipedal mutant animals. A container with a mutant fox is labeled "Genlab Alpha specimen, collected 2113-03-17."

16. WORKSHOP

This room smells of oil and fuel. Tools such as wrenches and electronic tools (both artifacts) hang on the walls. In a corner is a can of aviation fuel (counts as the jerrycan artifact, see *Mutant: Year Zero*). It can be used to make a fire bomb or to refuel a PC's reconnaissance armor. It contains enough fuel for a day's use.

17. GARAGE

A silo with a ceiling 150 feet high. Two large yellow rectangles are painted on the concrete floor. On one of the rectangles stands the wreck of a hovercraft. It's similar to the model used by patrolling judicators, but it's hermetically sealed hull enables it to be used for trips to the surface world.

The vehicle is not operational and cannot be repaired – several vital parts have been removed. Oil stains and burn marks from a jet exhaust indicate that another vehicle recently sat on the other rectangle.

The ceilings of the silo can be opened using a terminal on the wall. The ceiling itself opens like the iris of an eye, allowing vehicles to take off or land. A metal ladder leads up to the ceiling for service work.

18. SECURITY CENTRAL

All security cameras in the cryolab can be monitored from screens mounted by a desk in the shape of a semicircle in this room. However, some cameras are out of order. All monitored areas are indicated on the map on page 234.

A speaker system allows the personnel here to talk to any room in the facility. From security central, all doors can also be locked and unlocked.

There are two Cravats here when the PCs arrive. However, they are not very vigilant and will watch the monitors only about 50% of the time.

19. LOUNGE

Low sofas are found inside this room. There is an ancient video projector that plays movies from the Old Age. Here, more than anywhere else in the enclave, videos deemed subversive or inappropriate by Elysium's founders can still be viewed, and the collection available is extensive. The black and white classic Casablanca is currently playing. Against the wall stands a vending machine that once offered small pastries and cigarettes. Other than some dry cigarette packages it is now empty. When the PCs arrive there are three Cravats sitting on sofas, arguing about what to watch next.

20. BARRACKS

A room with nine bunk beds, each with an accompanying locker. This room originally housed the lab's security force. It is now used by the novices and Cravats.

THE ALARM

The PCs can trigger the alarm in the cryolab if they are seen by a surveillance camera (see Security Central). The alarm will also be triggered if the PCs are spotted by an Eminence or Hector, unless they are broken in the first round of combat. If the PCs are spotted by a Temple Novice or a Cravat, they have several rounds to silence them before an alarm will sound.

If the alarm is triggered, a warning signal sounds and a loudspeaker announces that hostile intruders (the PCs) are in the facility. The Eminences and their underlings will organize a defense. The Gray will flee out into the Zone (via Port Mendel) if they are losing the battle. The same goes for the Scrap King and the Cravats, who have no deeper loyalty to the Eminences. Hector and the Temple Novices will sacrifice themselves without hesitation if ordered to do so.

21. MESS HALL

A large room with several round tables. In one corner stands an "autochef" unit that can cook simple dishes upon request. Unlike in the Eminences' kitchen, the options available here are limited to tasteless soups and stews. The food might not be flavorful, but it is protein rich thanks to the use of insects as a replacement for other raw materials now long depleted.

22. CELL BLOCK

Two cramped cells. Locking or unlocking the doors requires an ID card class V or higher.

23. OFFICERS' QUARTERS

A bedroom with two single beds and a small desk of dark wood. This room used to house the guard officers. Now, the Machine Guard Hector stays here whenever he is not out patrolling.

24. FITNESS CENTER

The smell of sweat is ingrained in this room. There are robotic training machines here and two robots for combat exercises (the robots fight back and have a Strength 3 and a Fight skill level of 4). A hologram wall displays archery targets.

25. SHOWERS AND BATHROOMS

A room with five stalls along the wall. Each booth is a combination of shower and bathroom.

26. BACKUP REACTOR

A worn control room for the cryolab's backup reactor, which is built into the bedrock next to it. The reactor's control room has Rot Level 3. With a successful Tinker roll, a character can cause a meltdown in the reactor that will trigger a chain reaction that will flood the entire cryolab with radiation (immediately dealing D6 Rot Points and then one Rot Point per minute to everyone in the facility).

NPCS

Of the campaign's key NPCs, Colonel Montague, the Eminence Creon, the novice Cassandra, the Scrap King, and Nutty Nadya all appear in this Incident. Other NPCs are described below.

THE SOOTY HAND

The remains of Nadya's gang are a few loyal young men and women. At this point, they fear for their lives. They are angry and violent but are willing to listen to the PCs if they have a compelling plan. At their height, the gang consisted of about 30 members, but now only five remain with Nadya. They all have their right hands painted black.

Personal Goal: To survive.

Reputation: 0
Attributes: Strength 4, Agility 3, Wits 2, Empathy 2.
Skills: Shoot 2, Fight 3.
Biomechatronics: Reinforced Skull, Machine Arm, or Pain Inhibitors.
Gear: Scrap pistol (five bullets) and a blunt instrument.

THE CRAVATS

The Scrap King allied himself with the Gray, and his gang now acts as henchmen for the Eminences in the Deep and the Catacombs. The gang's signature is a handkerchief tied around the neck worn by all members, men as well as women. There are eight Cravats in Cryolab Delta when the PCs arrive. They were tasked with guarding the Cryolab but are not very loyal. They will flee rather than fight to the death.

Personal Goal: To eat, fight, and make the Scrap King proud.

Reputation: 0
Attributes: Strength 4, Agility 3, Wits 2, Empathy 2.
Skills: Shoot 3, Fight 3.
Gear: Scrap pistol (D6 bullets), club.

THE GRAY EMINENCES

There are nine Eminences in Elysium I in addition to Creon. Five of them are women: Hestia, Rhea, Larissa, Selene, and Thalia. The other four are men: Moros, Nestor, Proteus, and Zephyros. They all have identical attributes and skills. Seven of them are in Cryolab Delta when the PCs arrive. Proteus and Rhea are traveling on the surface in a hovercraft looking for other Elysium enclaves and the Aros research station, while Creon is currently out but set to return soon.

Personal Goal: To preserve their psychotronic bond and kill anyone who threatens them.

Reputation: 10
Attributes: Strength 3, Agility 4, Wits 5, Empathy 4.
Skills: Fight 2, Move 2, Shoot 4, Comprehend 5, Sense Emotion 5, Manipulate 3.
Biomechatronics: Interface.
Gear: Gyrojet pistol (D6 rockets each), class V ID card.
Special: All Eminences except Creon have just recently woken from their cryosleep and therefore the psychotronic bond between them is overly sensitive. Each time an Eminence is broken, all other Eminences suffer one point of Fatigue and one point of Confusion. This effect does not apply to Creon.

HECTOR

A Machine Guard who acts as the Eminences' bodyguard in Cryolab Delta. All other Machine Guards are back in the Core or the Deep. Like other Machine Guards, Hector's original personality is non-existent. He can be remotely controlled by the Gray via a communicator, but he has a standing order to protect them and can act independently.

Personal Goal: To neutralize all threats to the Eminences.

Reputation: 1 (see below)
Attributes: Strength 5, Agility 5, Wits 3, Empathy 1.
Skills: Force 4, Fight 5, Shoot 4.
Biomechatronics: Reinforced Skull, Interface, Thermal Vision, Communicator, Machine Arm, Machine Legs, Targeting Scope, Pain Inhibitor, Overdrive.
Gear: Gyrojet carbine (six rockets), class V ID Card.
Special: Hector cannot be Manipulated or Prosecuted, and he cannot suffer Doubt.

TEMPLE NOVICES

In addition to Cassandra (if she is here) there are five other Temple novices in the cryolab when the PCs arrive. These five have implants in their brains and follow the Eminences' orders to the letter. They perform simple daily chores. They are not violent in nature and will not even fight in self-defense but can be forced to commit violence in defense of the Eminences.

Personal Goal: To follow the will of the Eminences.

Reputation: 1
Attributes: Strength 2, Agility 4, Wits 2, Empathy 3.
Skills: Sneak 2, Move 2, Sense Emotion 3, Manipulate 2.
Biomechatronics: Interface.
Gear: None.
Special: Temple Novices cannot be Manipulated or Prosecuted, and they cannot suffer Doubt.

PSYCHOTRONICS

All Eminences in the Sleeping Council are linked via microchips implanted in their brains. These microchips contain radio transmitters and receivers that trigger limited telepathic capabilities. This technology is called "psychotronics" and was developed in the Academy (see the Murder Incident).

The Gray can communicate with each other at a distance through the psychotronic bond. They can also benefit from each other's brain capacity, making them extremely intelligent. A side effect of long-term interconnection is that patients feel each other's pain and can suffer from severe trauma if someone else in the link is killed.

Recently, the Gray have also implanted psychotronic chips in some Temple novices and a unit of biomechatronic soldiers, the so-called Machine Guards. These psychotronic bonds are different – they give the Gray total control over the individuals by eliminating their personalities.

DEEP WATCH ELITE SOLDIERS

Colonel Montague leads an elite unit that consists of as many soldiers as there are PCs.

Personal Goal: To follow Montague's orders.

Reputation: 3

Attributes: Strength 4, Agility 4, Wits 2, Empathy 3.

Skills: Fight 3, Shoot 3, Press On 2.

Gear: Gauss carbine, an E-pack, combat armor, frag grenade.

EVENTS

What happens during the PCs' visit to Cryolab Delta can vary quite a bit. Let them explore the base as they like. The following are suggested events that you can use whenever you want to increase the pressure.

- The PCs run into Cassandra, who is distraught. She wants to avoid fighting and will instead try to negotiate with the PCs. She has realized that the Eminences plan to enslave Elysium I and rule the enclave themselves, and wants the PCs to stop them – if they promise not to hand back power to the Houses.
- The Scrap King attacks. If the PCs have met him before (in the Kidnapping Incident) he might be out for revenge. He will attack in a brutal but cowardly way, preferably picking off one PC at a time. If he gets the chance to use the trap door in the audience hall, he will gladly do it. The Scrap King is always accompanied by some Cravats. If he is defeated, he will try to negotiate with the PCs.

- Hector attacks. He is completely emotionless, and impossible to Manipulate. If he is overpowered, he will temporarily retreat, but will turn up later and attack again.
- If the PCs end up in serious trouble, the Sooty Hand can come to their rescue. Nutty Nadya realizes that the Gray will never let them live in freedom and is prepared to sacrifice herself to defeat them.
- At the appropriate time, preferably when the Gray and Hector are defeated and the PCs believe they have succeeded in their mission, Creon returns to the cryolab, along with a Machine Guard (Ariadne, in game terms identical to Hector) and some Temple Novices (as many as there are PCs). Creon knows what has happened thanks to his psychotronic bond to the other Eminences. He uses the speaker system to address the PCs. He states that the Council activated the Omega Protocol. The nerve gas has already killed many in the Deep and the survivors are fleeing up toward the Core and the Crown. Players must decide if they believe Creon or not.
- Creon realizes that the game is over – the Gray cannot stop the Omega Protocol. His goal now is to gather the Eminences and novices who survived the PCs' attack against Cryolab Delta and head out into the Zone. If the PCs have killed one or more Eminences, Creon will be filled with a holy wrath and thirst for revenge. If the PCs have taken Eminences as prisoners, Creon is ready to negotiate. He is pragmatic and realizes that he has nothing to gain from fighting the PCs at this point.
- While the PCs negotiate with Creon, an elite Deep Watch unit arrives, commanded by Colonel Casimir Montague. It consists of as many soldiers as there are PCs. Montague's orders are to clean up and eliminate all witnesses – both the Gray and the PCs, who were never meant to survive their mission. Creon and the Scrap King will fight alongside the PCs if offered an alliance. Montague fights to the bitter end. He is not interested in talking to the PCs, but he can confirm that the Council has activated the Omega Protocol. It may be possible to Manipulate Montague to have him spare the PCs.

THE OMEGA PROTOCOL

The Omega Protocol plan was created when Elysium I was built. Its purpose was twofold: to prevent the enclave from ever falling into enemy hands, and to guarantee that the enclave leadership could never be overthrown by an inner threat. The plan consists of two phases:

In Phase 1, a deadly nerve gas is released into the enclave from hidden canisters. It is a dense gas that accumulates in the Deep first. As the enclave is filled by the gas, it rises upwards. It takes about 30 minutes for the gas to reach the Core and another 30 minutes to get to the Crown. This phase will trigger total panic as people desperately try to escape from the Deep, seeking refuge higher in the enclave.

The gas, which is invisible but has a sweet smell, is treated as an attack with nine Base Dice each round (Weapon Damage 1). Armor provides no protection against the gas, but special protective gear like gas masks and sealed suits do. Anyone who is broken by the gas will die after D6 minutes if no one successfully Heals the victim (–2 modification to the roll).

In Phase 2, a large number of hidden charges are detonated. The explosions trigger a chain reaction, causing all floors of the enclave to collapse. Anyone still inside the enclave when Phase 2 commences will be immediately killed or trapped far underground amidst a twisted labyrinth of rubble.

The goal of the Council is to force the Temple's forces to the Crown as they flee from the poison gas, where the bulk of the Deep Watch will be waiting for them to finish them off. In this, the plan will succeed – the Temple's army of novices and Machine

Guards will be destroyed. Many innocents will die too, but this is a price that the desperate Council is prepared to pay – the way they see it, the power of the Houses must under no circumstances be broken.

The Council intends to stop the Omega Protocol before the gas reaches the Core, and before Phase 2 triggers. But they have made a grave miscalculation – the Omega Protocol cannot be stopped once it has been activated.

AFTERMATH

When the dust settles, the PCs are likely alone in Cryolab Delta. The Gray as well as the Cravats are probably either dead or on the run. The PCs have no choice but to leave the Catacombs the same way they came in, via Port Mendel and the surface world.

Regardless of whether the PCs fly with their reconnaissance armor or walk on foot, they will soon see a huge crowd of people on the surface. Hundreds, perhaps thousands of people, pour out through the Breach to see the sky and breathe fresh air for the first time in their lives. Many fall to their knees, shocked by the experience. Others, either injured in the fighting or affected by the poison gas, follow behind with the help of others.

The thunder of heavy explosions in the depths announces the final phase of the Omega Protocol. All 84 levels of the enclave fall one after another, the city's alleys and buildings are crushed as they collapse into the abyss. Elysium I is no more. The long atomic winter is over. A new dawn is here. A new kingdom will be built.

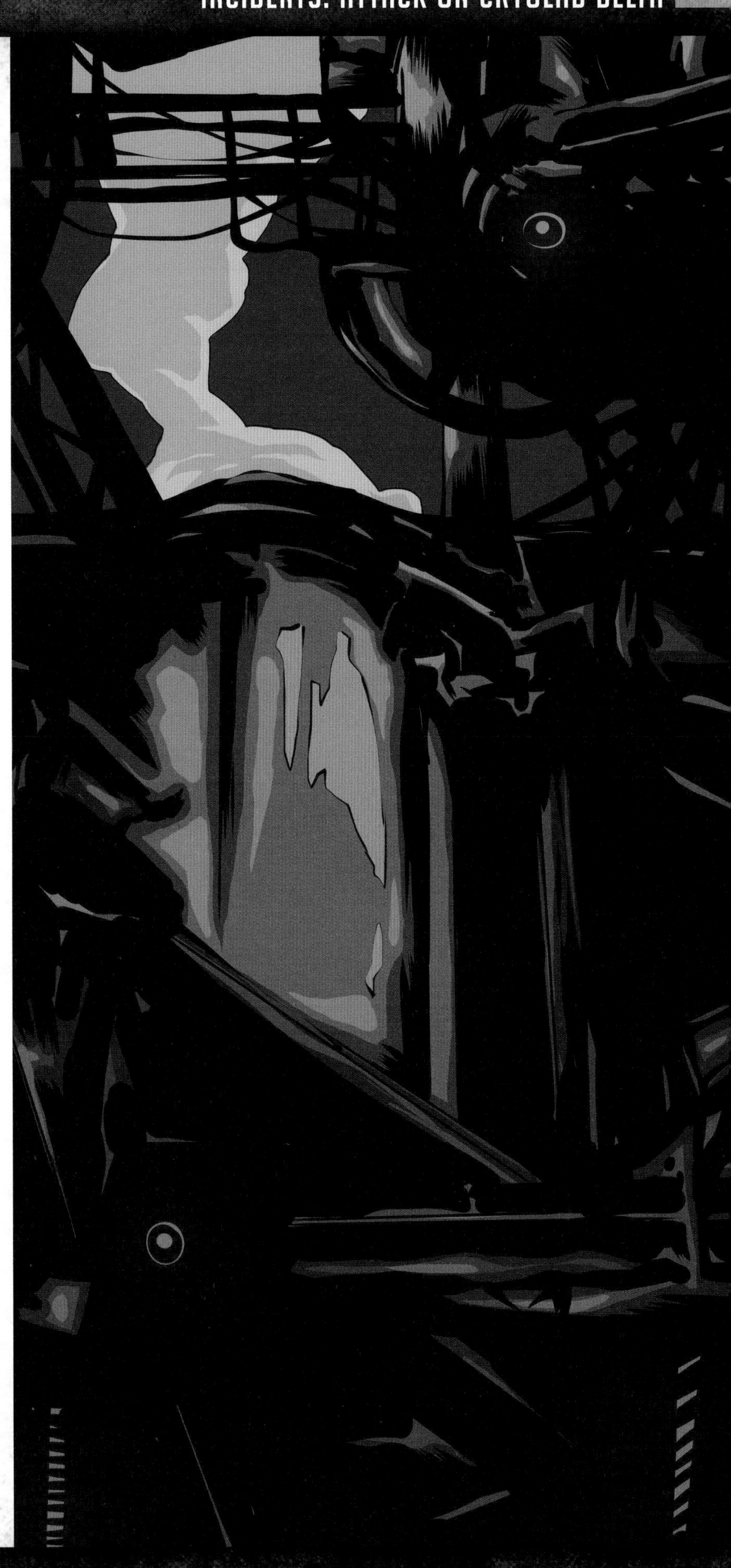

12

HUMANS IN THE ZONE

Many residents of Elysium I will lose their lives with the fall of the enclave – workers and highborn alike. After the initial shock of returning to the surface, the survivors will turn their anger toward the Council for not only triggering the Omega Protocol, but also for keeping the truth about the surface world hidden for decades.

Whatever remains of the Council collapses quickly. From now on, everybody must find their own way on the surface world. However, this doesn't mean that the Houses give up striving for power and influence. A whole new world lies before them.

When the *Guardians of the Fall* campaign is over, the story of the enclave survivors can continue in *Mutant: Year Zero* and be combined with the two previous expansions: *Genlab Alpha* and *Mechatron*. The humans from Elysium I reach the Zone at about the same time as the robots from Mechatron-7 arrive, and the mutant animals' long walk from *Genlab Alpha* reaches its end.

With the end of *Mutant: Elysium*, all classes of sentient creatures in the Mutant universe have finally arrived in the Zone. It's time to forge a new era.

Each player can choose to continue with his PC from *Elysium* or reprise a human mutant, an animal mutant, or a robot character from a previous campaign – or create a brand new PC. If you didn't run any of the previous campaigns in the *Mutant: Year Zero* world, this is a great opportunity to start a new one, creating PCs from any of the four classes in the available books.

MEETING THE DENIZENS OF THE ZONE

The meeting between the enclave humans and the previous inhabitants of the Zone is an overwhelming event for all involved. The meeting can take many forms and play out in different ways. You can let this encounter occur "off-screen" and fast-forward to a later point in the story, or play through the event.

The first option is preferred if you want to start playing a mixed group right away, but if you have time to play out the actual meeting it can be an exciting experience. Below is a possible sequence of events. See this as inspiration; feel free to change and modify whatever is necessary to best fit your campaign.

THE ARRIVAL OF HUMANITY

After the fall of Elysium I, the Houses still try to hold onto their power, but divisions occur and the enclave survivors split into smaller groups, each looking for a new place to settle.

WHERE WAS ELYSIUM I LOCATED?

Exactly where in the world Elysium I is located, and how long the walk to your chosen Zone takes, is up to you to decide. The enclave was completely destroyed by the Omega Protocol, and there is nothing down there for the denizens of the Zone to find but death.

The humans soon realize that they are not alone in the Zone. They will meet human mutants from the Arks, and possibly also mutant animals and robots. The surviving highborn humans tend to regard these strange creatures as a lower class, treating them as servants and laborers.

A group of about a hundred enclave humans settles down in an area of ruined buildings near an Ark. They use their enclave technology and technical skills to quickly build an advanced settlement with a water supply, medical care, and a disciplined militia. A marketplace is established inside the walls of the settlement, which rapidly becomes a major power in the Zone.

The Zone mutants quickly become dependent on their new neighbor: they receive medical care, food, and are offered work by way of various construction projects. The new settlement expands and soon begins to resemble a small town. Meanwhile, the gap grows between humans and mutants, who are treated as second-class people.

POSSIBLE EVENTS

Chapter 16 of the *Mutant: Year Zero* core book describes a number of events that might happen when humans reach the Zone. These are repeated here, in case you do not have access to that book:

- Humans and mutants unite in the fight against a common enemy, such as the Zone Ghouls, the Helldrivers or the Nova Cult. The struggle against these enemies is long and hard but finally, with help from the newcomers' technology, victory is achieved.
- A new watchtower is to be built in the human settlement. Many of the Ark mutants take part in the work. Then disaster strikes. The tower collapses, and several mutants die. A wild protest breaks out, tearing a rift between mutants and humans. But most mutants remain dependent on their new human masters.
- More enclave humans arrive at the settlement, doubling its population in a matter of weeks. New homes are built and trade routes with other factions in the Zone are established. Some of the humans grow very rich, while most of the mutants remain poor. Discontent is brewing.
- The conflict between humans and mutants intensifies. A militant human faction gives hate-stirring speeches in the marketplace, preaching that mutants are second-rate beings that have no place in the dawnworld. Some mutants are caught and beaten or burnt to death.
- The mutants have had enough of the abuse. In secret, they plan an attack against the humans. A bloodbath is imminent unless someone – the PCs? – can defuse the situation and give mutants and humans a common purpose.

NEW PCS

After the enclave humans arrive in the Zone, players can choose from four different classes when they create new characters: enclave human, human mutant (requires *Mutant: Year Zero*), mutant animal (requires *Genlab Alpha*) or robot (requires *Mechatron*).

PROFESSIONS AND ROLES

The newcomers bring new knowledge from their former life in the enclave and exchange their knowledge with the inhabitants of the Zone. When a new PC is created in the Zone, the player can choose between all the professions and roles described in *Year Zero, Genlab Alpha,* and Elysium.

Human and animal mutants can learn the professions from Elysium, but doing so requires that some projects have been performed in their settlement (see table). However, new human PCs can be created with these professions regardless of community projects, assuming they have been trained in the enclave.

Robots can never learn professions or roles and are limited to their models.

PROFESSIONS IN THE ZONE

PROFESSION	REQUISITE PROJECT
Scholar	Academy (new)
Officer	Army
Procurator	Code of Law (new)
Soldier	Army
Technician	Workshop
Investigator	Tribunal

NEW TALENTS

Talents can also be exchanged between classes. After the enclave dwellers arrive in the Zone, all PC mutants, animals, and humans have access to all the general talents described in *Year Zero, Genlab Alpha,* and Elysium. Talents associated with a particular role or profession remain exclusive.

CONTACTS

Belonging to a prominent family remains as important in the Zone as it was back in the enclave. The PCs' contacts (See Chapter 5) survive the exodus to the surface and are used the same way. Other classes cannot get contacts – they are only available to humans from the enclave.

How many IP a PC gets at the start of each game session is determined in the same way as before, by the total Control of the PC's House. Read more below on how Control works in the Zone.

REPUTATION

A human PC has a Reputation score, and they keep it outside the enclave. If the Social Ladder project is carried out in the settlement (below), human mutants will also get a Reputation score.

The table for starting Reputation on page 20 remains the same for humans outside of the enclave. All mutants automatically get a –2 modification to their starting Reputation however, because the humans find them less refined. All human mutants in the Arks of *Year Zero* start out as young.

The table below indicates how the starting Reputation score is modified by *Year Zero* and *Genlab Alpha* roles. Roles not listed in the table don't affect the starting Reputation. Mutant animals and robots don't have Reputation scores – the animals instead have Rank and robots have Hierarchy scores.

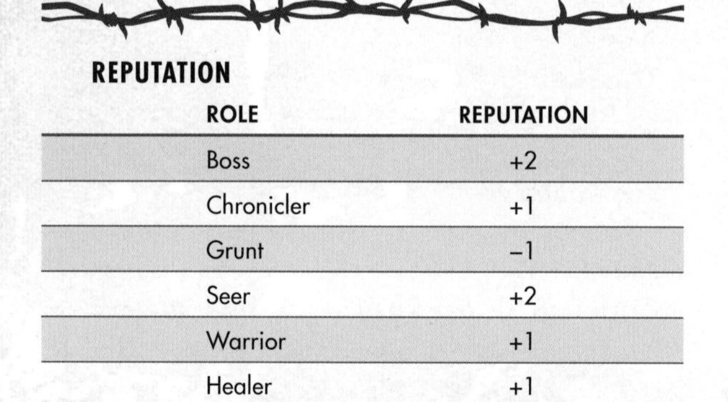

REPUTATION

ROLE	REPUTATION
Boss	+2
Chronicler	+1
Grunt	–1
Seer	+2
Warrior	+1
Healer	+1
Mutant	–2

Changing Reputation: How Reputation changes is handled differently out in the Zone. The list on page 25 is no longer valid. Instead, the following applies:

- If the PC has sacrificed or risked something for his House during the session, his Reputation increases by one.
- If the PC disappoints or betrays his House in any way, his Reputation drops by one.

You may also raise or lower a PC's Reputation as a result of exceptional actions in the game, provided the event becomes public knowledge.

RELATIONSHIPS

If a player creates a new human PC out in the Zone, the PC will not have relationships with other PCs and NPCs described for each profession as listed in Chapter 2. Instead, the player himself will need to create starting relationships.

GEAR

Leaving the enclave drastically reduces access to advanced technology. New PCs created with *Mutant: Elysium* rules, therefore, will not have access to the same starting equipment as the enclave dwellers had. Use the following table to replace the starting equipment listed in each profession description in Chapter 2:

ARTIFACT	REPLACE WITH
Stun gun	Sling
Stun baton	Spiked bat
Gauss pistol, gyrojet pistol	Scrap pistol
Gauss rifle, gyrojet carbine	Scrap rifle
Vibro knife	Scrap knife
Frag grenade	None
Comm radio	None
E-pack	None
ID-card	None
Credits	Bullets

PATROL LEADER & DOUBLE AGENT
After the fall of the enclave, the PCs are no longer judicators. They have no patrol leader, and nobody is a double agent. Instead, PCs are handled in the same way as in *Mutant: Year Zero*. Each PC should choose another PC as his buddy.

ARTIFACTS

After the fall of Elysium I, artifacts from the enclave can turn up out in the Zone. You can simply mix Artifact Cards from the custom card deck for *Mutant: Elysium* with cards from *Year Zero, Genlab Alpha,* and *Mechatron*. This will mean that a larger variety of artifacts, including more advanced enclave technology – such as gauss and gyrojet weapons – can now be found in the Zone.

OUTPOSTS

Human settlements in the Zone are called outposts. An outpost can consist of only humans, but more often humans from the enclave are joined by human mutants (see *Year Zero*) and/or animal mutants (see *Genlab Alpha*).

In the game mechanics, an outpost with enclave humans is handled like an Ark in Chapter 7 of the *Mutant: Year Zero* core book. Some differences are outlined below.

DEVELOPMENT LEVELS

A human outpost in the Zone uses the same Development Levels as an Ark: Food Supply, Technology, Culture, and Warfare. A newly established outpost begins with zero in all Development Levels.

NUMBER OF INHABITANTS

Unlike the Ark mutants, the humans from the enclave are not sterile but fully capable of bringing children into the world. This means that the population of such a society does not automatically fall, to the contrary, it can grow – and grow rapidly.

When you roll to determine the "session body count" at the end of each game session (see page 115 of the *Mutant: Year Zero* core book), also roll a die to determine how many people are born or have moved into the outpost. This roll is also made with a D6, modified by the current Food Supply Development Level. See the table below.

INHABITANTS IN THE OUTPOST

FOOD SUPPLY	NUMBER OF DEATHS	BORN/ SETTLED IN	POPULATION LIMIT
0–9	D6	D6	200
10–19	D6–1	D6+1	400
20–29	D6–2	D6+2	800
30+	D6–3	D6+3	1,600

Large Outposts: When the population in the outpost rises over 400, roll for population change once per month (in game time) instead of after each game meeting. Also, the dice result also shows the percentage change instead of the actual number of persons. Round to the nearest integer.

Population Limit: The current Development Level in Food Supply sets a limit for how large an outpost can get. This is shown under Population Limit in the table above. Note that the limit is per outpost – by establishing multiple settlements (as projects), an outpost can accommodate more residents. Robots do not count towards the population limit.

EXAMPLE

Pandora Kilgore's outpost in the Zone consists of 397 brave inhabitants – a mix of humans, mutants, animals, and robots. The Current Development Level in Food Supply is 24.

The game session is over and the group rolls for the session body count and newcomers. The first roll is a 3 and the other a 4. This means that one person dies (3-2) and six people are added (4+2). The population thus increases by five individuals to 402.

The society now counts as big, and the next population roll is made after a month of game time. The Development Level in Food Supply is unchanged.

12

The group now rolls a 5 and a 3, which means that 3 percent of the population dies, but it is increased by 5 percent due to births and new settlers - overall an increase of 2 percent. 2 percent equals eight persons, meaning the population rises to 410.

PROJECTS IN AN OUTPOST

All projects described in *Mutant: Year Zero* are available to a human outpost as well. In addition, there are several projects available only to settlements that contain human survivors from the enclave. These are described below.

CODE OF LAW

The outpost agrees on a regulatory framework of laws and that govern what is allowed and prohibited in society.

DEV Requirements: Culture 20, Warfare 10
Other Requirements: Tribunal
Skill: Comprehend
Work Points: 2 × number of PCs
DEV Bonus: Warfare +D6, Culture +D6
Special: Requirement to use the Prosecute skill

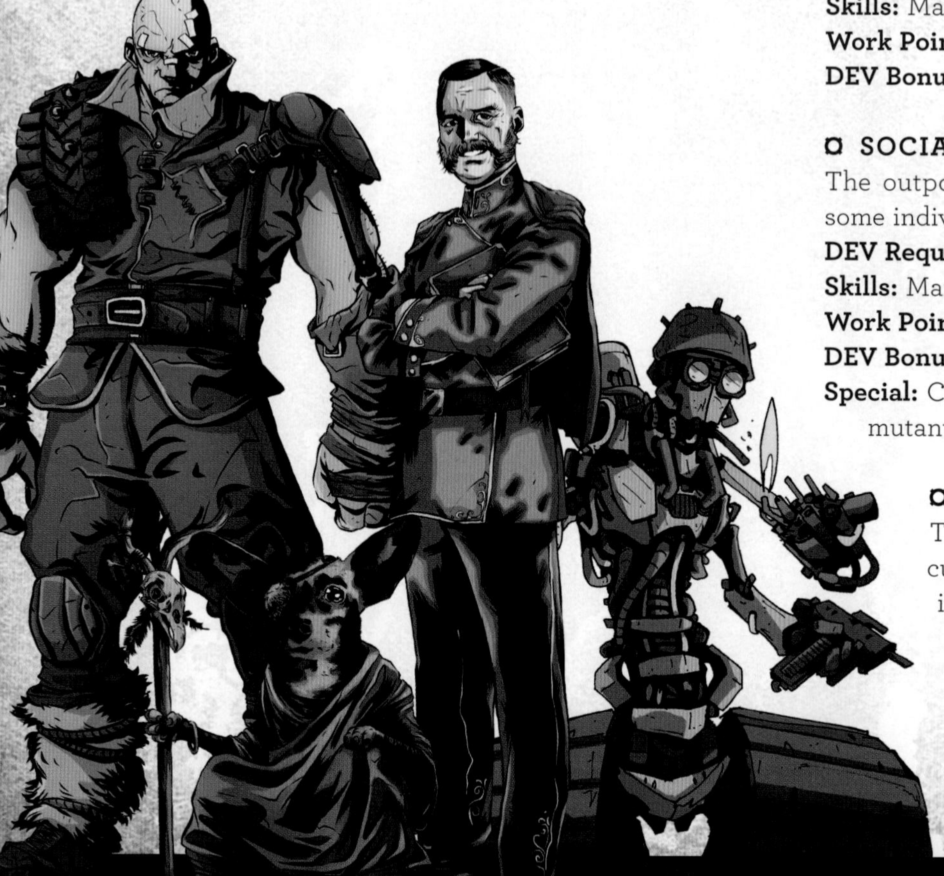

PRISON

A place where criminals are held under lock and key until they have atoned for their transgressions.

DEV Requirements: Warfare 20
Other Requirements: Tribunal, Code of Law
Skills: Comprehend, Endure
Work Points: 2 × number of PCs
DEV Bonus: Warfare +D6

SEWER SYSTEM

The outpost establishes a system of pipes for draining wastewater.

DEV Requirements: Technology 20, Food Supply 20
Other Requirements: Workshop
Skills: Comprehend, Jury-Rig, Tinker
Work Points: 2 × number of PCs
DEV Bonus: Culture +D6, Food Supply +D6

TRADING POSTS

The outpost establishes several small trading posts throughout the Zone to conduct trade and diplomacy with other groups.

DEV Requirements: Culture 20, Food Supply 20
Other Requirements: Market
Skills: Manipulate, Make a Deal
Work Points: 2 × number of PCs
DEV Bonus: Culture +D6, Food Supply +D6

SOCIAL LADDER

The outpost develops social hierarchies where some individuals rank higher than others.

DEV Requirements: Culture 25
Skills: Manipulate
Work Points: 1 × number of PCs
DEV Bonus: Culture + D6
Special: Completing this project means that even mutants in the outpost get Reputation scores.

CURRENCY

The outpost establishes a single common currency - credits - replacing the trade in bullets.

DEV Requirements: Culture 30
Other Requirements: Bank, Foundry
Skills: Comprehend, Make a Deal
Work Points: 2 × number of PCs

DEV Bonus: Culture +D6, Food Supply +D6
Special: A credit corresponds to a bullet in value.

STREET PLANNING

The clutter of hovels in the outpost is replaced by a planned and orderly pattern of streets and homes.
DEV Requirements: Culture 30, Technology 30
Other Requirements: Suffrage or Autocracy
Skills: Comprehend, Endure
Work Points: 3 × number of PCs
DEV Bonus: Warfare +D6, Food Supply +D6

NEWSPAPER

A periodic news publication is created. It covers many major and minor activities and daily life in the outpost.
DEV Requirements: Culture 30
Other Requirements: Ink & Paper, Printing Press
Skills: Manipulate, Enlighten, Investigate
Work Points: 1 × number of PCs
DEV Bonus: Culture +D6

COURIERS

A group of couriers are given the task of transporting important letters and other shipments between settlements.
DEV Requirements: Culture 30, Technology 30
Other Requirements: Settlement and either Suffrage or Autocracy
Skills: Comprehend, Endure
Work Points: 2 × number of PCs
DEV Bonus: Culture +D6, Food Supply +D6, Warfare +D6

INDUSTRY

Facilities for mass production of goods and gear.
DEV Requirements: Technology 35
Other Requirements: Foundry
Skill: Comprehend, Tinker, Jury-Rig
Work Points: 3 × number of PCs
DEV Bonus: Technology +D6, Warfare +D6, Food Supply +D6

COMMISSION OF ANCIENT TIMES

The Dawn Vault is replaced by an organized authority that collects, catalogs, and studies finds from the Old Age.
DEV Requirements: Technology 35, Culture 30
Other Requirements: Ink & Paper
Skill: Comprehend, Enlighten
Work Points: 2 × number of PCs
DEV Bonus: Culture +D6, Technology +D6

AIRSHIP

The brightest Technicians and Gearheads have invented an aircraft that can fly using a balloon filled with hot air or gas.
DEV Requirements: Technology 35
Other Requirements: Workshop
Skill: Comprehend, Tinker, Jury-Rig
Work Points: 2 × number of PCs
DEV Bonus: Technology +D6
Special: An airship can carry up to ten passengers and enables Zone travel (one sector per hour) without being exposed to the Zone's threats. Sectors passed by airships are not counted as explored, but Stalkers can Lead the Way from an airship in the same way as from an elevated position. To propel the airship a Steam Engine (separate project) is required, otherwise it will drift in the wind. Airships can also be used to flee from a conflict, granting a +1 Gear Bonus to the Move roll. Armor Rating 3, Resilience 10.

ACADEMY

The outpost establishes an institution for research and higher education.
DEV Requirements: Technology 40, Culture 35
Other Requirements: Collectivism, School
Skill: Comprehend, Enlighten
Work Points: 3 × number of PCs
DEV Bonus: Food Supply +D6, Culture +D6, Technology +D6

EMPIRE

The outpost designates an emperor to lead the people into the new dawn.
DEV Requirements: Warfare 40, Culture 40
Other Requirements: Autocracy, Settlement
Skill: Manipulate or Command
Work Points: 2 × number of PCs
DEV Bonus: Warfare +D6, Culture +D6

HOUSE CONTROL

Though battered, the Houses survive the fall of Elysium I and bring their old ambitions of dominance and conquest to the surface. Technically, each House retains Control even in the Zone, but only total Control is counted – it's not divided into sectors.

When the enclave is lost, each House loses 2 points of total Control (to a minimum of zero). It's only relevant to keep track of the Control of Houses represented by PCs in the group.

New Campaign: If you start a new campaign with enclave humans out in the Zone without having played *Guardians of the Fall*, each PC's House starts the game with D6 total Control.

USING CONTROL

A player with a PC belonging to one of the Houses can use its Control during the Assembly sessions in the outpost (see page 103 in the *Mutant: Year Zero* core book). Control can be used in two different ways:

- To contribute to projects being worked on in the outpost.
- To stage Incidents in order to increase the House's Control further.

A player cannot do both above options in the same Assembly – he must choose one of the two.

CONTRIBUTING TO A PROJECT

A House can use its influence to help finish projects in the outpost more quickly. The player simply distributes his House's total Control amongst the projects already in progress (including those commenced at that same Assembly meeting). Each point of Control assigned to a project reduces the number of remaining Work Points by one.

STAGING INCIDENTS

A House can also use intrigue and stage Incidents to strengthen its own power in the Zone at the expense of others, just as it did in the depths of the enclave. This can increase the total Control of the House but will lower a Development Level in the outpost.

The reason for a player to do this can be to get more Influence Points at the start of each game session. Thus, the player needs to weigh his own benefit against the interests of the outpost as a whole.

To stage an Incident, the player is first assigned two random Incidents just like back in the enclave (see Chapter 10). If you have access to the custom card deck for *Mutant: Elysium*, simply draw two random Incident Cards. The player chooses one of them, shows it to the group and its starting effect is immediately applied. The player then rolls dice to see if the Incident succeeds. Use the table on page 151 but use the Warfare Development Level instead of Security. If the Incident succeeds, the total Control of the House increases by one. Ignore the final effect of the Incident.

How the Incident affects the game is up to you as a GM. You can let the Incident happen in the background without affecting the PCs, or have the PCs get involved in the intrigue and build an entire gaming session around it.

DEVELOPMENT LEVELS

Use the table below to convert the Development Levels from *Mutant: Elysium* to the ones in *Mutant: Year Zero*, which are used for an outpost in the Zone.

Production	Food Supply
Defense	Warfare
Science	Technology
Culture	Culture

LOSING CONTROL

The struggle for power and influence is brutal – other Houses will always try to bring down the top dog. At the end of each Assembly, each player belonging to a House must roll a number of Base Dice equal to the total Control of their House. If the player rolls one or more ☣, the total Control of the House is reduced by one.

The player whose PC belongs to a House that loses Control can, if he wants to, come up with a story explaining the loss of Control.

INDEX

Name:		Age:
Profession:	House:	Reputation

TTRIBUTES

trength		Damage	○○○○○
gility		Fatigue	○○○○○
Vits		Confusion	○○○○○
mpathy		Doubt	○○○○○

ONDITIONS

tarving	○	Dehydrated	○
leepless	○	Hypothermic	○

ritical Injuries:

KILLS

ndure (Strength)	
orce (Strength)	
ight (Strength)	
neak (Agility)	
Move (Agility)	
Shoot (Agility)	
Scout (Wits)	
Comprehend (Wits)	
Know the Zone (Wits)	
Sense Emotion (Empathy)	
Manipulate (Empathy)	
Heal (Empathy)	

ROT POINTS

○○○○○○○○○○

EXPERIENCE POINTS

○○○○○○○○○○

APPEARANCE

Face:

Body:

Clothing:

GEAR

1
2
3
4
5
6
7
8
9
10

Credits:

TALENTS

CONTACTS

INFLUENCE POINTS

○○○○○○○○○○

ARMOR

Armor	Rating

WEAPONS

Weapons	Bonus	Damage	Range	Special

RELATIONSHIPS

Relationships	Patrol Leader
PC 1:	○
PC 2:	○
PC 3:	○
PC 4:	○

I Hate:

I Need to Protect:

My Big Dream:

PEOPLE I'VE MET	Role	Notes

THE PATROL

Designation:

Patrol Leader:

Other:

MY DEN

Description:

Gear Stashed:

Other:

TINY ITEMS

NOTES

ENCLAVE SHEET

EVELOPMENT LEVELS

roduction		Security		Culture		Science	

HE CORE – INFLUENCE

ector	Warburg	Fortescue	Kilgore	Morningstar
ova Paloma				
ld Koly				
irius				
indertuft				
ortholme				
alista				
indenburg				

HE DEEP – INFLUENCE

ector	Warburg	Fortescue	Kilgore	Morningstar
osel				
aborum				
rcadium				
inderfalls				
ogs of Hel				

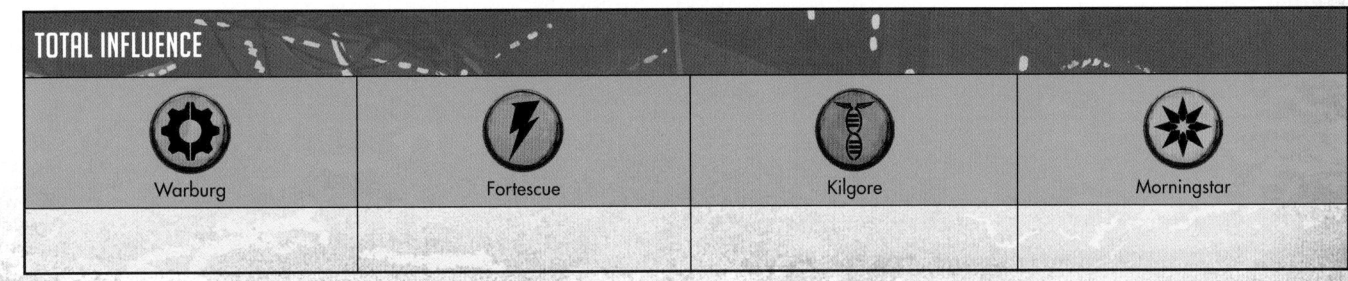

TOTAL INFLUENCE

Warburg	Fortescue	Kilgore	Morningstar

Round	THE CORE – INCIDENTS							THE DEEP – INCIDENTS				
Sector	Nova Paloma	Old Koly	Pirius	Tindertuft	Northolme	Calista	Hindenburg	Mosel	Laborum	Arcadium	Cinderfalls	Cogs of Hel
Warburg												
Fortescue												
Kilgore												
Morningstar												

Round	THE CORE – INCIDENTS							THE DEEP – INCIDENTS				
Sector	Nova Paloma	Old Koly	Pirius	Tindertuft	Northolme	Calista	Hindenburg	Mosel	Laborum	Arcadium	Cinderfalls	Cogs of Hel
Warburg												
Fortescue												
Kilgore												
Morningstar												

OUR BACKERS

HEIRS OF DOOM

Adam Woogie Woloshuk, Andree Henriksson, Andrew Hurley, Cali, Colin Bolger, Dennis Hardarsson, Ethan "Tex" Sims, J.M. Sunden, Jeff Robinson, Joe McLean, Justin Crowther, Kenneth Krammager, leifdaviking, Mad Jay, Nicolas Lapointe, Rune Stræde Andersen

SUPERINTENDENTS

Alexander Herring Orby, Arttu Rajamäki, Audun Løvlie, Bart Gelens, Ben Gunderson, Ben Sutter, Birk Hauke Wildhirt, Blaine Salzman, Bo Ahlgren, Bozz, Bret Jordan, Bryan Considine, Cameron & Madison Straka, Cato Vandrare, Chris Slowinski, Christopher Gunning, Cody Swatek, Damian Dhar, Daniel Penninck, Daniel Pervan, Dany Leclerc, David S. Robinson, Edgardo A. Montes Rosa, Edward "MilesAnP" Miles, Eric "Scales" Campbell, Erik Malm, Filipe Cunha, Geoffrey M Allen, Glenn Massoeurs, Greg Higgins, Hayden Bailey, Ignatius Montenegro, Jack Holden, Jakob Collins, James Hawkes, James "The Great Old One" Burke, Jason "Atomics" Unck, Jason A. Curiel, Jason Coleman BX, Jean-Michel Trudeau, Jeff L. Thomas, Jens Thorup Rasmussen, Joe Ross, Johan Mihailovici, John Noad, John Robinson, Jonas "ari" Hällström, Jonne "Comissar Claw" Kuokkanen, Joshua Moldenhauer, Julian d'Agostino, Justas Tomkus, Karl Vollan, Kenny Tripoli, Kevin Coleson, KnuT, Kris Kelly, Kristian Brodin, Larry T, Lee Langston, Lee Lomax, Lorenz "Silversteel" Aschaber, Lukas Buergi, Mark Hutton, Mark Solino, Martin Goodson, Martin Legg, Martin Petchey, Matt Pearce, Matthew "Thundermonk" Orwig, Matthew Thomas, Mattias Pettersson, Mattiaz Fredriksson, Mel "Insanity Rocks" Riffe, Michael "Chef Pandakage" Salas, Michael Lawrence, Morgan Weeks, Odyssey Vekshin, Our Hero Andy, Pangur Bán, Papa Nurgle, Paul Huey Hubbard, Pedro(Te), Pieta Delaney, Rene Bariteau, Richard E. Trub, Jr., Robert Calpo, Robert Rauschenberg, Roberto Bellesia, Roman Thöni, Rune Karlsson, Ryan Dukacz, Ryan Seguin, Ryan Wittig, Saty, Scott Bates, Sean Keating (Blastit52), Sean Wilcox, Sebastian "Vive la Legion" Este, Shaun Jenkins, Shawn P, Shawn Polka, Shervyn, Simone Colombo, Sławomir "Serox" Kopeć, Stuart Rickards, Terry L Pike, The Crowbar Lifestyle, Thorsten Wolk, Timothy D. Martin, Todd Stephens, Trevor P. Marshall, Tsapki Jose Perez, Tuomas Ristimäki, Willem Pypers, William Asico, Zachary Guenther, Zorlun

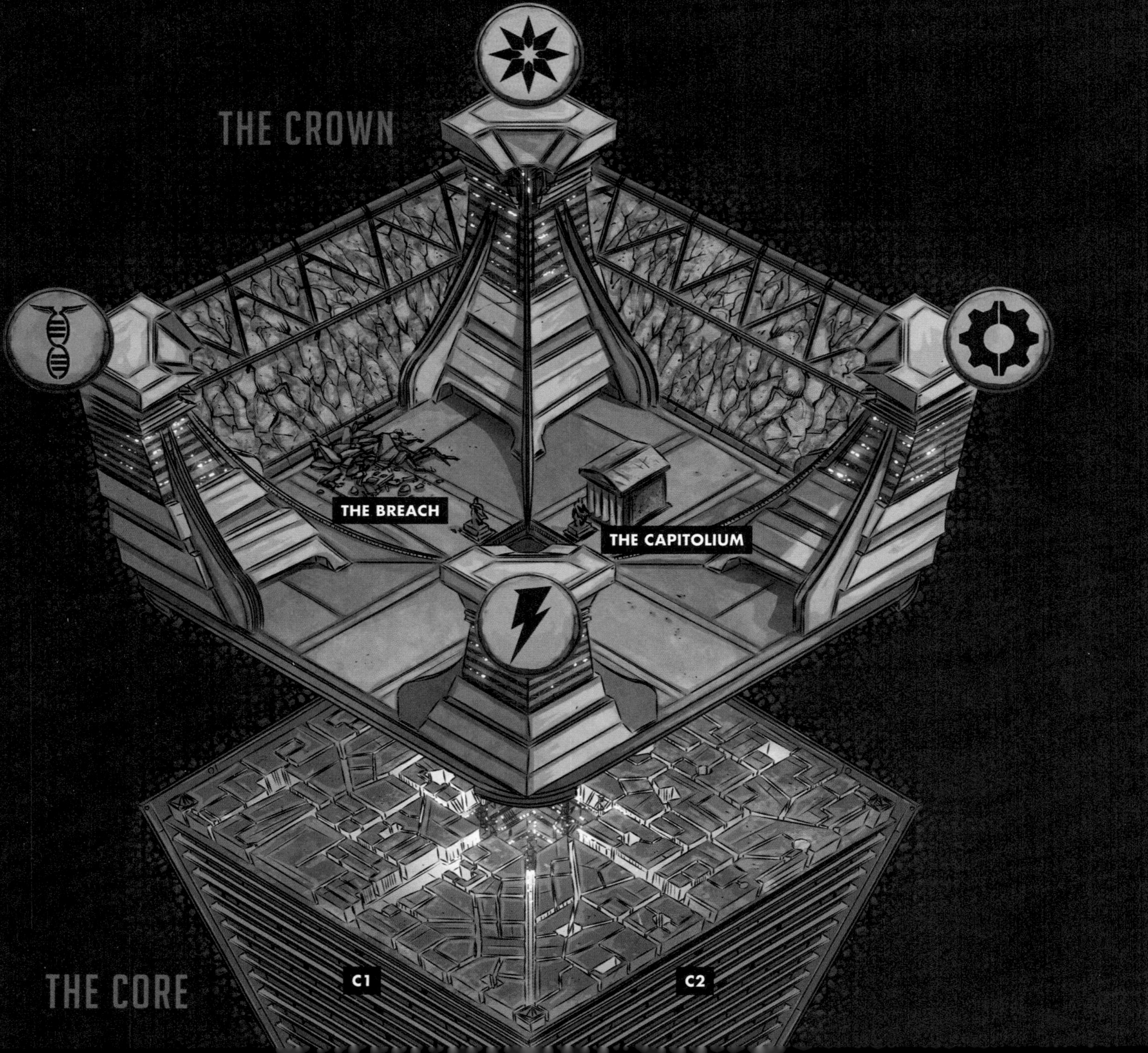

THE CROWN
THE BREACH
THE CAPITOLIUM
THE CORE
C1
C2